The Health and Safety Survival Guide

The Health and Safety Survival Guide

A comprehensive handbook for managers

Terry Brimson

McGRAW-HILL BOOK COMPANY

London · New York · St Louis · San Francisco · Auckland · Bogotá · Caracas
Lisbon · Madrid · Mexico · Milan · Montreal · New Delhi · Panama
Paris · San Juan · São Paulo · Singapore · Sydney · Tokyo · Toronto

Published by
McGRAW-HILL Book Company Europe
Shoppenhangers Road, Maidenhead, Berkshire SL6 2QL, England
Telephone 01628 23432
Fax 01628 770224

British Library Cataloguing in Publication Data
Brimson, Terence J.
  Health and Safety Survival Guide:
  Comprehensive Handbook for Managers
  I. Title
  344.104465

  ISBN 0-07-709049-7

Library of Congress Cataloging-in-Publication Data
Brimson, Terence J. (Terence John)
    The health and safety survival guide: a comprehensive handbook
  for managers/Terence J. Brimson.
      p.   cm.
    Includes bibliographical references and index.
    ISBN 0-07-709049-7
      1. Industrial safety–Handbooks, manuals, etc.   2. Industrial
  hygiene–Handbooks, manuals, etc.   I. Title.
  T55.B746
  658.4'08–dc20   95-9896
                                                                        CIP

Reprinted 1997

Typeset by Paston Press Ltd, Loddon, Norfolk
and printed and bound in Great Britain at the University Press, Cambridge
Printed on permanent paper in compliance with ISO Standard 9706

Contents

List of abbreviations

AC	Alternating current
ACOP	Approved Code of Practice
AIDS	Acquired Immune Deficiency Syndrome
AOTC	Associated Offices Technical Committee
AW.Regs	Abrasive Wheels Regulations 1970
BCF	Bromochlorodifluoromethane – or Halon 1211
B/F	Bring forward
BS	British Standard
BSI	British Standards Institute
CADCAM	Computer-aided design and computer-aided manufacture
CEN	European Standards Organisation
CHIP Regs	Chemicals (Hazard Information and Packaging) Regulations
CiP	Clean in Place
CL	Cycle limited
CO_2	Carbon-dioxide
COP	Code of Practice (*see also* ACOP and SCOP)
COSHH	Control of Substances Hazardous to Health
CPLDS Regs	Classification, Packaging and Labelling of Dangerous Substances Regulations 1984 (superseded by the CHIP Regs 1993)
dB	decibel
dB(A)	decibel adjusted for frequency
DC	Direct current
DSE	Display screen equipment
DSS	Department of Social Security
DT_p	Department of Transport
EC	European Community (or Commission)
EEC	European Economic Community (*see also* EC)
EEMUA	Engineering Equipment and Materials Users' Association
EHO	Environmental Health Officer
ELF	Electric Light Federation
ELF	Extra-low frequency
ELI	Employer's liability insurance
EMAS	Employment Medical Advisory Service (of the HSE)
EMR	Electro-magnetic radiation
EPA.90	Environmental Protection Act 1990
ET	Employment Training
F.	Factories – used in HSE form numbers to denote relevance to premises covered by the Factories Act 1961

FA.61	Factories Act 1961
FPA.71	Fire Protection Act 1971
FPOs	Fire prevention orders
FPO.72	Fire Precaution (Hotels and Boarding Houses) Order 1972
FPO.89	Fire Precaution (Factories, Offices, Shops and Railway Premises) Order 1989.
FPR.95	Fire Precaution (Places of Work) Regulations 1995
FSA.90	Food Safety Act 1990
HACCPS	Hazard Analysis and Critical Control Points System
HASWA	Health and Safety at Work, etc, Act 1974
HMIIP	Her Majesty's Inspectorate of Industrial Pollution
HMSO	Her Majesty's Stationery Office
HSC	Health and Safety Commission
HSE	Health and Safety Executive
HTST	High temperature short time
IAC	Industry Advisory Committee
IEHO	Institution of Environmental Health Officers
IIP	Investors in People
IPCS	Integrated Pollution Control System
IR	Infra-red
ISBN	International Standard Book Number
ISO	International Standards Organisation
IT	Initial Training
ITD	Institute of Training & Development
JCITB	Joint Council of Industry Training Boards
LECs	Local Enterprise Companies
$L_{ep,d}$	Mathematical equation to express measurement of average noise levels over given TWA (db(A)$L_{ep,d}$ in full)
LFS	Labour Force Survey
LPG	Liquid petroleum gas
Man.Hdlg.Regs	Manual Handling Operations Regulations 1992
MEL	Maximum exposure limit
mG	milli-Gows
MHSW Regs	Management of Health and Safety at Work Regulations 1992
MOD	Ministry of Defence
MOE	Means of escape
MSC	Manpower Services Commission (now superseded)
NCTEC Regs	Notification of Cooling Towers and Evaporative Condensers Regulations 1992
NHS	National Health Service
NIC	National Insurance Contributions
nT	nano-Tesler
O^2	Oxygen
OES	Occupational exposure standard

OS.	Offices, shops and railway premises – used in HSE form numbers to denote relevance to premises covered by OSRP
OSRP	Offices, Shops and Railway Premises Act 1963
OTJ	Off-the-job (training)
pH	potential of Hydrogen (measurement of acidity or alkalinity)
PAYE	Pay as you earn (income tax)
PDS	Product data sheet
PESF	Personal executive stress factor
PHLS	Public Health Laboratory Service
PLI	Public Liability Insurance
PPE	Personal protective equipment
PPE.Regs	Personal Protective Equipment at Work Regulations 1992
PSTGC Regs	Pressure Systems and Transportable Gas Containers Regulations 1989
pvc	Polyvinyl chloride
QA	Quality assurance
QC	Quality control
RCB	Residual contact breaker
Reg	Regulation
RF	Radio frequency
RIDDOR	Reporting of Injuries, Diseases and Dangerous Occurrences Regulations 1985
RIPHH	Royal Institute of Public Health and Hygiene
NRPB	National Radiological Protection Board
RSI	Repetitive strain injury
RTITB	Road Transport Industry Training Board (now closed)
s.	Section (of an Act of Parliament)
ss.	Sections (of an Act of Parliament)
SBS	Sick building syndrome
SCOP	Statutory Code of Practice
SI	Statutory instrument
SOS	Sick office syndrome
SPATA	Swimming Pool and Allied Trades Association
TB	Tuberculosis
TECs	Training and Enterprise Councils
TFE	Training for employment
TL	Temperature limited
TWA	Time-weighted average
UHT	Ultra heat treatment
UNEP	United Nations Environment Programme
ULD	Upper limb disorders (see also WRULD)
UMIST	University of Manchester Institute of Science and Technology
uPVC	ultra Polyvinyl chloride
UHF	Ultra-high frequency

VDE	Visual display equipment
VHF	Very-high frequency
VDT	Visual display terminal
VLF	Very-low frequency
VDU	Visual display unit
WC	Water closet
Wk.Eqpt.Regs	Provision and Use of Work Equipment Regulations 1992
WRULD	Work related upper limb disorders
YT	Youth Training

Acknowledgements

A person can have a broad knowledge and understanding of many things but no one can be 'expert' on everything. Thus, this book is not the work of just one person, but is a tribute to the support and encouragement of the following specialists in their fields.

For their patience and diligence throughout, I would like to sincerely thank:

Jim W. Davenport, JP, MIOSH, MIIRSM, Group Safety Manager, MB-Caradon PLC
Hugh Toomey, Institute of Training and Development (ITD Journals)
Brian F. Cockbill, MIOSH, Safety Officer, Kalamazoo (retired).

Also, grateful thanks to the following for checking, and providing technical input for, particular chapters (number in brackets):

Charles (Jim) Golding, Product Manager, Portables, Chubb-Fire Limited, Sunbury-on-Thames (12)
Clive Raybould, MIFireE, Station Officer, West Midlands Fire Service (Commercial and Industrial Training Unit) (12)
Adair Lewis, Manager, Information Services, Fire Protection Services (12)
Hazel Montague, Director, Berry, Birch & Noble, London (19)
Mrs M. Dummer, General Manager, Healthcall Optical Services, Milton Keynes (20)
Antonia Carr, Stress Management Counsellor, London (27)
Sandra Ridley, Manager, Stress Care, Care Assist Group Limited, Birmingham (27)
Margaret Brimson, for her artistry in Chapter 23.

Introduction

After the first Safety and Welfare Act was put on the statute book in 1802, progress in health and safety legislation was patchy, inadequate and very slow. From the 1950s, there was a steady development in health and safety legislation aimed at improving working conditions for employees. However, despite many laws, the incidence of deaths and injuries in industry continued to rise. Concern increased from the 1960s onwards, resulting in the commissioning of the Robens Committee from 1970 to 1972 to investigate and report on industrial safety. The 'Robens Report' culminated with the introduction of the Health and Safety at Work, etc. Act in 1974; many new regulations followed in the 1980s and 1990s.

With the new laws in the 1970s came new definitions of safety and, since, the introduction of other concerns, such as health, welfare and, more lately, hygiene, which, hitherto, had not generally been considered priorities by industry. There were a few large, paternalistic companies, such as Rowntree and Cadbury, that made good welfare provisions, but they were the exceptions. Also, for the first time, legislation enacted since the 1970s has brought about enforced responsibilities and accountabilities at corporate and individual level, so that the subjects of health, safety, welfare and hygiene have taken on, and continue to take on, new and more pertinent meanings for both employers and employees.

How often have you heard it said that health and safety is just common sense? Well, if it *is* just common sense, why are there so many accidents? We say that to err is human, and people do take risks every day. The problem is in the perception of hazards and degrees of risk.

It is hazardous to cross a road. The differences in the levels of risk between crossing a village high street early in the morning on a Sunday and crossing a motorway in the rush hour are obvious. Yet, faced with similar degrees of danger in factories, on farms, in shops, garages, offices, on construction sites and on training employment schemes, people take risks without realizing the potentially terrible consequences.

Sometimes, we may be tempted to play a game of Russian roulette, taking a chance on the way we handle a particular work situation. But we must not take that kind of risk, because, although the fatal bullet may not be in the chamber *this* time, eventually the odds narrow right down and we lose. No employer can afford to take chances by gambling against probabilities in the people business, particularly in health and safety. In horse racing, it is well known that the bookie plays to *win* and does in the long run. So, why not bet *with* the odds instead of *against* them?

It is commonly said, 'It won't happen to me', 'I will only be a minute', 'We haven't had an accident — yet' or 'You don't need to tell me, I've been doing this job for years'. Such confidence invariably precedes horrific accidents.

Safety is seen by many as a 'cost', something we do on sunny days but not on rainy days. It is also often seen as something that is not urgent — we can take our time about evaluating that 'urgent' health and safety audit report. But, can we afford *not* to be concerned about health and safety or to give it the priority it deserves?

Developments in the field of health and safety legislation have increased apace, with ever-increasing numbers of Acts of Parliament and their accompanying Regulations.

There is now even greater concern for the quality of working life, the environment in which work takes place and its effects on the wider environment. In Europe, the number of health and safety directives issued by the Council of Ministers of the European Community (EC), called EC Directives, with their increasing administrative and practical requirements, are evidence of this growing awareness of the actual and potential dangers that the individual faces while at work. It is this awareness that governments wish to instil into management.

The busy manager says, 'I cannot be expected to understand every bit of safety legislation that affects my business or my department'. But, of course, we soon find out that ignorance is no excuse, legally or morally, when confronted by a factory inspector or, worse still, a magistrate or judge with the prospect of *unlimited* fines and, in many cases, huge financial compensation awards to injured or killed employees or their dependants.

> It is not managers' business to be expert in health and safety; but neither is it their business to leave it to safety officers . . ., as is too often the case. Management needs to manage in this area as in any other and if it does it will find that there are plenty of spin-offs.

> Dr John Cullen, Chairman, Health and Safety Commission, July 1990

In the companion to this volume, *The Employer's Survival Guide*, I said that employment law has rightly been described as a veritable minefield. The many laws and regulations mean that managers have to tread very warily, because the way is strewn with very hazardous devices.

Health and safety laws in the United Kingdom are among the most complicated and certainly the most comprehensive of all employment laws. Consequently, responsible employers and employees are looking for guidance and professional advice on the best means of complying with and achieving the spirit as well as the letter of these laws.

A major objective of this guide is to provide authoritative and up-to-date guidance in most areas of health and safety so that you can travel through the minefield of health and safety law and practice, avoiding the many pitfalls that exist for the unwary.

Whatever your situation or level of experience, this guide will lead you through all the many legal requirements for health, safety, welfare and hygiene, whether you are considering employing or already employ people in their occupations. It will suggest to you what you should and must do to protect employees, customers, non-employees and others who may be affected by the acts or omissions of yourself or others whom you employ or control as a manager. That is the general aim. The following points relate to specific sectors.

- *Larger businesses* with your own personnel professional but without your own health and safety specialist. The necessity of keeping up to date with all that is going on in the health and safety field and keeping pace with laws affecting you is formidable. You must also give information, training and instruction to newly recruited and established employees. But, how can you do that effectively? This guide will direct you and lead you to sources of information and guidance.

- *Managers in high-tech growth companies*, perhaps newly established. Professionals in your particular technologies and specialism, without a personnel function and charged with recruiting your employees and keeping them safe. Technological innovations and growth bring with them obligations under health and safety law, but how can you know all that you need to know? This guide will help you.
- *Owner-managers of small businesses and the self-employed sole operator*, the entrepreneur with specialist skills, such as electronics, nursing, finance, selling, construction, joinery or engineering. You decided to work for yourself and sell your skill instead of being employed, and immediately you did so (whether you realized it or not) all sorts of health and safety laws applied to you, plus even more when you started employing people. What is not encouraging is that you are 'deemed to know', and ignorance of the law is not accepted as an excuse.
- *Headteachers*, particularly those of you struggling with local management of schools, are accountable for your own employment conditions. The specialist services of education authorities are no longer immediately available *free* — you have to 'buy in' health and safety or do it yourself. This guide will assist you greatly in discharging your important obligations to teachers, pupils, visitors and the public.
- *NHS managers* in health authorities. You are now personally accountable for health, safety, welfare and hygiene in hospitals and district health centres, including community care staff (Crown immunity was removed under 1990 legislation). You need to be aware of your responsibilities and how you can fulfil them. This guide will greatly assist you in this.
- *Private-sector nursing homes* are businesses in their own right, with the same accountabilities, especially in health, safety, welfare and fire precautions. You have duties to your staff and a 'special *duty* of care' to those in your care.
- *Managers of Investors in People (IIP) initiatives*, which provide training for employment under government and other sponsored training and work experience schemes, including Initial Training (IT), Youth Training (YT), Employment Training (ET), Job Clubs, Job Search and Re-start. Funding and lack of expertise often being a problem, you may not be able to afford your own full-time specialist practitioner, yet the health, safety, welfare and hygiene of your trainees is no less important, particularly as they work in widely varying environments. Also, the Health and Safety at Work, etc. Act 1974 (HASWA) plus 1990 Regulations clearly lay down the duties of training providers.
- *Students of and recent appointees in health and safety*, perhaps in training or studying for a recognized qualification to enter the health and safety field. There are many aspects of your profession for which this book will remove much of the 'mystique' and help you through it to a successful and rewarding career.

Whatever your situation, this guide will assist you in discharging your important legal and moral obligations towards your employees and others, including trainees, teachers, staff, pupils, charges in care or members of the public.

The aim, here, is to help you to avoid the potentially hazardous devices of the law and come through this minefield unscathed—but how? One way is by knowing *what* the 'mines' are, *where* they are, how you can *identify* them, *how* you can *avoid* them, and *why* you need to know and avoid them. There is considerable detail on many health, safety, welfare and hygiene aspects, so that you will have all the available and up-to-date information at your fingertips, and it is presented in a readable fashion, so it is easy to absorb, unlike the legal documentation itself!

To this end, much of the official gobbledegook has been removed. You will find that the subject matter has been divided into clearly defined areas so each chapter can cover it in depth, with appendices giving suggestions on relevant documents and procedures. There is also a detailed index to help you find what you need when you need it.

With this guide, you will be able to negotiate your way through what is perhaps the most hazardous part of the employment law minefield, led by a health and safety adviser who has been through, has survived, and now leads others safely through.

Note, however, that the material specific to the industries of construction and mines and quarries is so vast and complex that it cannot be covered completely in this book. Thus, the *principles* of this guide will apply equally to the needs of *all* industries, but those specialist aspects peculiar to construction and mines and quarries are only addressed here in a general sense.

1

Why health and safety?

A safe workplace is an efficient workplace. You can fill a workplace with machines and materials, but without people, your production processes are useless. Employees are your most valuable asset and need to be protected; managers have a vested interest and a legal duty to protect them.

The lack of safety awareness in workplaces continues to wreak much havoc in human lives. We cannot adequately describe the trauma experienced, such as the shock and fear felt by the child who has just been told 'Daddy has had an accident at work' or the grief of the widow at the graveside, but we can see some of its effects.

The size of the problem

Statistics vary over time because of differing and incomplete methods of reporting, but in UK industry in the 1960s and early 1970s, over 700 people were killed and over 180 000[1] seriously injured every year. In the 1980s, improved reporting procedures produced more accurate and meaningful figures, from which we see no real improvement in accident rates. In 1993, the European Commission quoted statistics that showed that approximately 8000 people die in occupational accidents in the European Community (EC) each year; further, that, each year, almost 10 million of the 120 million workers in the EC become victims of accidents and diseases that have occupational causes.

Since the advent of new legislation in 1974, the numbers *killed* at work have dropped but *serious injuries* have risen dramatically, giving enforcement authorities considerable cause for continued concern. Table 1.1 shows figures extracted from Health and Safety Commission (HSC) Annual Reports and Tables 1.2 and 1.3 show the breakdown of types of accident by industry sector.

Injury ratios

Despite the strict requirements of the Reporting of Industrial Diseases and Dangerous Occurrences Regulations 1985 (RIDDOR), it is recognized that many injuries and ill-effects suffered as a result of work practices still go unreported to enforcement authorities. This is, in part, due to the (illegal) non-reporting of 'reportable' occurrences, but is also due to the fact that many injuries do not result in time lost from work and therefore, although medically treated, are (also illegally) not included in reporting procedures.

For example, if an administrator injures their *left* arm, but is *right*-handed, they may return to work after hospital treatment, while a similar person with a similar injury to

1

Table 1.1   UK accident statistics[2]

Year	Killed	Major injuries	Serious injuries
1982	468	12 001	375 530
1986/87	355	20 695	159 011
1987/88	361	20 057	159 852
1988/89	362	19 944	163 119
1989/90	370	20 396	165 244
1990/91	346	19 896	160 811
1991/92	295	17 088	148 625
1992/93	430	28 018[5]	140 365
1993/94	235	16 326	132 343

Table 1.2   Reportable non-fatal major and over 3 days injuries by industry (excluding mines and quarries), 1986 to 1992[2]

Year	Agriculture	Energy, water	All manufacturing	Construction	Service	Unclassified	Total
1986/67	1043	19 621	54 046	16 468	65 958	1875	159 011
1987/88	1349	15 798	53 734	16 622	69 085	4264	159 852
1988/89	1973	13 728	56 141	16 597	71 268	3912	163 119
1989/90	1496	11 684	60 006	17 177	74 405	476	165 244
1990/91	1733	11 139	62 395	19 284	80 676	984	176 211
1991/92	1787	8990	57 459	17 479	78 604	1394	165 713
1993/94	1732	5120	49 356	11 118	78 875	2468	148 669

Table 1.3   Fatal injuries by industry (excluding mines, quarries and public services) 1986 to 1992[2]

Year	Agriculture	Energy, water	All manufacturing	Construction	Service	Unclassified	Total
1986/87	27	30	109	99	80	10	355
1987/88	21	33	99	103	96	9	361
1988/89	21	36	94	101	109	1	362*
1989/90	23	31	108	100	108	0	370
1990/91	23	27	85	93	98	0	326
1991/92	17	31	67	82	98	0	295
1993/94	16	11	64	65	79	0	235

their *right* arm who is *right*-handed could, possibly, become a lost time (over three days' absence from work) statistic. Additionally, many employees foolishly do not bother to report injuries.

The Office of Population conducted a labour force survey of some 40 000 households, interviewing nearly 80 000 people, of whom 45 000 were in employment. The 1990 survey arrived at an injury ratio that was somewhat at variance with that extrapolated from statistics derived from records under RIDDOR 1990/91, as shown in Fig. 1.1.

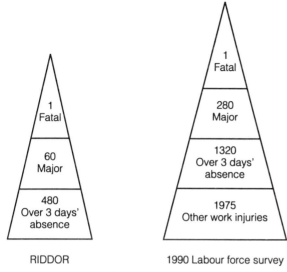

Fig. 1.1 Injury ratios[2]

The ratios from the RIDDOR statistics suggest that, for example, for the 326 fatal injuries in 1990/91, there were 19 560 major injuries and 156 480 injuries causing three days' absence (actual figures are 156 604). However, based on the 1990 labour force survey's figures, the 326 deaths in 1990/91 would have been accompanied by 91 280 major injuries, 430 320 over three days' absence injuries, and a staggering 643 850 other work injuries (less than three days' absence), which gives a total of 1 165 450 injuries *per annum*. These are horrifying statistics to wake up any complacent manager.

Furthermore, in addition to estimated differences between reported and unreported industrial injuries and ill-health, the 1990 labour force survey[2] revealed the following staggering statistics of the probable costs of industrial accidents:

* there are nearly 1.5 million work-related injuries every year, of which only just over half are reportable as laid down in the definitions given in RIDDOR
* there are over 2 million people, annually, who suffer from illnesses that they believe were caused or aggravated by their work
* there are approximately *29 million days* lost in industry *each year* due to injuries and the effects of ill-health — the equivalent of one day for *every* person in work
* HSE research found that, in 1988/89, the cost to the country of accidents occurring during manual handling operations was £90 million; they confess that this is probably an underestimate
* further HSE research found that the cost to the country of musculoskeletal disease among the working population exceeds £25 billion, £1.5 billion of which was caused by occupational factors
* between nine and ten million people are employed in occupations that include manual handling tasks and those in this group who complain of illnesses caused by occupational factors constitute 6 per cent of people who visit doctors' surgeries.

Source: HSC Annual Report 1990/91/92/93/94

Can there be any greater argument for why health and safety should be a top priority than the foregoing statistics?

Table 1.4 Disablement benefit awards (1978 to 1991²)

Year	Lung disease and deafness	Other disease and injury
1978	□□□ 1410	□□□□□□□□□□□□□□□□□□□□□□□□□□□ 12 502
1982	□□□□ 1849	□□□□□□□□□□□□□ 6408
1987	□□□□□ 2964	□□□□□ 2381*
1988	□□□□□ 3061	□□□□□ 2610*
1989	□□□□□□ 3095	□□□□ 1817*
1990	□□□□□ 2754	□□□□□□ 3504*
1991	□□□□□ 2832	□□□□□□□□□□□ 6609*
	□□□□□ 3075	□□□□□□□ 3932*
1993	□□□□□□□□ 4689	□□□□□ 3229

Source: HSC Annual Reports 1990/91/92/94.

*Rules on the degree of disability required to qualify for disablement benefit varied — 14 per cent or more disability generally, but, from 1987, figures also include degrees of disablement from 1 to 13 per cent.

Having considered industrial injuries and the effects of ill-health, let us now look at some other statistics that are also very revealing.

Occupational diseases Most occupational diseases have incubation periods of many years, with the penalty for ignorance, carelessness or complacency being paid between 10 and 40 years² after the event. Compare the annual notifications of such diseases as pneumoconiosis, asbestosis, mesothelioma, occupational asthma and occupational deafness (281 in 1986/87, 323 in 1987/88, 305 in 1989/90 and 273 in 1990/91) with the numbers actually awarded disablement benefit under occupational diseases and injuries schemes in Table 1.4. These benefit awards have steadily increased since 1978.

Prosecutions The number of successful prosecutions by the Health and Safety Executive (HSE) have risen from 1654 in 1981, with average fines of £189, to 2289 in 1990/91, with average fines of £739 (excluding exceptional fines, as given in Table 1.5). Table 1.5 illustrates the rise in prosecutions.

Enforcements There are two types of enforcement notices: improvement notices and prohibition notices. Prohibition notices may either be deferred or take immediate effect. The numbers of enforcement notices issued have risen steadily, as shown in Table 1.6.

Prosecutions and enforcements are both on the increase, with fines of up to £750 000 for very serious cases (as we have seen above). Is this due to worsening safety standards or increased activity by the HSE? The answer is that it is probably a combination of the two.

The enforcement notices given in the years 1987/88 to 1989/90 are acknowledged to be the result of continuing blitz inspections by the HSE in accident-prone construction and other sites. Also, since 1990/91, the HSE has begun to vigorously enforce the Control of Substances Hazardous to Health Regulations 1988 (COSHH) as *all* employers (and self-employed people using hazardous substances) should have completed COSHH assessments by 31 December 1989. Even by 1992, however, many had still not done so.

Table 1.5   Successful prosecutions and average penalties

Year	Prosecutions	Convictions	Average fines
1981	1838	1654	£189
1985	2258	1915	£436
1987/88	2337	2053	£427
1988/89	2328	2090	£541
1989/90	2653	2289	£739
1990/91	2292	1991	£903
1992/93	2157	1865	£1390
1993/94	1793	1507	£3061

These averages do not include the following exceptional fines which, if taken into account, would distort average trends upwards:

- for 1987/88, a fine of £750 000 against BP
- for 1989/90, a fine of £100 000 against Nobels Explosives
- for 1990/91, fines of £250 000 against Nobels Explosives (second successful prosecution), £100 000 against Tate & Lyle and £750 000 against British Rail.

As yet, two people have actually been imprisoned, both of them company directors. In 1989, and 1992, three company directors were sentenced to suspended terms of up to two years' imprisonment (plus fines to be paid by themselves and their fellow directors of up to £47,000). This included the first ever prosecution for manslaughter following an industrial accident after what was described as inattention to legal responsibilities and the ignoring of warnings given by the HSE (David Holt Plastics Limited v HSE).

Also, a managing director of a demolition firm was given a suspended sentence after endangering his workforce by failing to protect them against known asbestos. If he *had* gone to prison, the company would have been compelled to close down.

Employees are also often prosecuted, as well as employers.

Table 1.6   Enforcement notices issued (1981 to 1992)

Year	Improvement notices	Prohibition notices
1981	5921	2108
1986/87	6577	2903
1987/88	6631	4530
1988/89	6693	4853
1989/90	7610	4532
1990/91	8467	4232
1992/93	7642	4452
1993/94	6472	4051

The nature of the problem

If we bring another dimension into those statistics, we can see 'what people were doing' when they were injured. The figures shown in Table 1.7, expressed as percentages of all deaths and injuries, may surprise you. Note the continuing increase in the numbers of people suffering from falls since 1988 and that those accidents arising from handling goods have remained consistently very high.

Table 1.7 Causes of accidents

Activity	1984*	1988[†]	1989[†]	Percentages 1990[†]	1991[†]	1992[†]
Operating machinery	16.0	5.4	5.6	5.3	5.3	5.2
Firm's transport	7.0	2.5	2.7	2.7	2.5	2.6
Persons falling	16.0	**29.7**	**29.5**	**30.0**	**31.4**	**28.0**
Striking against object	8.0	6.4	6.5	6.3	6.2	5.9
Struck by falling object	6.0	15.6	15.4	15.4	14.4	15.0
Handling goods	**30.0**	**30.5**	**30.6**	**30.7**	**30.8**	**34.0**
Using oils/chemicals	4.0	2.7	2.7	2.8	3.0	2.8
Hand tools and others	13.0	7.2	7.0	6.8	6.4	6.6

Source: Manpower Services Commission and safety training manuals and statistics.
[†]*Source*: HSC/HSE annual reports for 1989, 1990, 1991, 1992 and 1994.

Statistics have a habit of extrapolating themselves into future events and proving that the law of averages is tough to beat. I want to ensure that neither your company nor your employees become part of those statistics, so I shall guide you as to what you need to know and do, to help you keep safe and within the law.

Notes

[1] This figure was that for 'reportable' accidents, that is, those resulting in absence from work of four days or more. If non-reportable accident statistics were available, they would probably at least double these figures. Indeed, an estimate of 'non-serious', non-reportable injuries (that is, fewer than three days' absence) is 1.25 million per year.

[2] The source of this information is the HSC's annual reports of 1990, 1991, 1992, 1993 and 1994.

[3] Reporting criteria changed after 1970.

[4] This figure does not include the 167 people killed in the Piper Alpha disaster on 6 July 1988.

[5] These figures are provisional (as at the 1993 report); they are likely to be revised upwards.

2

The costs of health and safety

In every aspect of business there are costs. These include staff, money, machines, materials and time.

When an item is required in the interests of health and safety, the question invariably asked is, 'How much will it cost?' We need to assess whether or not costs are reasonable and practicable (see Chapters 6 and 31), but with health and safety there are two ways to view costs, encapsulated by two questions:

'Can you afford to do it?'
'Can you afford *not* to do it?'

The costs of providing for health and safety

Personal
The first cost is a personal one of commitment. When the lives and limbs of your employees and yourself are at stake, leadership from the top is vital. A *safe* workforce is a *happy* workforce. You need to demonstrate and encourage two things:

- *safety consciousness* the attitude of mind to 'think safety' about everything that is done; to assess (*before* a hazard is created) the consequences of what you do or fail to do
- *safety awareness* the ability and keenness to look for health and safety issues in the workplace, to recognize hazards and take action to prevent them from causing accidents.

Time
It will take time to organize safety, but time taken at the outset to ensure the health, safety and welfare of your employees (and yourself) will more than pay dividends later. Employees who see that their boss is interested enough to take the time to attend to health and safety matters will be happier and better motivated. Time given to these matters at meetings or discussions will always be of benefit. A few minutes spent putting something right and making it safe will save possibly hours of lost time and heartache associated with accidents and injuries.

Money
Health and safety always cost something in financial terms. Time costs money, but there are also costs in terms of protective wear, modifications to plant and machinery (guards, fencing or mechanical), time devoted to safety and safety training. There may be professional advice needed from a health and safety specialist. These costs

will be well worth while, in that efficiency will be increased and costly accidents will be prevented. But, what if the cost is too great and unreasonable? You have to work out the cost–benefits in your case and if the *cost* is out of proportion to the *benefit*, perhaps the best advice is not to do that job at all.

The costs of avoiding health and safety provision

Experience and statistics have proven that the costs of *not* being healthy or safe are greater in the long run than those of making safe.

Personal

A lack of safety consciousness and awareness will reflect how the company's image or prestige is viewed by your employees, customers and the public — even if no accidents occur. When an accident does occur, especially one with serious consequences, employees become unsettled and concerned for their welfare, the firm loses the confidence of its customers and its good reputation generally (or gains a bad one). The embarrassment and pressures all this causes managers personally will certainly take its toll.

Time

For every hour *not* given to health and safety, there is a penalty to be paid many times over later.

Much more expensive time is lost because of accidents and accident investigations than is invested in accident prevention. How *much* time is lost, by everyone, as a result of accidental injury? The answer is as follows:

- time is lost by the victim
- time is used by first-aid attendants, doctors, nurses, hospital staff
- time is taken to investigate the incident, write a detailed report and console grieving loved ones
- time is spent dealing with safety inspectors, police and inquisitive reporters
- time is taken to restore the status quo
- time is taken to reassure worried employees
- time is taken to answer questions asked by curious customers.

There are also further hidden time losses: how much time (and money) is lost by those who work inefficiently in unsafe conditions, who feel insecure in their jobs, who have low morale and lack motivation because of little or no management concern and who take time off 'sick' regularly? How much does sick building syndrome or sick office syndrome cost? (See Chapter 26 for more on this last point.)

Money

Time lost is money lost. Add to this the costs of:

- damaged machinery and equipment and their reinstatement
- damaged or lost materials
- lost production
- lost orders due to lost customer confidence (it does happen)
- payment of company sick pay and SSP
- increased insurance premiums
- defending prosecutions (on the increase)
- paying fines (also on the increase)

- recruiting and training a replacement employee
- high labour turnover
- and so on.

Morale

'Well, the bosses don't care, so why should I?', is a comment sometimes heard during health and safety audits. But bosses who show that health and safety *are* important, who take time to train their employees in health and safety and keep them informed of essential matters of law (while not frightening them with legal gobbledegook) and who take remedial action, will demonstrate to employees that health and safety *are* important, that they care and (most important of all) that *employees* are important. It is also a form of recognition, especially when employees' observations and suggestions are listened to and acted on by management.

Of course, another 'cost' of *not* taking care of health and safety needs is becoming one of those terrible accident statistics.

3

The need for legislation

The statistics quoted in Chapter 1 speak for themselves. But, what concerned many was not so much the figures as the underlying reasons for them. In 1969, Lord Robens (then Chairman of the Coal Board) was appointed to undertake a review of safety in Britain to discover the root cause of our appalling record.

The Robens Committee worked for two years from 1970, its findings and recommendations being set out in the Robens Report and forming the basis of the Health and Safety at Work, etc. Act 1974.

The Robens Report made six basic criticisms of safety in Britain, in response to which six corresponding recommendations were made. Health, *per se*, had not really been considered to be part of safety up to 1972, as evidenced by the disablement benefit awards quoted in Chapter 1. The six main criticisms in the Report were as follows:

1. There was a mass of legislation with no systematic approach to implementation (safety law consisted of 30 statutes, often conflicting, and nearly 500 regulations)
2. Enforcement was unrealistic and almost impossible; there had become a contempt for safety law by default
3. Existing laws covered buildings and machines, but not people or what they did; nor did it cover visitors, customers or the public
4. Undue emphasis was placed on technical and mechanical safety at the expense of systems of work and management responsibilities
5. There was little or no active involvement of workers in accident prevention
6. There was a problem of attitude, in particular with that of complacency towards safety, with the result that there was little safety organization or initiative and no real involvement of workers.

Thus, a new law was enacted with a number of important features that gave a whole new approach to (health and) safety. These features were:

- a comprehensive, unified system of law enforcement contained in a single statute
- an enabling legislation, capable of encompassing changes in conditions and technology in the introduction of new regulations without new laws being passed (such as the Control of Substances Hazardous to Health (COSHH), noise, lead, asbestos, nickel and other regulations)
- concern for people, systems and procedures — not just machines and buildings
- encouraging self-regulation regarding risk prevention
- bringing the concept of personal accountability of everyone at all levels in every organization
- providing for enforcement with prosecution as a last resort.

4

The structure of laws

Throughout this book, I refer to Acts of Parliament, Regulations, codes of practice and Guidance Notes. It may be of interest to readers to know precisely what status and authority these different pieces of law have in the overall context of health and safety management and enforcement.

The nature of laws

The body of English law governing health and safety issues is quite extensive, complex and ever-growing. There are five main *types* of law:

- Acts of Parliament
- Regulations made and issued under those Acts
- Approved Codes of Practice (ACOPs)
- Statutory Codes of Practice (SCOPs)
- Guidance Notes.

Acts of Parliament (Acts)

The process by which a piece of law comes onto the statute book in Britain is quite lengthy and subject to Parliamentary procedures. The steps are as follows.

- *Green paper* At first, an 'idea' is put out by government in the form of a 'green paper' — so called simply because it is printed on green paper. This is an initial consultative document in which views of various bodies and individuals are sought by the minister responsible for the particular matter raised in the green paper.
- *White paper* After all initial consultations have been completed, all responses are considered and the original idea formulated into something more concrete and in what is called a 'white paper' — again, so called because it is printed on white paper. This is a second consultative document and has a similar wide circulation.
- *Bill* When the second consultative stage is complete, the minister then formulates a Bill, which is the final draft, and this is submitted to Parliament. It is fully discussed, amended after discussion and study by committees and finally voted on to become an Act of Parliament and then law.
- *Act of Parliament* When the Bill has been passed by Parliament, it is then passed to the monarch for royal assent, after which it is placed on the statute book and becomes law. Some Acts assert legal rights for the individual and so form part of civil law, which are enforceable by individuals through the process of civil law.

Regulations

The various Acts empower the appropriate Secretary of State to make and issue Regulations under the Acts. The purpose of this is that the Acts themselves cannot contain every detail of how the content and context of an Act will be enacted, so Regulations, which give that detail, are published. Regulations may be one of four types:

- general in scope, such as concerning the environment or accident reporting
- limited in scope, say, be specific to a particular hazard (such as lead or asbestos) or particular occupation (such as the operation of grinding wheels)
- functional, for example dealing with electricity
- industry related, such as construction, pottery or the docks.

Regulations are instructions to industry on how it should implement the requirements of the Acts. The Secretary of State does not need to go back to Parliament to obtain approval — the Act empowers them to make and issue the Regulation. However, there is always (or mostly) a consultation period with 'consultative documents' being produced, rather like the green and white papers produced for an Act, after which the full regulations are issued and become law.

Approved Codes of Practice (ACOPs)

Just to complicate things a little further — though, in fact, the purpose is to make matters easier — a code of practice is issued with the Regulations and this gives detailed guidance as to how industry can conform with the detail of the respective Regulations. ACOPs are usually drawn up in wide consultation with representatives of employers, trade unions and professional bodies and then, when the code is agreed, it is 'approved' by the Secretary of State and becomes an ACOP.

Statutory Codes of Practice (SCOPs)

A further complication is the issue of SCOPs. These are not usually generated from industry, but, rather, issued by the Health and Safety Executive (HSE) on behalf of the Health and Safety Commission (HSC), Industry Advisory Committees (IACs) set up by the HSC or possibly in conjunction with a body such as the British Standards Institution (BSI).

Guidance to ACOP/SCOP

From time to time, often when an ACOP or a SCOP is issued, Guidance booklets will be issued along with or supplementary to Regulations. Guidance booklets may be issued by the HSC, HSE, IACs or by industry itself.

Quasi-legal status

ACOPs, SCOPs and Guidance Notes have a 'quasi-legal' effect, not unlike that of most parts of the Highway Code (except those dedicated to the Road Traffic Act) in that they are not mandatory and you cannot be prosecuted for failing to comply with them. However, beware: if failure to comply with ACOPs, SCOPs or Guidance Notes should result in infringement of the law or lead to an injurious accident or dangerous occurrence, then *that* failure may be used in evidence against you.

European Community Directives

The United Kingdom, within the European Community (EC), is subject to many EC laws passed down from the European Commission in the form of EC Directives.

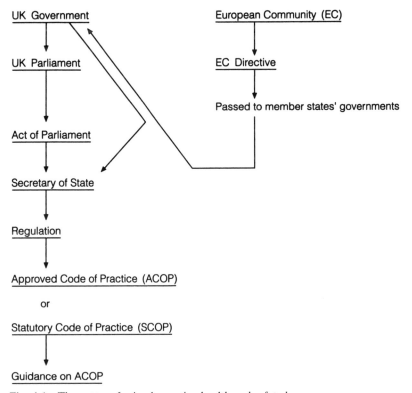

Fig. 4.1   The pattern for implementing health and safety laws

These Directives are instructions to the governments of member states to implement a particular aspect of EC law.

EC Directives, *per se*, have no power over employers in the UK. The power comes from the fact that the UK Government issues Regulations under an appropriate Act of Parliament, for example, the Management of Health and Safety at Work Regulations 1992 (MHSW Regs) were made under the HASWA. ACOPs, SCOPs and Guidance Notes are issued with these Regulations (as above). The pattern for implementation of EC Directives and other health and safety laws in the UK is as shown in Fig. 4.1.

Enforcement

For details of enforcement of health and safety laws, see Chapter 31.

5

Health and safety laws existing up to 1975

The Robens Committee, which met from 1970 to 1972, and from whose work the Health and Safety at Work, etc., Act 1974 (HASWA) evolved, found that there was a 'mass of laws and regulations'.

There is sometimes a misconception about the HASWA in that people think that it replaced and repealed all previous laws. The purpose of the HASWA was, however, not initially to repeal or to replace but to enforce. There was little wrong with the laws themselves, the problem was the lack of enforcement and powers for inspectors.

Although we discuss here the situation before the HASWA 1974, we include the HASWA to place the various laws into context.

Previous health and safety laws

Since 1802, there were numerous attempts to legislate for safety in British industry, but the laws that were passed were ineffective in the main, too narrow in their scope and unenforceable. The first real Safety Act was in 1901 and empowered the Secretary of State to issue Regulations on specific aspects of health and safety, but, after that, there was silence in terms of new safety legislation until the 1950s.

Following the pattern described in Chapter 4, a number of laws concerning health and safety were enacted in the UK in the 1950s, 1960s and 1970s, each governing particular industries:

- Agriculture (Poisonous Substances) Act 1952
- Mines and Quarries Act 1954
- Agriculture (Health, Safety and Welfare Provisions) Act 1956
- Factories Act 1961
- Offices, Shops and Railway Premises Act 1963
- Fire Precautions Act 1971.

Each of these has a series of Regulations that have been made and issued under them, such as the Abrasive Wheels Regulations issued under the Factories Act.

Factories Act 1961
Before the advent of the new 1974 Act, the Factories Act 1961 formed the main basis of penal law in relation to health and safety. The Act covered five main areas:

- health
- safety
- welfare
- home workers
- notices, returns and records.

Some parts of the Act have now been replaced or repealed by parts of the HASWA, the Reporting of Injuries, Diseases and Dangerous Occurrences Regulations 1985 (RIDDOR), the Fire Precautions Act 1971 and the Control of Lead at Work Regulations 1980. However, the Factories Act will still set the main standards for health and safety to be complied with in factories for some time to come. Note that the word 'factories' has a much wider meaning when it comes to the enforcement of this Act than it does in common usage.

Offices, Shops and Railway Premises Act 1963 (OSRP)

This follows broadly similar principles to those found in the Factories Act 1961 but applies to different types of working situations, as its name suggests.

The Health and Safety at Work etc. Act 1974 (HASWA)

The HASWA was given royal assent on 1 July 1974 and became law on 1 January 1975. After a period of grace, it was fully implemented on 1 April 1975. As with other Acts, many Regulations have been, and continue to be, issued under it, including the recent United Kingdom 1992 Regulations, which implemented the EC Directives on various aspects of health and safety. The HASWA did not, *per se*, repeal all previous laws that went before it, but, rather, reinforced them and gave powers to inspectors to enforce those laws. For example, one offence under section 14 of the Factories Act 1961 is failing to fit a guard or removing a guard from a machine, but such contravention of that Act would be prosecuted under a relevant section of the HASWA, not the Factories Act.

Other Acts affecting health and safety

There are other laws that stand alone, including:

- Food Safety Act 1990
- Environmental Protection Act 1990.

These also have Regulations issued under them, such as the Food Hygiene Regulations of 1970 and the Food Hygiene (Amendment) Regulations of 1990 and 1991, all issued under the Food Safety Act.

Regulations, ACOPs and SCOPs

These continue to be issued under the respective Acts, together with Guidance Notes. Certain Regulations issued under the HASWA will, progressively, repeal certain sections of the Factories Act and the OSRP so that those aspects will be enshrined in law under one Act, the HASWA.

6

The Health and Safety at Work etc. Act 1974

The Health and Safety at Work etc. Act 1974 (HASWA) came into force on 1 January 1975, with the normal period of grace following its introduction. There are significant differences between this Act and previous safety laws. Several important sections of the Act are discussed in detail later (in Chapters 7, 8 and 9), but here we examine the direct effects the Act has on employers, including managers, and the self-employed.

The terminology

The title of the Act was itself a revolution in safety law, with each word having significance.

'Health'

For the first time, health was specifically legislated for in the 1974 Act. Many diseases, such as pneumoconiosis, mesothelioma, asbestosis, silicosis, other cancers, dermatitis, eczema, acne, occupational deafness, and occupational asthma, had gone unchecked by regulation. This was often due to complacency and ignorance of the ill-health effects on workers of various substances and processes — until it was too late.

More recent legislation has been passed on specific matters affecting health, including lead, asbestos, noise, food safety and hygiene, and environmental pollution. Some of these are Regulations issued under the HASWA, while others are Acts in their own right (these are dealt with in detail in later chapters). The health considerations of the HASWA also incorporate emissions into the atmosphere that could adversely affect the local population (section 5). In addition to the standards of the HASWA, the Environmental Protection Act 1990 has been introduced and it has far-reaching implications, bringing in separate legislation covering the effects of employers and their operations on the general environment outside their premises (see Chapter 14).

'Safety'

The 1974 Act brought all the existing industrial safety laws together under one all-embracing statute. The old Factories Act 1961, Offices, Shops & Railway Premises Act 1963, Mines and Quarries Act 1954, Agriculture Acts 1952 and 1956, *et al.*, were not repealed but all enforced by the HASWA, though some sections (only) of these

Acts were replaced by the HASWA. Thus, a company or individual can be prosecuted under the HASWA for contravening a section of one of these earlier Acts, as we saw in the last chapter (see page 15).

'At work'

This was a new concept in safety law. Until the HASWA, only approximately one in twelve of the workforce in Britain enjoyed any protection in matters of safety, which left up to eight million people without protective legislation. There was no law to protect such workers as teachers and barristers, traffic wardens and policemen, bakers and milkmen, nor bus and taxi drivers (except by the Road Traffic Act). Nor was the army of self-employed workers either protected or made responsible (except for civil liability under common law). And travelling salespeople were protected while on their employer's premises, but once they drove off in their company car they were not protected at all. Now, anyone who is 'at work' in any situation or location is covered by this law — except domestic servants.

'Etc.'

This means that it is an enabling piece of legislation, that it is all-embracing and provides for every aspect of occupational health, safety, welfare and hygiene. It provides for Regulations to be enacted without recourse to Parliament (some of these are dealt with later).

The philosophy of the Act

Certain key points permeate the Act throughout.

- '*It shall be the duty* . . .' This is a recurring phrase in every section. It is the *duty* of every employer and employee to fulfil every aspect of the HASWA with no excuses. It is not a question of 'I will do it when I get round to it' nor 'no one has been killed, yet' nor even 'we cannot afford it'. This duty is *absolute*.
- '*So far as is reasonably practicable*' This is not a get-out clause as many at first thought. If it is reasonable and practicable then it *must* be done. Determining what is 'reasonable' is a matter of judgement and there is no clear legal definition of what it is, but if an item of safety engineering is unreasonable because of 'cost' or is impractical due to genuine technical and/or engineering difficulties, then steps must be taken to eliminate the hazard, minimize the risks and/or issue personal protective equipment — without these, the job should not be undertaken.
- *Who decides what is reasonable and practicable* The onus is on the employer (or owner of the premises) to prove that something in the interests of health and safety is *not* reasonable or practicable. It is not for the Factory Inspectorate or Environmental Health Department to prove that it *is* practicable. While, as we have seen, there is no legal definition of 'reasonable', in normal circumstances the professional opinion of a factory inspector carries considerable weight in a court of law and it is for the defendant to prove them to be wrong (section 40 of the HASWA).
- *Guilty or innocent* The normal principle of British justice is 'innocent until proved guilty' ('proven guilty' in Scottish law). However, in matters pursued under the HASWA, you are, in essence, guilty until proved innocent. It is for the defendant to prove innocence, that is, that they did their duty, so far as was reasonable and practicable, and that it was *not* reasonably practicable to do more than in fact was done (section 40 of the HASWA). In many court cases brought under the

HASWA, pleas like 'We were about to do it', 'We have operated for 20 years without trouble' or, 'I did not know . . .' have held little or no sway as mitigation.

The HASWA was designed so that another Act affecting health and safety in the employment of people would never be required to replace it. It is an all-embracing Act, bringing every statute and Regulation concerning health and safety (that had not been repealed before its inception) within its scope. It also provides for Regulations to be made under the Act, of which there have been many.

7

Duties of employers

The main duties of employers are detailed in sections 2, 3, 5, 6 and 9 of the HASWA. These include:

- duties to employees (section 2)
- duties to non-employees, including the duties of the self-employed (section 3)
- duty to control emissions into the atmosphere (section 5)
- duties of designers, manufacturers, importers and suppliers of substances (section 6)
- duties concerning personal protective wear (section 9).

Two key phrases begin each section: 'It shall be the duty', and 'so far as is reasonably practicable'.

Because of developments in legislation, we extend the scope of our discussion to health, safety, welfare and hygiene.

Duties to employees (section 2)

Who is an employee?

Two categories of persons are classified as employees for the purposes of health and safety:

1. any person who is permanently or temporarily on your payroll for the purpose of PAYE and class 1 National Insurance Contributions (NIC)
2. all initial training (IT), Youth Training (YT) and Employment Training (ET) trainees, as such trainees are classified as employees of the company that pays them (in the case of IT and YT) or the training agent who arranges and provides their training (in the case of ET). That IT and YT trainees' training allowances are funded by TECs (or LECs) or that ET trainees are paid benefits by the Department of Social Security (DSS) is not a get-out clause.

The European Commission issued a Directive to protect young people at work, which came into effect on 31 December 1993. A 'young person' is defined in the Directive as a person under the age of 18 years, while an 'adolescent' is one aged between 15 and 18 years and a 'child' is aged under 15 years. The Directive also sets maximum working hours for these categories of young people.

There was a period during which ET and YT trainees placed for work experience were *not* regarded as employees, but the final ruling on this is given in the Health and Safety (Training for Employment) Regulations 1990, which states:

> all people receiving training or work experience from an employer are deemed to be employees .... Previous provisions covering participants on government training schemes are re-enacted.

These 'previous provisions' date back as far as the Health and Safety (Youth Training Scheme) Regulations of 1984, which were enacted because of the horrific accident rates among young trainees.

What of IT, YT and ET trainees who are *not* on your payroll, but are with you as a 'training placement', directed by their training agent (who employs them) for work experience? They are *not* your employees, but the same Regulations require you to afford them the same health and safety protection as you do other employees. Also, Job Club, Job Search and Re-start members on government job finding schemes who are visitors to come and go as they please, are to be afforded the same protection as if they were employees while they are on your premises.

So, in other words, anyone who is regularly on your premises for training and/or work experience and who is not a visitor, contractor, self-employed person or customer is to be treated as you would an employee. (The situation regarding contractors, agency temps, self-employed people and visitors is dealt with under section 3.)

Plant and equipment

All plant and equipment must be safe, without risks to health and must be regularly maintained under section 2(2)(a). The implication here is that planned preventative maintenance must not wait until plant and equipment has caused an accident. It means testing for safe operation and keeping maintenance records of all preventative and remedial maintenance undertaken. It includes maintaining all necessary guards on machines and testing protective devices such as fail-safe mechanisms. Concerning records, you may have maintained a machine, but if it fails in any way, what proof will you have that you have maintained it if you do not have adequate records? Many a defence argument has failed because of the lack of written records.

Systems of work

It is not just machines or processes that are important, but the system of work, that is, the method of doing the job must be safe and without risks to health (section 2(2)(a)). So, you need to look not only at *what* is done (operate plant or machinery or make a product, say) but *how* it is done. This includes the provision of protective equipment and personal protective clothing, firefighting equipment and safety signs (see below).

Handling goods

Remember those terrible statistics for injuries caused by handling goods of Chapter 1? There must be safe systems of handling, storage and transportation of substances used or produced at work (section 2(2)(b)). 'Substance' is defined in section 53 as:

> any natural or artificial substance, whether solid or in liquid form or in the form of a gas or vapour.

Literally anything from handling a drum of chemicals or the office typewriter to moving a three-ton power press is included here (see also Chapter 10).

So serious is the problem of injuries arising from handling goods that the EC issued EC Directive 90/269/EEC, effective from 31 December 1992. It lays down minimum health and safety requirements for the manual handling of loads where there is a risk, particularly, of back injury to workers (this is dealt with in detail in Chapter 4).

Information, instruction and training

Every employee must be given all necessary information, instruction and training about job safety, the nature and hazards of substances used at work and the safe methods to use when doing their jobs (section 2(2)(c)). This is such an important subject that it is dealt with on its own in Chapter 29.

Supervision

Companies must ensure that employees are properly supervised so they are kept safe, operate in the correct and safe manner and comply with health and safety rules (section 2(2)(c)). Saying 'I gave them the instructions' or 'I have issued protective gear and told them to wear it' and then leave them to get on with the job is not enough. It is the *duty* of employers to ensure compliance with the law and their company's health and safety rules. If an enforcement officer (factory inspector or environmental health officer (EHO)) observed an employee not wearing safety helmet or goggles when the health and safety policy or safety rules say they should, the inspector would enforce that policy and those rules.

It is an offence *not* to provide supervision in the job in the same way that it is an offence to fail to give information, training and instruction and, for this reason, many firms do not allow 'lone worker' operations.

All employers have a special duty of care to young people under the age of 18 years. They must be supervised at all times and must never be left alone in the workplace. This latter point is a rigid rule of Training and Enterprise Councils (TECs) (Local Enterprise Companies (LECs) in Scotland).

Drug and solvent abuse

1990 Regulations place the responsibility for 'knowingly' permitting drug or solvent abuse in the workplace on the employer. The special duty of care includes this aspect. What the employee does off duty, off their employer's premises is their own affair, but you now have a clear duty to prevent ill-health effects of drug or solvent abuse at work and, of course, the negative effects this has on employees' safety performance.

In this respect, you have a clear duty under the Control of Substances Hazardous to Health (COSHH) Regulations 1988 to assess substances, inform employees of their ingredients and hazards, to train employees in their use, to protect employees from those hazards and to prohibit any person from abusing any of those substances that may harm them. Young persons can just as easily sniff an industrial solvent in a factory as they can sniff glue in a back street.

HSE Guidance Note regarding this area (IND(G)91L) is available free of charge from your local HSE office.

A safe place of work

Section 2(2)(d) requires that you must provide a safe place in which to work. The premises or grounds in which your employees work must be safe and without risks to health. The Act specifically mentions maintenance of buildings, but also such things as fire doors, routine access into and through workstations and emergency egress from the place of work to a fire door or exit. Also, what of the layout of the factory floor, the warehouse, machine shop and workshop? What about the office layout — are the desks too close together, providing little space for movement? They are *all* part of a safe place of work under section 2(2)(d).

Housekeeping

One of the most needy areas for training is housekeeping. By this is meant maintaining a safe place of work, ensuring employees keep their workplace and the area around their workbench clear of obstructions, with no clutter in gangways, no boxes or rubbish in access ways to fire doors or exits and so on. Floors in restaurants, hotels, residential and nursing homes and children's homes/play schemes must be kept clear at all times. Other common but avoidable hazards are caused by carelessly placed electric cables for the office typewriter, computer, photocopier and (most lethal of all) the office kettle. *Never* keep a kettle or boil water in it on the floor — this creates a deadly risk of scalding. Keep kettles in kitchens or at least on tables in the office.

Environment

You must provide a safe and healthy work environment (section 2(2)(e)). By this is meant that there should be adequate lighting, heating and ventilation in the workplace. Also, the decor and cleanliness should be attended to, and a healthy, risk-free atmosphere maintained. Here are some specific points.

- *Lighting* There must be adequate natural and/or artificial lighting — not too dim and not too bright. Remember that people's eyesight can be adversely affected by both poor light and glare from lights that are too bright. Fluorescent lights cause glare, which can be damaging to eyesight, and so diffusers should be fitted to tubes to eliminate or reduce this (especially important where computers, computer terminals and word processors with visual display units (VDUs) are in use (see Chapter 19 for more on this).
- *Heating* The *minimum* temperature you must achieve in workplaces where a substantial proportion of the work is sedentary or requires no serious physical effort is 16°C (60°F) within one hour of commencing work (section 3 of the Factories Act 1961 and section 6 of the Offices, Shops and Railway Premises Act 1963). There is no *maximum* temperature, but conditions must still be 'reasonable', and you must not use energy to create a temperature above 19°C (66°F) (Fuel and Electricity (Heating Control) Order 1980).
- *Ventilation* There must be adequate ventilation in the workplace, but it must not be so great as to create draughts. This can be achieved by ensuring that windows can be opened or by installing extractor fans and/or air conditioning. But, beware of relying *solely* on extractor fans for ventilation, as this could present problems when it is necessary to use extinguishers in the event of a fire (for example, Halon (BCF) gives off harmful fumes that need to be dispersed; see Chapter 12).

- *Atmosphere* The atmosphere in the workplace must be clean and free of harmful or unpleasant gases or fumes. This includes the dispersal of gases and dust from the atmosphere. Surprisingly, there are known instances of people having been killed by exploding dust in the atmosphere. Two come to mind. One of these was when a manager and a foreman died in a flour mill and another was when six employees died in an ammunition plant. All the dust hazards needed in these cases was a spark.

Good housekeeping, therefore, is important to the working environment and is key to a *safe* working environment.

Smoking
There is growing concern about smoking in the workplace and its ill-health effects upon workers who do *not* smoke (called passive smokers). Ill-health can be short term, with bronchial, throat or asthmatic problems, or it can become permanent, say in the form of nicotine-related cancers. Even many smokers are beginning to recognize the benefits of a smoke-free atmosphere. Regulations likely in the future will make it possible for employers who permit smoking that affects the health of non-smoking employees to face prosecution. In August 1990, the EC Court judged that a lady who suffered lung damage due to passive smoking was the 'victim of an industrial accident', opening the way for claims for industrial injury benefit and/or compensation.

Sick building or sick office syndrome

Another area of concern is the sick building syndrome (SBS) or sick office syndrome (SOS). Experts warn us of the danger of allergies and diseases caused by poor working and other environments, due to various factors. These are dealt with in Chapter 26.

Welfare

The Act reiterates the phrase 'health, safety and *welfare*' throughout. Welfare is important for employees. In addition to environmental matters, the law requires that there be a minimum provision of sanitary conveniences and wash basins, the numbers required being dependent on the ratios of males to females, as laid down in section 7 of the Factories Act 1961 and section 9 of the Offices, Shops and Railway Premises Act 1963. Where from one to five people are employed in a single employer's premises, one communal (male and female combined) toilet is acceptable, but, where *more* than five people are employed, there *must* be separate conveniences for male and female employees (quite separate from any dedicated disabled facilities).

Factories
There must be one sanitary convenience (WC) for each 25 male employees and each 25 female employees separately. In factories that employ more than 100 males, one WC for every 25 males up to 100, plus, thereafter, one WC for every 40 (or part thereof) males is acceptable — providing there is also an adequate provision of urinals. Sanitary conveniences must be so constructed that their interior is not visible from outside the convenience. Separate approaches must be provided for male and female facilities, and suitable signs or symbols must be fixed to the doors. Walls of all sanitary conveniences must be washed down at least every 14 months, while floors must be swept daily and washed at least weekly (section 7 of the Factories Act 1961).

Building sites
The requirements for the provision of sanitary conveniences for building site operations are similar to those for factories, except that the ratios for more than 100 employees are one per 35 (male and female) employees.

Offices, shops and railway premises
The ratios of WCs to employees required for offices, shops and railway premises are different to those for factories. The ratios of WCs to male and female employees separately is one WC for every 15 (or part thereof) employees up to 100 of each sex; with a ratio of one WC for every 25 (or part thereof) over 100 employees of each sex. Where urinals are provided for males, the figure is more complicated (see Table 7.1).

Where there is shared occupancy of premises, the *aggregate* numbers of male and female employees determine the numbers of conveniences there should be. Where customers are also present in premises — say for a restaurant or supermarket — an addition of one convenience for each sex must be added to the above.

It is unlawful to have no provision for female employees. If a female is refused (or declines) a job because there are no toilets, she can sue for sex discrimination at an Industrial Tribunal and be awarded compensation (as in the case of Anderson *v* Alexander Pollock Limited, August 1990, when an award of £4600 was made to the lady concerned).

Food consumption
There must be adequate facilities to enable employees to eat food away from workbenches and the factory floor, but *not* adjacent to toilets. Employees must especially *not* consume food in factories where lead, ionizing and non-ferrous metals are worked.

Hand washing
In kitchens where food is prepared for sale or supply to employees and/or members of the public, there must be separate wash-basins away from sinks for washing dishes and utensils; they must also be separate from non-catering employees and the public.

Clothing
Facilities must be provided for outdoor clothing/footwear away from kitchens and from places of food manufacture, such as meat pie factories. Cloakroom facilities

Table 7.1 Ratios of WCs and urinals to males employed

Numbers of males employed	Numbers of WCs	Numbers of urinals
up to 15	1	—
16 to 20	1	1
21 to 30	2	1
31 to 45	2	2
46 to 60	3	2
61 to 75	3	3
76 to 90	4	3
91 to 100	4	4
Over 100	4	4*

*Plus one WC *or* urinal for every 25 (or part thereof) employees over 100.

should also be provided, for safety reasons, away from factories and machine shops.

HASWA information poster

Requirements to display the Factories Acts and/or Offices, Shops and Railway Premises Acts were repealed on 18 October 1989 by the Health and Safety Information for Employees Regulations 1989 (SI. 682). You may, if you wish, still display the old posters in training centres, as they are still law and useful training aids for, say, IT/YT/ET trainees.

The 1989 Regulations require you to display the laminated-plastic HSE poster 'Health and Safety Law: What you should know' (available from HMSO) ISBN 0.11.701424.9, price £3.20 + VAT in 1991. It must be displayed in a place where all employees can see and read it daily (not just the manager or administration staff).

Other notices

You will be required to display copies of various Regulations according to the particular operation undertaken in your workplace, for example:

Abrasive Wheels Regulations 1970
Aerated Water Regulations 1921
Celluloid Regulations 1921
Cinematograph Film Stripping Regulations 1939
Clay Works (Welfare) Special Regulations 1948
Cotton Cloth Factories Regulations 1929
Dry Cleaning Special Regulations 1949
Factories (Testing of Aircraft Engines and Accessories) Special Regulations 1952
Food Hygiene Regulations 1970, as amended
Foundries (Protective Footwear and Gaiters) Regulations 1971
Highly Flammable Liquids and Liquefied Petroleum Gases Regulations 1972
Horizontal Milling Machines Regulations 1928
Iron and Steel Foundries Regulations 1953
Locomotives and Wagons (Used on Lines and Sidings) Regulations 1906
Magnesium (Grinding of Castings and Other Articles) Special Regulations 1946
Non-ferrous Metals (Melting and Founding) Regulations 1962
Pottery (Health and Welfare) Special Regulations 1950
Power Presses Regulations 1965, and 1972 amendment
Self-acting Mule Spinning Regulations 1905
Woodworking Machines Regulations 1974
Work in Compressed Air Special Regulations 1958.

Health and safety policy

Every firm employing five or more persons (including the director(s)/owner-manager(s)) must have a written statement of their policy on health, safety and welfare (section 2(3)). If you have four or fewer, including the boss, you are not *required* to write one, but it is still a good idea to do so.

Do remember that IT/YT/ET trainees are employees for the purposes of health and safety, as outlined earlier. Thus, a director or owner-manager plus three employees, plus one such trainee, gives a total of five, so you must have a written statement of your health and safety policy, which must be brought to the attention of every employee.

There is no set format for health and safety policies, though the HSC and HSE have published several booklets to assist in drawing up health and safety policies, including:

Effective policies for health and safety (available from HMSO)
Safety policies in the educational sector (by the Education Services Advisory Committee, available from HMSO)
Writing your health and safety policy statement (a model statement for small businesses, available from HMSO)
Guidance on implementation of safety policies (for the construction industry, by the Construction Industry Advisory Committee, available from the HSE)
Our health and safety policy statement (ISBN 0.11.885510.7, by the HSE, available from HMSO).

A policy must contain the following basic themes:

- *what* you will do
- *how* it will be done
- *who* will be involved
- *who* is responsible.

Your policy must cover at least the five subsections of the Act as outlined above, that is:

- 2(2)(a): provision and maintenance of safe plant and equipment
- 2(2)(b): arrangements for safe handling, storage and transportation of substances
- 2(2)(c): provision of supervision, information, training and instruction
- 2(2)(d): maintenance of a safe and risk-free place of work, including safe access and egress
- 2(2)(e): maintenance of safe and healthy working environments
- COSHH: arrangements for compliance with COSHH Regulations 1988
- substances: arrangements for safety and health regarding substances used or encountered, such as lead, nickel, ionization, asbestos.

Really, for the first part, all you need to do is look at the headings in this chapter and say 'that is what we are going to do'. Your policy is already well underway.

You should include in your policy *all* those aspects relevant to your industry, products and processes *required* by statute (of which the list seems endless) and those you *need* to include due to your local situation, plus those which, as manager, you personally feel appropriate. Do think long term, not just what could happen today or next month. If some process or event *could* take place only once a year or is merely *possible*, you should include it. Otherwise, you will end up revising your policy more frequently than is necessary.

Responsibility

The responsibility for health and safety must lie with a senior executive and the policy document must be signed by the chief executive (yourself?). In the case of multisited establishments, the overall company policy should be signed by the company's chief executive and the individual unit or site policies by the unit or site senior manager.

Delegation

Your policy should include an organization chart, family tree style, which shows the levels and channels of communication in the company through which accountability for health and safety is delegated. Remember, however, that although authority can be delegated downwards in the organization, the ultimate responsibility for health and safety rests and remains at the top — with the chief executive or site/unit manager.

Beware

Your policy should be realistic. Whatever you state in your policy becomes law (in effect) and, as indicated above, employees are required by the HASWA to obey it. Thus, if, for example, you decide that all employees must wear safety helmets everywhere and you put notices up to that effect, even though there is, in reality, no need for helmets, a HSE inspector or EHO would enforce the wearing of helmets because your policy and the signs say 'helmets must be worn'. Do you really want the secretaries to wear safety helmets at their desks or when walking through your warehouse area? Be realistic.

A brief outline of a typical health and safety policy, which you may use as a guide, is given in Appendix 1. The HSE's booklet *Our health and safety policy statement*, mentioned above, will also greatly assist you in writing your own policy; you can use it as a guide or just fill in the blank spaces for your organization.

Safety representatives

If you have a recognized trade union, that union's members are permitted to nominate their own appointed safety representatives (section 2(4), HASWA, and Safety Representatives and Safety Committees Regulations 1977).

Elected safety representatives have certain rights. They may:

- carry out workplace inspections not more than once every three months, with written notice one week prior to each occasion
- inspect new machinery or major changes in machinery as they occur and without notice
- independently investigate any accident or serious incident that occurs in the workplace they represent (that is, not in another department or workplace not represented by them)
- make reports and recommendations to management concerning safety
- receive copies of all relevant documents relating to occurrences
- represent the workforce (including non-members) to management in matters of health, safety, welfare and hygiene.

Section 2(5) of the Act also provides for the appointment of safety representatives by non-union employees, but this has not yet been backed by any Regulation. Even if you do not have a recognized trade union, I suggest that it would be a good policy to permit the appointment of representatives. Many non-union companies have representatives who do a very valuable job, but it is a matter for you, the employer, to decide on.

Whether elected and appointed by trade union or non-union employees, management has no legal right of influence in election of representatives. It is the duty of employers to consult with safety representatives and involve them in the health and safety process (section 2(6)).

Health and safety coordinators

Where there is no professionally qualified health and safety practitioner appointed in a company, management may wish some functional employee involvement at worker level. A very useful method is the appointment of health and safety coordinators in the junior management structure, perhaps as an additional duty for an existing job description. They do not feature in law, there is no legal requirement to appoint them, but wide experience suggests that such an appointment can prove a valuable link between management and employees, and provide a way of ensuring that things happen instead of being perpetually overlooked.

What do health and safety coordinators do?

The short answer is, whatever you want them to do, within their level of competence, plus act as facilitators, ensuring that where requirements for health and safety exist or arise, they are organized. Their basic duties could follow the pattern of health and safety representatives, plus this element of ensuring that where requirements exist or arise for health, safety, welfare and hygiene matters, they act as facilitators to them being met. However, it would be grossly unfair to make such an appointment without giving them correct training for the job — health and safety is a complicated and demanding job!

Should they be qualified safety practitioners?

Not necessarily, as the function of a health and safety coordinator is to 'coordinate' and to facilitate, which may mean obtaining the services of people who are suitably qualified to satisfy the particular needs that exist or arise. An ability to organize and enthusiasm for health and safety, plus good basic training, therefore, would be the main assets of the post-holder.

Safety committees

The above-quoted Regulations state that if two or more elected safety representatives (not coordinators) request that a safety committee be established, then you must set one up (section 2(7)). If no formal request is made, there is no statutory obligation. Membership of the committee should be by election from the employees and appointment from management, with equal representation. Safety representatives may also serve on the committee, but this is not necessarily so. The function of the safety committee should be similar to that of safety representatives, but more inclined towards the *management* of health, safety, welfare and hygiene than *policing* them. It should, for example:

- examine accident, injury and diseases statistics and trends, conditions and practices
- discuss and analyse health and safety audits or investigation reports and recommendations
- advise management on safety policy or rules and on safe systems of work
- assess the effectiveness of safety training and of health and safety communication in the workplace.

Always ensure that a committee has an *agenda* and that the agenda is strictly adhered to. Avoid the item 'any other business' to ensure that *only* health, safety, welfare and hygiene matters are discussed. Experience has shown that where these principles are not followed, the committee develops into a 'talking shop' and a platform for airing a variety of complaints, often nothing to do with health and safety. The result is a costly waste of time and resources.

Even if you have no statutory obligation to have one, a committee is, nevertheless, a very useful instrument. Very small firms probably cannot afford the time for health and safety committees, but, then, putting health and safety items on the production meeting agenda or setting up a small, informal working party would prove valuable.

Safety supervisors

Various Regulations require that safety supervisors be appointed in certain sensitive industries. These industries are:

- construction
- cinematograph film (manufacture and stripping)
- potteries
- shipbuilding and repair
- diving
- ionizing.

It is not essential for safety supervisors to be qualified health and safety practitioners (though it is useful), but they must be competent, suitably qualified and experienced in the particular industry or process being conducted. Indeed, qualified safety officers may *not* be 'competent' in the particular circumstances of the job.

Safety supervisors should check that Regulations relating to their industry and process are being complied with and promote health and safety in the systems of work. They would also provide advice to the employer.

First aid

There are three requirements on employers with regard to first aid:

1. to provide adequate first aid facilities, which will be determined by:
    - the numbers employed
    - the nature of the undertaking
    - the physical size of the establishment and how employees are deployed within it
    - the location of the premises and of employees (on site or mobile and in transit, for example)
2. to inform employees of the arrangements and procedures for first aid
3. where a first aid room is provided, it must conform with the standards set out in the 1900 ACOP
4. to appoint suitably qualified first aid attendants.

First aid attendants

Every employer must appoint first aid attendants (known as first aiders) where access to medical treatment in an accident and emergency centre (such as a hospital or doctor's surgery) outside the workplace is too distant to obtain medical help quickly and easily. There is no threshold laid down for how many employees you need to have to appoint first aiders, so, theoretically, if you have only one employee you should have at least one first aider (though it is doubtful that this would be enforced).

The ACOP does not lay down any rigid rules as to the numbers of first aiders there should be, but says that *sufficient* numbers should be appointed. When deciding how many to appoint, you should consider not only the numbers of employees to be serviced, but also the nature of your undertaking, the physical spread of your operations and the processes and products of your business. The ACOP suggests a ratio of first aiders to employees of a *minimum* of one or more first aiders per 50 employees (or part of 50 for hazardous situations). Do remember that you should allow for absences on holiday, training, sickness, meetings and lunchbreaks, so the advice is to add, say, one suitable person for each three appointed permanent first aiders.

Small firms In small firms of a non-hazardous nature (not a building site or engineering establishment) employing, say, 25 people or fewer, the ACOP permits 'appointed persons'. An appointed person in this respect is not a qualified 'suitable person' (see below), but one who has undergone only basic first aid training (what to do in an emergency, how to call an ambulance, how to maintain a first aid box, and so on). *They are neither qualified nor authorized to administer first aid.*

Suitable persons The 1990 ACOP refers to first aiders as 'suitable persons'. No one *except* a 'suitable person' shall be permitted to administer first aid to any patient. Anyone who is unqualified, not appointed and who gives first aid treatment to someone lays themselves open to civil action in the event of erroneous treatment and any adverse reaction to the treatment given. Also, the employer could be similarly liable for aiding and abetting this. Who, therefore, is a suitable person? The answer is as follows:

- a person appointed by the employer who holds a *current* first aid certificate as a result of undergoing an approved course at a training organization approved by the HSE (these are normally the St John Ambulance, Red Cross and some Training and Enterprise Council (TEC) accredited training organizations)
- a person who has undergone training and obtained qualifications approved by the HSE for the purposes of the Regulations, which are:
  —a qualified doctor (MD), registered with the British Medical Council
  —a qualified nurse (say, a state registered nurse (SRN), registered general nurse (RGN) or state enrolled nurse (SEN)) who holds a *current* registration with the United Kingdom Central Council for Nursing, Midwifery and Health Visiting (UKCC), parts 1, 2 and 7 of its Single Professional Register.

No other people are acceptable. Thus, a person who was a qualified ambulance driver or Army medic ten years ago does not qualify for this role.

First aid boxes
They should be of a 'suitable material', able to protect the contents and keep them clean. On the front, clearly visible, should be a white cross on a green background, with perhaps, similarly, the words 'first aid'. They should contain the minimum of materials suitable for the working environment, as laid down in the Regulations and ACOP. The *minimum* contents of static workplace boxes should be as follows:

- general guidance card (see below)
- 20 individually wrapped, sterile, assorted dressings ('detectable' dressings for catering establishments)
- 2 sterile eye-pads with attachments
- 6 individually wrapped triangular bandages
- 6 safety-pins
- 6 medium-sized, individually wrapped, sterile, unmedicated wound dressings (approximately 10 × 8 cm)
- 2 large, sterile, individually wrapped, unmedicated wound dressings (approximately 13 × 9 cm)

- 3 extra-large, sterile, individually wrapped, unmedicated dressings (approximately 28 × 17.5 cm)
- if no running water is available, sterile water or saline solution (0.9 per cent), in sealed, disposable containers.

AIDS First aid is administered to many people from all walks of life and to those not known personally to the first aider. It is important to protect first aiders against the possibility of contracting the HIV virus and/or AIDS. Although not on the 1990 ACOP approved list, it is also strongly advised that you include the following two items in the first aid box:

- a box of disposable plastic gloves
- a resusciade (not a Brookes airway, as only medically qualified people can use these).

You will need to have a policy on AIDS. It is suggested that this be included in your overall company policy or, in very small companies with only one or two first aiders, be made known by written instruction to your attendants and in the first aid box.

Portable or travelling first aid boxes These should contain the following:

- general guidance card (see below)
- 6 individually wrapped, sterile-adhesive dressings
- 1 large, sterile, unmedicated dressing
- 2 triangular bandages
- 2 safety-pins
- individually wrapped moist cleaning wipes.

Other points to remember Standard first aid boxes are readily available. The contents of first aid boxes must be kept up to the minimum levels listed above, so a weekly or monthly check by the 'suitable person' is recommended. If you have several first aiders, it is advisable to appoint one (the senior) of them, otherwise each will think the other has done the job and it may be neglected.

No other items (such as safety helmets, office keys, flask and sandwiches or any item not on the prescribed list) should be in the box. If you want to keep such items as eye lotion, antiseptic liquid, scissors or non-listed bandages (*not* creams), they should be kept in a separate container.

Never keep or administer (or allow first aiders to administer) pills or tablets (such as paracetamol) or creams of any kind (even antiseptics) to anyone — refer the patient to a doctor. You never know what other drugs a person may be taking (or may have taken) or what allergies a person may have. This is why the specified plasters and bandages are '*un*medicated'.

You may also consider keeping adjacent to (but not *in*) the first aid box such items as plastic gloves, aprons, blankets, blunt-ended stainless steel scissors and disposal bags.

A 'General Guidance Card' to be kept *in* the first aid box is contained in the Regulations and government copyright is waived so that you may reproduce it.

Most importantly:

- always keep all items scrupulously clean
- always dispose of any plaster or bandage that has been opened or partially used as *an opened item is no longer sterile.*

The first aid room

There is no legal obligation to provide a first aid room, but, where one *is* provided, it must conform to the ACOP and should have:

- sink with hot and cold water
- soap and paper towels
- drinking water and disposable cups
- smooth-topped work surfaces
- suitable store equipped as for first aid boxes
- refuse containers and plastic bags
- couch with waterproof surface and clean pillow/blankets
- clean protective garments for first aiders
- chair
- bowl
- records, such as first aiders' certificates, accident books, accident investigation reports (company and HSE Forms F2508/F2508A; see Chapter 30)
- a trained and appointed first aider available at all times when people are working.

The provision of first aid facilities on employers' premises is governed by the Health and Safety (First Aid) Regulations 1981 (as amended). These Regulations are supported by the 1990 ACOP on first aid. Copies of both of these are available from HMSO. These Regulations apply to all employers, employees and self-employed alike.

Incident or accident?

'Incident' and 'accident' have different meanings. An *incident* is an occurrence that, although potentially dangerous and with possible health and/or safety consequences, does not result in injury, ill-health effects or damage. An *accident* is an occurrence that *does* result in injury, ill-health effects or damage, no matter how slight.

Incidents

Under the Reporting of Injuries, Diseases and Dangerous Occurrences Regulations (RIDDOR) 1985 (as amended), all major incidents are called 'dangerous occurrences' and must be reported to your local HSE office or environmental health officer within seven days of their occurrence on HSE Report Form F2508 (available, in pads, from HMSO, ISBN 0.11.883853.9). The form includes such things as explosions, major collapses, fires. The list of 'dangerous occurrences' is quite extensive and is to be found in the RIDDOR.

Injuries

All injuries, however trivial, must be reported to management by the victim or, if unable, another responsible person within 24 hours. Details of first aid and/or medical treatment given must be recorded in an accident book. You can design your own accident book or you may use Accident Book DSS Form BI510 (ISBN 0.11.761384.3, price £1.25 each, 10 for £8, or 50 for £33, from HMSO). Your accident register must contain the following information (for which DSS Form BI510 is ideal):

- full name, home address and occupation of the patient/victim
- signature of the person making the record entry and the date, plus their address if not the patient/victim

- details of the accident, including when, where and *how* it happened, with as much detail as possible (not just 'cut finger')
- details of the injury or ill-health effect suffered
- a box for the employer's signature if the accident is 'reportable' under RIDDOR.

Although not required by RIDDOR, it is also strongly advised that you record the details of first aid treatment given by the first aider, medical practitioner or hospital, with the signature of the person giving treatment if possible. This will provide valuable support information in the event of future enquiries, say, if there is a compensation claim.

Reportable occurrences Under RIDDOR, *all* injuries that result in absence from work of four days or more (called an 'over 3-day injury' in the HSE's annual reports) or are fatal, certain major injuries even where there is no absence from work, certain industrial diseases, and other major incidents, such as fires and explosions, *must* be reported to your local HSE office or environmental health officer. This should be by the quickest possible means (normally telephone) and followed up by sending a completed HSE Report Form F2508 or F2508A within seven days of the occurrence. Note that the requirement under RIDDOR to record the above dangerous occurrences, fatalities and injuries that result in absence of four days or more in the 'Register of reportable accidents, dangerous occurrences and ill-health enquiries register' (HSE Form F2509) has been discontinued.

Protective wear

In addition to the duty to provide protective equipment and clothing as part of the 'safe system of work' (discussed above), section 9 of the HASWA makes it unlawful to levy any charge for any protective device, clothing or equipment that is a requirement either because of company policy or health, safety and hygiene regulations. The test is, does the law or do you *require* employees to wear or use personal protection in the interests of health, safety or hygiene? If the answer to this is 'Yes', you must provide it free of charge, because to charge employees for it is an offence under the Act. However, if you only 'recommend' their use (for example, of safety shoes), then you may seek payment, but you cannot compel employees to wear or use them. You can reasonably insist on *sensible* footwear in these circumstances, though (wearing slippers or open-toed sandals in a factory is downright irresponsible, after all).

Notifiable diseases

Under section 29 of the Public Health (Control of Diseases) Act 1984, employers must notify their local environmental health department if any employee is suffering from a notifiable disease. You must also notify the local authority of any employee suffering a disease that can infect food and cause food poisoning (see also Chapter 30).

Duties to non-employees

Both you and your employees have a duty to people who are not your employees. This duty applies in two ways:

- directly to others
- indirectly, through the environment.

Directly to others

This duty is to ensure that every task undertaken by you and your employees in your business (on or off your premises) is safe and without risks to the health and safety of visitors, customers, suppliers and the general public (section 3(1)). Self-employed people have the same duty (section 3(2)). Employers and the self-employed must provide information to those who are not their employees about things they do, materials they use or goods they supply that may affect them (section 3(3)). An example of what can happen if you do not exercise this duty comes to mind. In mid 1991, a firm of consulting engineers whose design and advice led to hazards to the public when a building fascia collapsed was fined £20 000, plus £75 000 costs.

IT, YT and ET trainees, students on work experience schemes, subcontractors and Job Club and Re-start members are to be regarded as employees while on employers' premises for the purposes of health, safety, hygiene and welfare. They must be given full protection under section 2 as detailed under 'Duties to employees' at the beginning of this chapter, as required by the Health and Safety (Training for Employment) Regulations 1990.

Remember, *all* IT, YT and ET trainees have the status of employees of the company on whose payroll they are (in the case of IT/YT) or with whom they have been placed for work experience (in the case of ET). Job Club and Re-start members are *not* employees — they are technically 'visitors' — but they are, nevertheless, to be afforded the same protection as employees while on the employer's premises.

Indirectly, through the environment

This duty is to ensure that there are no harmful emissions into the atmosphere (section 5). This means not emitting noxious and offensive substances and rendering harmless and ineffective any substance that may be emitted. It would appear from section 5(3) that what is 'noxious or offensive' is not confined to the description on a label but what is perceived by a user or third person to be noxious or offensive, including noise. Section 5(4) of the HASWA attributes responsibility to the person in control of the process of manufacture and not solely to the owner of premises.

There have been instances where employers have been doing their sincere best to expel fumes, dust and gases from inside their workplace (obeying section 2(2)(e)), only to find themselves in trouble for polluting the external environment (under section 5). Hence the duty of 'rendering harmless' mentioned above (see also Chapter 14).

Other duties

There are other duties that employers have to their employees and these are so significant that they justify separate chapters. Many health, safety and hygiene aspects are now given special status by UK laws and Regulations and by EC Directives. These are dealt with in the following chapters: 10 on the COSHH Regulations; 12 on fire; 13 on noise; 14 on environmental protection; 15 on electricity at work; 18 on management of health and safety; 19 on VDUs and VDTs; and 27 on stress management. Also, there are further Regulations that apply to employers, too numerous and complex to include in this volume. Included here are those Regulations that will apply in part or in whole to *all* employers.

There are sanctions and penalties for failure to comply with the HASWA that were increased from 1 October 1992. See Chapter 31 for details of these.

8

Duties to customers

The duties of firms as suppliers of goods and services to their customers (and to their customers' customers) are laid down in section 6 of the HASWA. These duties are extensive and relate to the design, manufacture, construction, supply or sale, installation and servicing of any article or substance 'for use at work'.

The supply of goods and services for retail sale to and consumption by the public is covered by the Consumer Protection Act 1987. Some of the duties of section 6 are repealed by the Trades Descriptions Act, but the principles still apply.

The Food Safety Act 1990 also has similar and far-reaching duties (see Chapter 13).

The terminology

An article is any item of plant, machinery, instrumentation, equipment, electronic apparatus, raw or worked material or clothing supplied or installed for use at work.

- *Substance* A substance is any liquid, oil, chemical, solvent, gas or powder supplied for use at work.
  In other words, articles and substances are anything you sell or supply for use in a working environment.
- *Electricity* Electrical or electronic equipment and apparatus *are* 'articles', but electricity, *per se*, is a substance and the mode of 'supply' is unlikely to be encountered outside the electricity supply industries. However, do remember that electricity actually *used* in any working environment comes under the controls of the Electricity at Work Regulations 1989 (see Chapter 15).

Duties as a supplier

Design and construction
The article must be safe by design and so constructed as to be safe and without risks to health when properly used by a person in their work (section 6(1)(a)), which means that it must not be cobbled together in some unprofessional make-shift 'that'll do' manner. When designing your product, you must examine all the possible health and safety risks that could possibly arise. For example, you may design a wonderful fork-lift truck that is safe and reliable in its performance, but what happens when an overweight driver's anatomy protrudes from the recesses in the seat?

You must ensure that your article is foolproof, as a person may, unwittingly or wilfully, place themselves in a hazardous situation. This is why fail-safe devices are fitted to many machines in addition to the guards required by section 14 of the Factories Act 1961 and section 17 of the Offices, Shops and Railway Premises Act 1963. An excellent help on this subject is the book *British Standard Code of Practice for Safety of Machinery*, BS.5304: 1988, published by the British Standards Institution, 1988.

Tests and examinations

There are important duties placed on you as a designer and manufacturer to make sure, by conducting tests and examinations on those articles and substances you supply, that they are completely safe and without risks to health. You must:

- test each article designed and manufactured by you to ensure that it meets required standards (section 6(1)(b))
- ensure that it is safe and without risks to health when in use, by including the fitting of guards and fail-safe devices and so on (section 6(4)(b))
- provide information about those tests and any necessary rules for safe working conditions that the user must ensure are followed and which you prescribe for that article or substance (section 6(4)(c)).

Your customer/user *must* be able to rely on your research and test data and not have to replicate your tests in order to assess any possible hazards or risks to health (section 6(6)).

Information

You must provide information about your article and/or substance, its make-up, construction, chemical ingredients, the hazards associated with your product and the necessary precautions to take against those hazards. You must also provide information about the safe use of your product and conditions necessary to put it to that use (section 6(1)(c)).

Research

You must carry out research into the design of your article (section 6(2)) or substance (section 6(5)) before it is made and conduct research into that article or substance itself. This is to discover what hazards there may be, what the risks of that hazard to safety or health are and whether or how they can be eliminated, minimized or protected against (in that order!)

Installation

If you erect any article, it must be in such a state as not to pose a threat to health and safety when properly used (section 6(3)). This article might be a power press, centre lathe, grinding machine, computer, typewriter, coffee machine, electronic control panel, a chimney, whatever. It might be a chemical, gas or solvent for use at work.

Use

Whatever you design, manufacture, import, supply or install, you *must* ensure that it is safe and without risks to health when used (section 6(4)(a)). This should be provided for by your tests, as noted above.
Question: What information will you give about the conditions in which it should be used or *not* be used.

The user's responsibility

It is possible that you may include in a contract of sale and purchase that the purchaser will carry out their own tests in their working environment. For example, this may be necessary when it is not possible for you to replicate your customer's working situation in your own design or manufacturing premises. Where your customer, in a *written agreement*, undertakes the proper use of the article or substance that you have supplied, in a manner that is safe and without risks to health of the users, then those duties are transferred to your customer.

However, this will not absolve you of any liability for any malfunction due to manufacturing faults that may lead to injury or ill-health. You cannot simply pass that responsibility on to your customer by placing a disclaimer on the product or in support literature. Substances have been found with a disclaimer on the label and words to the effect that it is the customer's responsibility to conduct their own tests and assessments, but this is illegal.

The relationship between supplying and selling

Although consumer laws place the responsibility for trade descriptions on the person who actually *sells* (retails) an article or substance to the end user — the 'ostensible supplier' — under section 6(9) it is the manufacturer — the 'effective supplier' — who carries the liability for the article or substance being safe and without risks to health. You cannot pass the buck down the line!

Leased equipment

'Any person who sells or lets on hire, or as agent of the (seller or) hirer causes or procures to be (sold or) let on hire, for use in a factory in the United Kingdom, any machine intended to be driven by mechanical power which does not comply with the requirements . . . (of the regulations pertaining to that equipment) . . . shall be guilty of an offence' (section 17(1) of the Factories Act 1961).

Under this law, the hirer (or seller) of prime movers, transmission machinery and dangerous parts of any machinery has a duty to see to it that it is safe, including ensuring that every set-screw, bolt or key on the revolving shaft, spindle, wheel or pinion is so sunk, encased or otherwise safely guarded as to present no danger to the user. Revolving shafts, flywheels, couplings, belts and pulley drives, and chain and sprocket drives, wheels or pinions must be securely fenced. Also, any spur and other toothed friction gearing that does not need frequent adjustment while in motion must be completely encased. The only exception to these rules is if an item is so 'safe by position' as to be as safe as if it were encased; but beware when maintenance is underway!

These rules apply equally to items sold as to items hired out, but the duties of hirers are emphasized here. Further provisions to this rule apply to equipment used in construction and jute industries and to the supply of abrasive wheels. The specific Regulations are:

Construction (General Provisions) Regulations 1961 (SI 1580)
Jute (Safety, Health and Welfare) Regulations 1948 (SI 1696)
Abrasive Wheels Regulations 1970 (SI 535).

Leased vehicles

There have been instances of vehicle hire companies supplying cars, vans and lorries to lessees and, apart from collecting rents, seeking to shed their responsibility for that vehicle. Unless there is *written agreement* with the lessor to the effect that they are responsible for all repairs, maintenance and satisfying Department of Transport requirements for MOT certificates, the responsibility rests with the vehicle hire company.

If, for example, a lease is within, say, one month of expiry, the vehicle is at or past the date when an MOT inspection is due and the vehicle fails the test but the lease company refuses to carry out the necessary work for the MOT certificate to be granted (because the vehicle is going to be auctioned), then that hire company is committing an offence under both section 6 of the HASWA and under the Consumer Protection Act 1987, as the vehicle is manifestly unsafe. It also, of course, contravenes the Road Traffic Act 1991.

It must also be remembered that, where a vehicle is provided to a customer company for use by its employees, and the vehicle is in an unsafe condition, without an MOT certificate, perhaps during that final one month of the lease, then the lessor will cause the employer (that is, the customer) to commit an offence against their employee under section 2(2)(a) of the HASWA in that they are supplying an article for use at work that is in an unmaintained and unsafe condition. Drivers of company vehicles on the highway when on firm's duty are at work and entitled to protection in this respect. Such neglect on the part of the lessor would also cause *both* employer and employee to break the Road Traffic Act.

9

Duties of employees

Very clear duties are placed on employees with regard to themselves (to protect themselves from their own acts or omissions) and others (who may be affected by their acts or omissions). This does not absolve management from its responsibilities for what employees do or fail to do. It must also be remembered that, in incorporated companies, directors and managers are also employees of their own company and have the same duties of care as their employees.

The philosophy

The philosophy that governs the duties placed on employers by the HASWA also governs those placed on employees concerning:

- their 'duty'
- what is 'reasonable and practicable'
- and the 'burden of proof' (see Chapter 5 for more on this).

Under civil law, the manager is responsible for the actions of his 'servants' (called 'vicarious liability') and can be sued in a civil court for compensation or recompense of the acts and/or omissions of those 'servants' ·(employees). But, under the HASWA, as at criminal law, the employee is singly or mutually responsible for their own acts and omissions (quite apart from any civil proceedings).

Employees' duty to themselves

Employees have a duty to themselves that they must take reasonable care that their acts or omissions do not endanger their own health, safety and welfare (section 7(1)). The strong emphasis here is on personal accountability and, by inference, any employee who causes serious consequences for themselves is liable to prosecution. Numerous prosecutions of individual employees have followed, even when no accident or injury has occurred.

Employees' duty to others

By the same statute there is a duty *not* to commit any unsafe act or omission to the detriment of the health, safety and welfare of other employees or of those who are not employees (visitors, contractors, customers, suppliers, the public) who might be affected by those unsafe acts and omissions (section 7(1)). The Food Safety Act 1990 adds the dimension of food safety and hygiene to this duty.

Employees' duty to the employer

It is the duty of all employees to cooperate with their employer, to comply with the requirements of the HASWA and to obey the company's health and safety policy and all the health, safety, welfare and hygiene rules of the company. They must also use or wear all necessary protective wear and equipment provided by their employer in the interests of health, safety and hygiene (section 7(2)).

Beware: managers who turn a blind eye and fail to enforce health, safety and hygiene rules are themselves committing an offence of condoning offences and may themselves be liable under the HASWA (sections 2 and 7).

Employees must not misuse or abuse any equipment provided in the interests of health, safety and hygiene (section 8). Such high-spirited pranks as setting off fire extinguishers or the misuse of compressed air lines are both highly dangerous and criminal.

There are sanctions and penalties under the HASWA that affect the employee to the same extent as they do the employer. These are covered in Chapter 31.

Drug and alcohol abuse

It is worth reiterating here the duties of employees concerning drug and alcohol abuse. They must not indulge in any form of drug-taking or consumption of alcohol (whether on or off the premises) that will cause them to be incapable of undertaking their duties safely and without risk to themselves or others who may be affected by their acts or omissions. This is particularly important to operators of industrial, agricultural and catering machinery, bus and taxi drivers, train and tube staff, and so on.

Employees should be reminded that taking drugs at work will place an obligation on you (the employer) to take disciplinary action and possibly remove them from the premises for their own and others' safety. You could cover this in your induction process and should include it in your health and safety policy (not in memos to employees or individual briefing, as this may be misinterpreted as a personal slight). The employer's duties in these respects were detailed in Chapter 7.

10

Control of substances hazardous to health

The 1970s and 1980s saw a tremendous upsurge in concern regarding anything connected with 'health' in the workplace, not least with the realization of the harmful and ill-health effects of the many substances used in a variety of industries and processes (some after incubations of 10 to 20 years).

Controlling hazardous substances is not new to industry. What *is* new in Britain is formalized assessments of hazardous substances, defined methods of use and the setting of minimum standards for the safe handling and storage of those substances.

There are procedures that you must follow in order to protect your own employees, customers or end users and their employees.

The Control of Substances Hazardous to Health (COSHH) Regulations 1988 became law in October 1989. They incorporate the EC Directive on the protection of workers' health and came into effect on 1 January 1990 after three months' grace given to complete assessments. These Regulations are further amended by the COSHH (Amendment) Regulations 1990, 1991 and 1992.

To whom do these Regulations apply?

No employer, however small, no matter how few they employ or whatever their industry, is exempt from COSHH — not even the self-employed. Even if the result of carrying out the procedures is a nil return, they must be followed.

It is better to check and *know* that you have no hazardous substances than to assume you have none and later make a grim discovery.

The terminology

* *Assessments* You must assess what hazardous substances you use and/or produce at work, their nature (whether they are oils, chemicals, powders, gases), description, the hazards associated with them and the risks involved in using and/or producing these substances.
* *MEL* This stands for 'maximum exposure limit', which means the maximum airborne concentration of any substance (as determined by the European Commission or HSC) *up to* which an employee is permitted to be exposed during a reference period — usually presented as a time-weighted average (TWA) of minutes or hours, such as 8-hour TWA or 10-minute TWA.

- *OES* The 'occupational exposure limit'. This is the maximum airborne concentration of certain substances *down to* which emissions into the working environment must be controlled.
- *Carcinogenic* Something capable of causing or inducing cancer. Substances presenting this hazard are called 'carcinogens'.
- *Systemic* This term is used for any substance — whether it be gas, liquid or powder — that can be absorbed into the nervous system or bloodstream by inhalation (through the mouth and nose into windpipe and lungs), ingestion (through the mouth into the gullet and stomach) or penetration (through the skin). The term comes from the fact that the substances get into the 'systems' of the body. Thus, for example in one factory, an employee who stepped into a bucket of phenol was dead in 20 minutes (despite immediate medical help) because of its very rapid systemic effects.
- *Hazard* This means any danger that may arise from a hazardous substance and the possible ill-health effects of such exposure on the users and others who may be affected by that substance (see also under What is covered, later in this chapter).
- *Hazardous* Section 2 of the COSHH Regulations defines a hazardous substance as one that falls into any of the following five categories:
  —that substance which is classified as toxic, very toxic, irritant, harmful, corrosive, flammable, explosive or radioactive under the Chemicals (Hazard Information and Packaging) Regulations 1993 (CHIP Regs) which replaced the 1984 Regulations
  —any substance for which a MEL has been set in Schedule 1 of the COSHH Regulations or which has an OES set by the HSC
  —any micro-organism that creates a hazard to the health of any person, such as Legionellaceae, which causes legionnaires' disease
  —any dust particles in a substantial airborne concentration
  —any other substance not mentioned above but that, none the less, creates a comparable risk of ill-health effects to any person.
  The above categories include anything that can be taken into the body by inhalation, ingestion and through the skin that, as explained under 'Systemic', above, have ill-health effects including systemic ones.
- *Risk* This is the likelihood that a person will be exposed to a hazard and be affected by it. How can we eliminate or at least minimize that risk? To use a very simple example, a bottle of spirit-based correction fluid contains a 'hazardous' substance (1,1,1-trichloroethane, listed as harmful), but the element of 'risk' is negligible if the cap is kept on the bottle and the user does not inhale or ingest the contents. You can eliminate the hazard completely by using a water-based alternative.
- *Safe* This is when we can say that the risk of exposure to a hazard is nil or so negligible as to be acceptable. We can render a situation safe by eliminating the hazard, for example by engineering it out or by the use of protective wear and equipment.

Objectives

If you follow the advice given and comply with the Regulations, the following objectives should be achieved:

- identify the processes where hazardous substances are used in the workplace or produced by your company

- obtain and collate all the data on each substance used or produced at work and assess the results of any environmental tests
- obtain the data on control measures for these substances (this would normally be on a product data sheet (PDS), available from your supplier, and, of course, if *you* are a supplier, you must compile PDSs and will need to obtain all the necessary information from *your* suppliers, scientists or chemists), but also, note that obtaining a PDS is *not* an 'assessment' under the COSHH Regulations, it is merely an important aid to help you carry out those assessments
- identify those workers who are likely to be affected directly or indirectly by those substances
- assess the likely exposure of each worker to each substance and monitor their exposure and possible ill-health effects
- provide medical/first aid action in the event of exposure
- determine what action is required to eliminate exposure or at least minimize the risk of exposure to these substances
- provide information, training and instruction for all employees required to handle these substances and to others who may also use them and be affected by them, including customers, their employees and end users.

What is covered by the COSHH?

The COSHH Regulations cover any hazardous substance that is included in any of the five categories listed under 'Hazardous', above, and include any natural or artificial substance that is solid, liquid, dust, gas or vapour. Note that the COSHH (Amendment) Regulations 1990 and Carcinogenic ACOP set MELs for carcinogens. These Regulations (obtainable from HMSO) have been extended by the 1991 Amendment Regulations with new *lower* MELs, which took effect on 1 January 1992, but, being very detailed and technical, are not included here.

The following are *not* included under the COSHH *per se*, but are each controlled by specific regulations with their own COSHH-style rules:

- lead (see Chapter 17)
- asbestos (see Chapter 18)
- explosive or flammable substances
- mining substances used below ground
- substances used in medical treatments.

Electricity is not specifically excluded from the COSHH, but is covered by the Electricity at Work Regulations 1989.

Policy

If your firm employs five or more people (including the director(s), manager(s) and IT/YT/ET trainees), remember that you must have a written health and safety policy (see Chapter 5). Under the COSHH Regulations, you must include the COSHH in your policy in exactly the same manner as for health, safety and welfare, generally including additional factors below it.

What about very small firms with *fewer than* five employees? While there is no *legal* obligation to have a written policy, you will find that it is very advantageous to have one. Many customers now require their suppliers to provide them with a copy of their health and safety policy, so even though you may be a small firm, a COSHH-based policy may help you get that order!

Responsibility

A person at senior level (normally a director or owner-manager) must be appointed with overall responsibility for the COSHH. Remember that, although *authority* may be delegated, *responsibility* stays at the top.

Delegation

There is a sequence of actions that must be followed in order to comply with the COSHH. These should be carried out by a competent person who has received the necessary information, training and instruction. That person may be within your own organization, with the necessary addition being made to their job description, or (if a small business or if such training and appointment is impracticable) a competent person from outside, such as a health and safety adviser.

Each member of management should have their duties defined in the COSHH policy statement and in their job descriptions. (See *The Employer's Survival Guide* in which I offer guidance on delegation and job descriptions.)

Handling materials

You must include in your health and safety policy the procedures for the *safe* handling, use, storage and transportation of all hazardous substances that you use or produce. These procedures must include reference to the COSHH assessments and hazard data sheets (see below). This is a requirement of the COSHH Regulations and of section 2(2)(b) of the HASWA.

Assessments

The first step in your policy on hazardous substances is to undertake assessments. The assessments involve the discovery, identification and health-risk assessment of every work activity where any hazardous substance is used in the workplace and/or produced. This is the most important part of the COSHH as it is the foundation of your safe systems of work in relation to hazardous substances (as required by the HASWA section 2(2)(a) and the COSHH Regulations).

COSHH Regulation 6(1) states:

> an employer shall not carry on any work which is liable to expose any employees to any substance hazardous to health unless he has made a suitable and sufficient *assessment* of the risks created by that work to the health of those employees and of the steps that need to be taken to meet the requirements of these Regulations.

The assessments referred to here should have been completed by 31 December 1989. In the case of newly formed businesses, assessments should be completed immediately the business starts.

The many firms that have not completed their assessments are, therefore, breaking the law. The HSE started blitz inspections in the year 1990/91, which partially accounts for the increase in the number of enforcement notices (see Chapter 1) and local authority environmental health officers began a 'high level of activity on COSHH assessments' from 1 January 1993. There is every indication that these COSHH checks will continue for some time, together with their routine audits.

The assessment process

This includes the following steps.

1. *Identify substances* Identify and list each substance made/used, giving:

   - its name and chemical name/formula (if applicable)
   - how it is recognized (colour, smell, consistency)
   - manufacturer/supplier
   - its classification ('toxic, etc.', as given under 'Hazardous', above, and as shown on the label — if it does not have a label, contact your supplier)
   - its MEL
   - its OES
   - any other identification: micro-organism, dust (including innocent-sounding names like flour; dust can explode).

2. *Determine the hazard* What is the hazard that this substance presents in its unprotected state? Record the hazard; the following questions are helpful in this.

   - Is it poisonous, carcinogenic or noxious?
   - What ill-health effects can it have if it is inhaled, ingested (eaten or drunk) or touches the skin (systemic)?

3. *Assess the risk* What is the degree of risk to which the employee (or end user or their employee or the public) is exposed?

   - Is the substance (an oil or chemical, for instance) open to direct contact or is it enclosed?
   - How likely is it that an employee may come into contact with it and be adversely affected by it?

   Record the risks.

4. *What medical steps are needed*? Even where a substance is enclosed or encased, there could be a leakage, spillage or explosion. So, what first aid and/or medical treatment should be made available to cope with this? Do remember that not all medical practitioners are fully conversant with every hazardous substance, their ill-health effects and their antidotes, and so advice to them in the form of a substance and medical treatment data sheet will be very helpful. (A suggested outline of such an advice sheet can be found in Appendix 4.)

Sources of information necessary to complete an assessment To help you, such information should be readily available or you should have access to sources of information and advice. For *existing* substances there should be either of the following.

- A label on the tin, bottle or drum. It will have affixed one or more of six labels that contain a black symbol on an orange background, which indicates that the substance is hazardous, and the appropriate word (Corrosive, Flammable, Explosive, Toxic, Harmful, Irritant, or Oxidizing) underneath. Similar symbols are enclosed in a diamond-shaped sign on vehicles that carry hazardous substances. When you decant a substance, remember to transfer the information to the new container.
- A product data sheet (PDS) from the manufacturer/supplier. This should contain all the above information and appropriate first aid treatment in the event of exposure to the substance. Data sheets must by law be made available by a manufacturer or supplier, so if they haven't given you one, ask for one!

For *new* substances, that is, those substances you produce or intend to produce, contact a source of expertise and advice (a chemist, chemical company, oil specialists, research laboratories, say). You *must* carry out assessments before using or producing any new substance *and* provide information, training and instruction on that new substance to your employees. You must also provide information in a product data sheet (as outlined earlier) to your customer and end user.

Records You should maintain a register of all hazardous substances that contains the following information:

- name of substance, with a serial number for easy reference
- any other names (trade name, additional to chemical name)
- MEL
- all ingredients
- chemical and physical properties
- nature of hazard
- details of the manufacturer/supplier
- reference to hazard data sheet
- whether/when obtained from the manufacturer/supplier.

Prevention and control

Having assessed what you have in use in your workplace or production, your next step is to take the necessary measures to achieve one of two things: either prevention or control of the hazard. Section 7(1) of the COSHH states that:

> every employer shall ensure that the exposure of his employees to substances hazardous to health is either *prevented* or, where this is not reasonably practicable, adequately *controlled*.

Prevention

If possible, you should prevent any hazard (risk to safety and health) arising at all. To do this, answer the following important questions.

- Can you eliminate the hazard?
- Can you manufacture your product in another way without this substance?
- Can you use a safer alternative to make your product?
- Do you really need to do this job?
- Do you really need to use that substance?

If the answer to the first three questions is 'Yes' and to the fourth and fifth questions it is 'No', then you should act accordingly to eliminate the hazard: dispense with the job or substance, or find an alternative. This is a requirement of the COSHH Regulations.

Control

With regard to MELs and OESs for inhalation, if you cannot eliminate the hazard, follow the steps given below.

- Can you eliminate the risk? If the answer is 'No', ask the next question.
- Can you minimize it? Can you:

   —take steps to neutralize the substance?
   —completely enclose it?
   —adapt the plant/machinery to eliminate the risk? Or:

—provide protective equipment?
—provide personal protective wear?
—adapt the plant/machinery to minimize the risk?

Control measurements

If MELs and OESs lay down differing exposure levels for a substance, it is the OES that is regarded as an *adequate* control level. To assure compliance with MELs and OESs, measurements of the exposure of employees should be taken using the instruments and procedures outlined in the HSE's Guidance Notes on this subject (EH/42, available from HMSO).

For other risks of exposure via the skin or ingestion, the standard to be observed should be such that if the majority of employees were exposed to it continually, they would not be adversely affected. For example, say they were to be exposed to oils that cause skin diseases. If almost everyone contracts dermatitis, the control measures are inadequate; but if only an allergic person could be adversely affected (and you provide them with adequate protection), then the control measures are adequate.

Standards of protection

You must ensure that whatever control measures or protective equipment/wear are decided on, they are adequate for the job. So, for example, rather than just specifying 'a respirator', say what *kind* of respirator is required — the one that will fully filter out those harmful gases, dusts, fumes, and so on.

You must also ensure that the protective wear and equipment are regularly and properly maintained and that those for whom the wear or equipment is intended actually wear or use it and do not tamper with it.

Medical and first aid cover

You must provide adequate medical and/or first aid facilities, according to the nature of the hazard and degree of risk. Even where a substance is enclosed, there could be a leakage, spillage or explosion. So, what medical and/or first aid treatments should be made available? (See step 4 under the assessment process, above.) Don't go overboard but don't skimp either; provide that which is adequate for the situation. Remember also to maintain the first aid box as per the 1990 ACOP (see Chapter 7).

Monitoring

Having assessed the hazards and risks, taken preventive or protective measures and provided medical cover, the next step is to maintain a watching brief on those substances. This means monitoring what is happening. You monitor in exactly the same way as you control for MELs and/or OESs. Don't forget to wear that protective clothing, as necessary, when monitoring — a good example works wonders!

Health surveillance

Where employees are exposed to hazardous substances and are at some risk even though they have protective equipment and clothing, you must carry out periodic health surveillance (see also Chapter 11). This includes employees who work with certain hazardous substances such as lead, nickel, asbestos, silver and so on. These medical checks should be appropriate to the substance concerned, and an occupational medical adviser (doctor) or industrial nursing service will assist here. Where lead is used, though, *only* an EMAS-approved employment medical adviser is permitted to conduct such medical surveillance.

Records

In addition to the COSHH records of the substances themselves (through the use of the product data sheets and assessments), you must maintain records of all monitoring, all exposures and all medical and first aid treatments (Regulation 10(3)). You must keep records available for inspection for:

- *30 years* records of personal exposure monitoring and first aid for employees
- *5 years* records of general MEL, OES and other monitoring.

The reason records are kept for so long is because many occupational diseases (such as those given with statistics in Chapter 1) take a long time to surface or develop.

Note that if a company ceases trading, the directors or managers of that company must notify their local HSE office and hand all records over to them for retention.

Legionellae records of examinations and tests carried out on local exhaust ventilation plant and other control equipment in the interests of preventing and controlling *Legionellae* must be kept for the period during which the 'appointed person' holds that appointment and for a minimum of two years after that person has relinquished that appointment. (See also Chapter 25.)

There is no prescribed format for records of assessments and control systems, but suggestions for simple COSHH assessment forms for the job, the substance and medical surveillance are given in Appendices 2 and 3.

The COSHH has now been explained in some detail. How much of this material applies to your company will, of course, depend on its size, the nature of the substances used at your workplace, your products and the *amount* of each hazardous substance used and made. Remember, though, that the basic rules of the COSHH apply to *all* firms, even if the result is a nil return. Also, all COSHH Regulations apply to self-employed persons; they are simply viewed as if they were both employer and employee.

Information, training and instruction

You now have all the necessary information on your hazardous substances, control measures and the medical/first aid arrangements. Your next step (to comply with both the COSHH Regulations and section 2(2)(c) of the HASWA) is to give all concerned employees adequate information, training and instruction. This should consist of:

- *information* written information, as either individual handouts or notices posted at the workplace, about the substances, their hazards, risks and protective measures to be taken (remember to communicate your health and safety and COSHH policies to employees)
- *training* verbal communication (teaching) in a lecture situation away from the job where discussion and tests of knowledge and understanding should take place; if your employees have not understood what you have said, the training may not be adequate
- *instruction* skills and knowledge about the job given on the job where the hazardous substances are actually used and/or produced.

It is an excellent idea to get your employees to *sign* to say they have received and understood the information, training and instruction. This prevents any lapses of memory as to whether or not you have done this, which can cause problems later.

It is worth recalling here the rest of section 2(2)(c) — that of providing *supervision*, which is very important under the COSHH.

Do remember, in both your assessments and training, your special duty of care to young people under the age of 18 years. Remember also that all IT/YT/ET trainees are employees for the purposes of health, safety and welfare.

Occupational asthma

An estimated 30 employees develop occupational asthma after being exposed to a wide range of respiratory sensitizers that range from grain dust to isocyanates. The HSE has announced a programme of action, commencing in 1994, that is aimed at reducing the incidence of this disease. The programme seeks to improve controls on respiratory sensitizers by raising the levels of awareness of the risks involved. The programme will be four-fold:

- further amendments to the COSHH general ACOP, highlighting particular hazards associated with respiratory sensitizers
- publishing comprehensive guidance on the control of respiratory sensitizers
- publishing an information card for use by employees
- launching an enforcement campaign to ensure compliance with the COSHH Regulations and the general ACOP.

The HSE has published Guidance Notes on this subject: 'Medical Effects of Occupational Asthma' (reference MS.25 (ISBN: 0-11-885584-0) price £2 (available from HMSO).

Sources of help

For assistance, the following are available to give guidance and practical help.

- Your local HSE office (you will find their address and telephone number in your local and/or business directory).
- Abundance Management Services, Abundance House, 17 St Michael's Crescent, Oldbury, West Midlands, B69 4RT (tel: 0121 552 2073).

11

Carcinogenic substances

Accidents leading to physical injury leave obvious evidence of their consequences, but illnesses that result from exposure to dangerous substances invariably do not provide early warnings. They only become evident many years, sometimes several decades, later.

Medical research on occupational cancer continues to find substances and processes that cause the disease or give varying degrees of indication that they cause cancer. It is thus very important to have an active precautionary policy of prevention and control of exposure to carcinogenic substances and (now by law) those suspected of being carcinogenic.

A European Community (EC) Directive, a new United Kingdom (UK) Regulation amendment and a new ACOP place new obligations on employers to prevent exposure to carcinogenic substances.

The terminology

There are a number of terms used in the Regulations and ACOPs and it is helpful to know their correct meaning. The following appear in paragraphs 1, 2 and 3 of the Carcinogens ACOP.

- *Carcinogenic* now has three meanings in the ACOP. It means any substance or preparation that:
  1. is included under the CHIP Regs and is labelled with the risk phrase 'R45: may cause cancer'
  2. is listed in Appendix 1 to the Carcinogens ACOP, which is given here because this is a *new* list under the Carcinogens ACOP:

     - aflatoxins (carcinogenic metabolites of aspergillus (fungii) in soil, manure and therefore cereals)
     - arsenic and inorganic arsenic compounds
     - beryllium and beryllium compounds; bichromate manufacture involving the roasting of chromate ore
     - bichromate manufacture involving the roasting of chromate ore
     - electrolytic chromium processes, excluding passivation, which involve hexavalent chromium compounds
     - mustard gas (B,B'Dichlorodiethyl sulphide)
     - calcining, sintering or smelting of nickel copper matte or acid leaching or electro-refining of roasted matte
     - ortho-toluidine

- coal soots, coal tar, pitch and coal tar fumes
- the following mineral oils: unrefined and mildly refined vacuum distillers, catalytically cracked petroleum oils with final boiling points above 320°C, used engine oils
- auromine manufacture
- leather dust in boot and shoe manufacture, arising during preparation and finishing
- hardwood dusts
- isopropyl alcohol manufacture (strong acid process)
- rubber manufacture and processing giving rise to rubber process dust and rubber fumes
- magenta manufacture
- 4-nitrobiphenyl

3. any substance(s) arising from (that is, as a by-product of) a process listed under 1 and 2 above.

- *Hazard* An unsafe condition, act or emission that presents the potential for injury or ill-health effects.
- *Risk* The likelihood that a hazard may arise or exposure to that hazard may exist; risk is not the hazard itself, but the probability of that hazard arising. Risk is normally measured in three levels — high, medium and low (with variations on this being to express these in percentages or probabilities, such as 0.01 to 9.99).

The legislation

A European Community (EC) Directive on carcinogenic substances (90/394/EEC) was implemented in the UK by a new ACOP that is issued under the COSHH Regulations.

The existing COSHH Regulations (as amended in 1990 and 1991) have been further amended by the COSHH (Amendment) Regulations 1992, each of these amendments taking effect on 1 January following their publication.

The HSC issued an amended ACOP for carcinogenic substances (the Carcinogens ACOP) and it came into force on 1 January 1993. It is the basis of this chapter.

There is also the COSHH General ACOP, which is dealt with under the COSHH Regulations in Chapter 10. Reference is also made to the Chemicals (Hazard Information and Packaging) Regulation 1993 (CHIP Regs).

There is a direct relationship between the material in this chapter and that of the previous chapter, so it is best to read them both together.

Note that where a 'Regulation' is referred to in this chapter, this is one in the COSHH Regulations themselves and not the ACOPs.

The scope of the Carcinogens ACOP

The new ACOP is concerned principally with the following duties of employers:

- policy
- prohibitions
- assessments of risk
- prevention of exposure
- control of exposure

- monitoring
- health surveillance
- information, instruction and training
- records.

Carcinogenic substances and policy

As has already been established in earlier chapters, there is a need for every employer to have an effective health and safety policy (and where there are five employees or more, that policy should be set out in a written statement) covering:

- general health and safety (see Chapter 7)
- control of substances hazardous to health (see Chapter 10).

Paragraph 2 of the new General ACOP to the COSHH Regulations lists factors that employers have to take into account when considering whether or not a substance is hazardous. Included here is a strong suggestion that they have a further obligation to devise and set down a *precautionary policy*, that is, a policy that is designed to ensure that all reasonable precautions are taken to prevent or control the exposure of employees to any substances that are either:

- *known* to be carcinogenic
- are *suspected* of being carcinogenic.

There are so many substances about which little is known that 'better safe than sorry' is the best policy with regard to this ACOP. The problem is that if an employer or employee does *not* know or suspect that a substance is carcinogenic, then there may be a tendency not to take reasonable precautions until scientists confirm that it *is* carcinogenic, but then it is too late for those who have already been exposed to it.

Prohibitions

These relate to Regulation 4. There is a full list of prohibitions in Schedule 2 to the COSHH Regulations as amended. The following are given as specific prohibited carcinogenic substances in the Carcinogens ACOP:

- 2-naphthylamine
- benzidine
- 4-aminodiphenyl
- 4-nitrodiphenyl and their salts
- any substance containing any of these compounds in a total concentration equal to or greater than 0.1 per cent
- the importation of the four substances above
- benzene in a concentration of more than 0.1 per cent (except in industrial processes, research, development and analysis and for motor fuels covered by EC Directives).

Note that holders of exemption and import licences issued by the HSE under previous Regulations should reapply to the HSE under Regulation 14 of the COSHH Regulations as amended.

Assessments

Assessments have an especially vital role to play in the control of carcinogenic substances. Your assessments must identify (Regulation 6):

- whether or not carcinogenic substances are present in your manufacturing or processing operations
- any workers who may be at particular risk from carcinogens
- any specific group of workers, such as pregnant women, who may be at particular risk from carcinogens
- the extent of the risks to health
- the extent of exposure to those risks to health
- the nature of the hazard(s) to which employees may be exposed
- whether or not a substitute substance is reasonably practicable
- the operating and maintenance instructions and procedures, where relevant, that will ensure that exposure to them is minimized
- the control measures needed to prevent or reduce exposure
- the information needed to plan those control measures and make them effective
- the routine precautions necessary to prevent exposure, including the issue of personal protective equipment (PPE)
- the non-routine precautions necessary to prevent exposure, such as in emergencies
- procedures for reporting defects in plant, systems or precautions
- the monitoring procedures necessary to ensure controls are effective
- health surveillance procedures to be followed for those who may be at risk
- the arrangements for consultation with employees and their representatives on all the above.

Detailed advice on carrying out risk assessments is contained in Chapter 18.

Prevention of exposure

Your first duty as an employer is to *prevent* the exposure of employees and others who may be affected by your undertakings (Regulation 7). This is important, bearing in mind the very serious and often irreversible nature of diseases caused by carcinogenic substances. Prevention can be achieved by two means:

- *substitution* using an alternative and less hazardous substitute or a synthetic substitute if possible (synthetics should, for example, be chosen for the production of chemicals, but care should be taken to ensure that they do not present other hazards)
- *enclosure* completely enclose the process so as to eliminate exposure (you will need to build in precautions and emergency action should that enclosure fail, as with a leak).

When determining which substances to use, care should be taken that no by-products are produced that might be hazardous.

Control of exposure

If all attempts to prevent exposure by use of alternatives or enclosure have been exhausted and exposure still cannot be eliminated and/or if a resultant hazardous by-product cannot be avoided, then the next step must be to *control* the possible exposure of employees to identified and hitherto unconfirmed risks (Regulation 7). This can be achieved by a number of means, by:

- *minimizing* the amount of carcinogenic substances in use — maybe by using the minimum possible in production and limiting the personal issue of substances to employees to the absolute minimum essential for an operation

- *centralizing* storage of substances under carefully controlled conditions
- *limiting* the number of people who handle carcinogenic substances and further to only *authorized* personnel
- providing *separate* areas for eating, drinking and so on that do not present risks of contamination by the substance
- providing *separate* cloakroom facilities so that contamination cannot be carried from the person's clothing to, say, an eating and drinking area
- providing PPE where this is essential and unavoidable, and issuing this to maintenance and engineering personnel who may also be exposed to unforeseen risks (note, however, that the law requires such equipment to be used as a last resort only; you must seek to *prevent* exposure first).

Monitoring

Paragraph 14 of the Carcinogens ACOP reinforces the requirement of paragraph 68 of the General ACOP. You must have adequate programmes and systems of monitoring carcinogenic substances and the exposure of people to them (Regulation 10). Your programme should:

- confirm that your control systems are functioning correctly
- confirm that employees are obeying the rules correctly
- indicate the extent of exposure of individuals to carcinogenic substances
- confirm that prescribed MELs and OESs are being complied with, that is, that any exposure is within those prescribed limits
- detect any deterioration in standards of control.

Health surveillance

The Carcinogens ACOP reinforces the requirement (Regulation 11) that health surveillance must be carried out in cases of *all* carcinogenic substances unless the exposure is not significant. Health surveillance should be in accordance with the General ACOP and must, in most instances, be carried out by medically qualified persons (for specific guidance, see Chapter 1).

In the case of carcinogens, adequate health surveillance can be critical because the early detection of any health problems can offer a better prognosis and increased chances of recovery. Not all health surveillance is effective in susceptible persons in the very early stages of the onset of disease; therefore, the maintenance of full operational and exposure records is essential (see below).

Information, instruction and training

Unless you achieve the complete elimination of exposure to risks from hazardous substances, exposure to those substances cannot be presumed to be zero and so there is the possibility that ill-health effects may occur. In these cases, the provision of information, instruction and training (Regulation 12) is even more critical where carcinogens are used than other substances.

Such information, instruction and training given to employees must be of the highest standards with the fullest possible information being given. Sometimes, employers worry that by giving employees what they regard as 'too much' information, they may trigger unnecessary anxiety and even malingering, but withholding detailed information can produce the same effect plus suspicion and distrust.

In addition to the requirements of the General ACOP, your information, instruction and training to employees should include:

- the nature of the hazards involved with the substances
- the degrees of risk to which they may be exposed
- the special features of the carcinogenic substances used
- the circumstances in which they may become exposed to them.

Records

You must originate and maintain up-to-date records of all assessments, monitoring and health surveillance (Regulation 10(3)(a) and (b)). These records must be kept for *minimum* periods of time as follows:

- 5 years for general records, where no personal exposures of identifiable employees are included
- 30 years for records that relate to personal exposures of identifiable employees.

There was a suggestion in the consultative document for the Carcinogens ACOP that this latter time should be increased from 30 years to 40 years, but this was not incorporated.

12

Fire safety

Every two minutes, a fire engine is called out. Every year, half a million people have fresh memories of fire. Another 1000 have no memory of them because, for them, fire had fatal consequences. There are many terrible examples of the effects of fire, but here are some of significance. A total of 227 people died in the Joelma Building, Brazil in 1974, of whom 80 fell from the roof and 2 were firemen; 11 people died in the Woolworths fire in 1979; the Bradford football ground fire of 1989 claimed 56 lives; in a fire in a Yorkshire mill in 1961, 7 women died; while, in 1990, over 30 lost their lives in the King's Cross Underground disaster. Two firemen lost their lives fighting the Sun Valley Poultry fire in Hereford in September 1993. All these fires are significant because they were preventable and caused by lack of awareness.

The Woolworths fire went out of control due to poor procedures and people not taking the alarm seriously. In the Bradford fire, poor housekeeping meant rubbish and dust were not cleared, and ignited. Also, bad design meant that a heat trap was created in the apex of the roof of the stand, so in only $2\frac{1}{2}$ minutes the whole stand was ablaze, in 4 minutes it was totally engulfed, and in just 6 minutes it was completely destroyed. Naturally there was panic, but the final fatal flaw was that the turnstiles/exits were locked.

The Brazil fire also resulted from poor design: means of escape and fire doors were built to codes unaltered since the 1930s.

The loss of life in the Yorkshire mill fire occurred because the women went back into the burning building to collect their purses and wage packets.

In both the Woolworths and Bradford fires, flames, smoke and fumes moved upwards and then downwards when there was nowhere else upwards for it to go.

The King's Cross fire happened because of poor management systems and housekeeping, and the flammable paint and linings used in the escalators.

The financial penalties that accrue to the nation for these and other disasters are astounding. The average direct costs of all UK domestic and industrial fires are:

- per hour, £120 000
- per week, over £20 million
- per year, over £1000 million
- plus consequential losses.

In the 18 months to May 1992, fires during construction or renovation of buildings cost a staggering £250 million (these figures are from the Fire Protection Association).

The Associated British Insurers calculated the fire losses in 1992 to be:

- £774 million (over 70 per cent of all losses) for industrial/commercial fires
- £326 million for domestic fires.

This gives a total cost of £1.1 million for all fires in 1992, taking account of direct losses only and excluding consequential losses.

People's attitudes towards fire are somewhat like those towards the *Titanic* before it sank — 'We're unsinkable', 'It won't happen to us', 'It's been OK up to now'. No building is completely fireproof. Suddenly the unthinkable happens and you are helplessly watching an office, factory or training centre burning to the ground. Worse, far worse, when it becomes clear that there are human victims. Remember the young girls trapped in the Woolworths store in Manchester, smoke billowing round them and firemen unable to reach them, until cutting gear was brought in, and the bodies of 10 customers found within feet of a fire exit, unable to find or reach it because of the thick toxic smoke coming from burning foam furniture, plus the security person who went back in to help and died in the attempt.

In over 100 detailed audits I have conducted each year, the most prominent hazard found is consistently fire. Each audit, without exception, revealed examples of the major hazards outlined in this chapter, hence the space given to this very important aspect of safety here and in the appendices.

Fire safety is vital because, literally, people's lives and jobs depend on it.

Introduction

It is not possible to provide full technical advice that is relevant to *all* workplaces in just one guide. However, we hope you will gain a good overview of the main principles of fire precautions and fire safety, which *are* relevant to all situations. Professional advice will be particularly important in high-risk, very large or complicated premises and processes.

Legal definitions

Before proceeding with the legal aspects of fire safety, we need to be able to understand the language used. What do the Regulations, fire certificates and legal documents mean when certain terms are used? Here are some useful legal definitions to help you be clear about their terminology:

- *Employer* an owner, including a self-employed person, who has one or more employees; has the same meaning as 'occupier' except in multi-occupied buildings
- *Employee* an individual who works generally in the workplace in question or who uses it as a base, under a contract of employment or apprenticeship; the term also includes trainees under the Training for Employment scheme
- *access room* a room through which the only escape route passes from an inner room
- *inner room* a room from which escape is only possible via an access room
- *means of escape (MOE)* a structure that provides people with a safe route to travel from any point in a building to a place of safety

- *accommodation stairway* an additional stairway, not designed as a means of escape, but provided for the convenience of the occupants of a building
- *place of safety* a place sited away from the building, such as a street, passageway, walkway or open space, to which people can disperse and be safe from danger of fire
- *cavity barrier* the sealing of any concealed space against the spread of smoke or flames, such as ceiling voids
- *compartments* a building (or part of a building) constructed so as to prevent the spread of fire to or from another part of that building or adjoining building
- *compartment wall* a fire-resisting wall used to separate compartments
- *dead end* an area from which escape is possible in one direction only
- *distance of travel* the actual distance from any point in a building to a door for means of escape (MOE) in a compartment wall, protected route, protected lobby or final MOE
- *escape lighting* emergency lighting provided to illuminate escape routes at all 'material times'
- *material times* times when employees are at work on employers' premises
- *storey exit* an exit through which people are no longer at immediate risk from the effects of fire, heat and smoke
- *final exit* the direct access from the MOE into a street, passageway, walkway or open space where it is possible for people to rapidly disperse, safely, away from the hazard of smoke and flames from a building
- *fire door* a door or shutter in or leading to a MOE, that is resistant to the movement of smoke, flames and gases and capable of allowing the safe movement of personnel (fire doors with non-metallic leaves must be self-closing and constructed to BS 8214; fire doors will be specifically marked on the plans in a fire certificate)
- *fire hazard* the potential for injury or loss of life in a fire
- *fire risk* the likelihood that a fire could occur (in assessing buildings, a fire authority will be concerned with the potential risk of injury or death from a fire *should* it occur, not how likely it is that a fire *could* occur)
- *fire-resisting construction* a construction that can resist flames and smoke for a specified period of time (20, 30 or 60 minutes) to the standard of BS 476
- *fire/smoke stopping* a seal to restrict the passage of smoke or flames
- *protected lobby* a lobby protected from fire by fire-resisting construction
- *protected route* a route (including walls, partitions, ceilings and floors) affording adequate protection from smoke and flames by virtue of being separated from the rest of a building
- *workplace* a building or part of a building in which one or more employees work, as defined in section 43(1) of FPA 71, and to which Regulation 3 of FPR 95 applies, for example, where:
  (a) a fire certificate is in force under the Factories Act 1961 (FA.71) or the Offices, Shops and Railway Premises Act 1963 (OSRP); or
  (b) the fire authority has exempted the premises from the need to have a fire certificate under the Fire Precautions Act 1971 (FPA 71); or
  (c) the place of work does not require a fire certificate (for example, because not enough employees work in the premises to require a fire certificate to be issued); or
  (d) there are Crown-occupied and Crown-owned premises (albeit that the Crown itself, but not its managers, have immunity from prosecution in respect of such workplaces)

- *relevant training* work experience provided by those training schemes and providers under the Training for Employment scheme under Regulation 2 of the Health and Safety (Training for Employment) Regulations 1990
- *material times* times when employees are present in the workplace.

The legislation

The ever-present threat of fire is well understood by fire officers, architects, engineers and many others who are engaged in the constant fight against fire and the protection of buildings from it. What is not so well understood is the increasingly complex nature of the law associated with fire. It sometimes comes as a shock to people . . . to discover what a minefield it can be.

B. L. Fuller, former Chief Fire Officer, West Midlands Fire Service,
in Foreword to *Fire Safety and the Law*
by Ann Everton and Jon Holyoak.

The general requirements for fire safety are laid down in the Fire Precautions Act of 1971 (FPA), which is the basic standard every fire authority works to. This is supported by other statutory instruments, which are:

The Fire Precautions (Hotels and Boarding Houses) Order 1972 (SI 238)
The Fire Precautions (Factories, Offices, Shops and Railway Premises) Order 1989 (SI 76)
EC Directive 89/654/EEC — Workplace Directive
EC Directive 89/391/EEC — Framework Directive
NHS and Community Care Act 1990
Fire Precautions (Places of Work) Regulations 1995 (FPR.95)
Fire Precautions (Application for Certificate) Regulations 1989
Building Regulations 1991.

The FPA applies to all premises except private single dwellings. Where a fire certificate is in force under the FPA (see below), it will set specific requirements for the particular premises to which it relates. The main effect of the FPA was to enforce fire certificate standards in relation to hotels, boarding houses, offices, shops, railway premises and factories. However, there were loopholes in the FPA in that, for example, schools, residential homes and so on, did not require fire certificates. These loopholes have now been plugged by the Fire Precautions (Places of Work) Regulations 1995.

The duties of employers with regard to fire safety are also laid down in section 2(2)(d) of the HASWA (to provide a safe place of work). The duties of employees are contained in section 7(a) of the HASWA (to take reasonable care), section 7(b) (to cooperate with the employer) and section 8 of the HASWA (not to interfere with or misuse anything).

The scope of the legislation

To what type of premises do these Regulations and Guidance Notes apply? Almost every type, including many not hitherto covered by any fire precautions law.

FPR 95 covers the following people and premises:

- all employers' premises (in this regard there are 1.1 million employers' premises registered with the fire authority but 1.7 million registered for VAT, which means up to 700 000 are not registered and may be breaking the law)

- all premises to which the public have access
- all self-employed persons who have one or more employees (30 per cent of self-employed persons have employees)
- hotels and boarding houses with more than six beds
- schools and hospitals, who will need to 'top up' their existing standards to meet the requirements of FPR 95
- Crown-occupied buildings, for example, penal establishments
- voluntary organizations with one or more employees
- employers' premises with domestic accommodation in the same building (whether with the same employer or not).

Many large premises not hitherto covered by FPA 71 or later FPRs/FPOs will need to abide by fire precautions legislation for the first time. This includes establishments like warehouses, exhibition halls, laboratories, lecture blocks, residential halls in universities and colleges, and country houses that open to the public; also, smaller premises, such as day-care centres, surgeries, small bed and breakfast houses with more than six beds, including those for employees.

All these types of establishment will be required to carry out risk assessments and formulate plans for upgrading the status of their premises' fire safety and fire precautions.

Exemptions The following are exempt from the requirements of FPR 95:

- self-employed persons with *no* employees, including small hotels and boarding houses with fewer than seven beds and run without assistance (those with one or more employees must comply in full)
- the storage of combustible refuse and the supervision of construction and maintenance work (covered by other Regulations)
- licensed premises (including public houses) and those premises with a public entertainment licence – *while it is in force*. Note that once the public entertainment licence has expired, these premises must comply in full
- voluntary organizations with *no* employees (if they have one or more employees, they must comply)
- underground transport stations, mines and quarries (covered by other legislation)
- moored vessels, tents, other movable structures and open air work (legislation to be determined in the future)
- home-workers, child-minders and domestic servants.

Small businesses
Guidance given by the Home Office to fire authorities includes the necessity of avoiding the imposition of administrative, financial and legal constraints on small- and medium-sized businesses 'which would hold back [their] creation and development' (see further under Compliance costs later in this chapter).

What are the ingredients of fire?

Fire is a chemical reaction called *combustion* (normally oxidation resulting in the release of heat and light). To initiate and maintain this chemical reaction — or, in other words, for an outbreak of fire to occur and continue — the following three ingredients are essential:

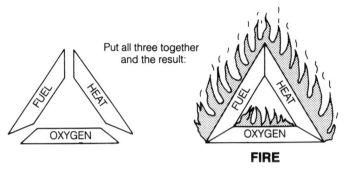

Fig. 12.1 Ingredients necessary for a fire

- *fuel* — a combustible substance that is either solid, liquid or gas
- *oxygen* — usually supplied by air, which is approximately 21 per cent oxygen
- *heat* — a certain temperature needs to be reached (once a fire has started, it normally maintains the required heat).

This is often represented as a triangle, as shown in Fig. 12.1.

Because three ingredients are necessary for a fire to occur and continue, it follows logically that to extinguish a fire you need to take away any one of the three ingredients. Either:

- cut off the oxygen supply (by blanketing or smothering the fire)
- remove the heat (by cooling it)
- remove the fuel source if possible (starving).

With regard to this last option, you can cut off gas, petrol or oil supplies, but it may sometimes not be practicable to try to remove the fuel source as wherever the fuel goes, the oxygen and heat will go with it. You can, however, prevent a fire by removing the fuel source from the risk zone before a fire starts. Many, however, erroneously believing that by removing the fuel they can put the fire out, have been badly burned. Two cases in Dudley in 1991 come to mind, both of 60-year-old ladies who, in attempting to remove burning chip pans from their kitchens, poured boiling fat over themselves, dropped the pans, the fire spread and they were badly burned and disfigured. The *only* effective way to deal with a burning chip pan, deep-fat fryer or similar fire is by smothering it (but only do this with a fire blanket or damp (not wet) towel)), *never* with *water*. Should an extinguisher be used, the velocity of discharge would cause the extinguishing media to be driven below the surface, resulting in an eruption of hot fat/oil.

What are the physical causes of fire?

Fire is mainly caused by any one or a combination of the following factors:

- heat
- electrical faults
- chemical reaction
- explosion.

Heat

Heat causes can include simply:

- very high temperatures in combustibles (wood, paper, hot ashes, oils and metal, which will all burn without an igniting flame if heated sufficiently)
- the sun's rays (electromagnetic radiation)
- sparks from welding, machinery or two vehicles colliding and, for example, a spark igniting petrol fumes
- friction (two materials rubbing together, such as machinery with no oil).

Remember that even metal can burn without an igniting flame if heated sufficiently and hot metal can set other things on fire.

Electrical

Electrical causes can include:

- faulty or loose electrical wiring or connections in cables/plugs
- a cable that is of too low an amperage rating for the load of the apparatus or machine
- fuses that are of too high an amperage rating, as they afford no protection to the apparatus or machine
- failure to protect by using residual current devices or residual contact breakers
- insulation failure (poor or decaying sheathing)
- cabling that is used still coiled, causing heat to pass through the plastic and melting it
- short circuits
- lack of earthing
- plugs and sockets in poor condition
- electrical equipment left switched on, including overnight.

Chemical

The reaction that takes place when two incompatible chemicals come together causes heat. This is sometimes done deliberately in manufacture (such as in mixing styrene and phenol to make styrenated-phenol, but this is carefully controlled), but at other times it is unintentional, with disastrous consequences, as when there are spillages or when that 'controlled' process goes terribly wrong.

Explosion

This happens when an explosive substance is ignited — often the result of an uncontrolled chemical reaction causing a rapid build-up of heat and/or explosion. This can happen, for example, if the styrene and phenol mixing process goes out of control, causing an accelerated build-up of heat in a pressure vessel or the reaction of two chemicals in an uncontrolled environment. In a Salford chemical plant in 1973, such a mixing process went out of control because steam heat was applied too rapidly to cool and unmixed styrene and phenol ingredients, resulting in a violent chemical reaction building up to an explosion and the death by phenol poisoning of an unsuspecting operator who had taken over an unsafe continuous-process operation.

A simple demonstration of this kind of chemical reaction and explosion is when a drop of water is added to boiling fat. The spitting that occurs is caused by the water expanding into steam, with the resulting fire in the spilled fat being a chemical reaction — a real hazard. That is just one drop of water in a little bit of fat, so try to imagine what happens when 3000 pounds of styrene and phenol explodes in a pressure vessel.

What are the human causes of fire and explosion?

Except for fires caused by lightning, *all* fires and explosions have human causal factors, that is, people did or failed to do something. Generally, human factors can be categorized under five main headings, and encapsulated by a sixth:

1. careless acts and omissions
2. misuse of equipment (especially electrical)
3. defective plant, machinery and equipment (poor maintenance)
4. deliberate acts (arson)
5. carelessness and faulty procedures by contractors
6. management failure.

Careless acts or omissions
These include:

- inadequate supervision, especially of cooking activities
- illicit or unsafe smoking
- a discarded cigarette or lighted match in an ashtray or waste bin, igniting paper
- careless disposal of waste, close to heat sources
- exposed, unattended waste in a factory yard, inviting vandalism
- flying brands from flues and ducts, with perhaps heat causing ignition of loose particles
- sparks from welding and machinery
- sparks from metal-to-metal/stone or static sparks igniting dust
- heating appliances left too close to combustibles (especially gas-powered heaters in factories and garage workshops)
- failure to uncoil extension leads (the heat caused melting of the sheathing)
- covering ventilation grilles of heaters, machinery and office equipment
- inadequate cleaning of work and leisure areas (remember the Bradford disaster).

Here are two examples of how carelessness regarding sparks can lead to deaths and injuries through dust explosions.

In 1973, a manager and a foreman in a Manchester flour mill were killed by a dust explosion when the foreman's boots (which he should not have worn) created a metal-to-metal spark on a staircase, which then ignited explosive airborne flour dust particles.

In 1974, six employees were killed in a Witton, Birmingham, ammunition plant when a lady switched on a transistor radio. The tiny static spark created ignited airborne gunpowder dust, resulting in an explosion. Twenty other people were seriously hurt.

Misuse of equipment
Some examples of this factor are:

- hot equipment, machinery and materials left unattended
- wrongly wired electrical cables
- fitting electrical fuses in plugs that are too highly rated for the equipment

- failing to follow safety instructions
- overuse of extension leads, overloading power circuits
- misuse of portable heaters.

There have been many instances of factories, offices and homes being burned down and lives lost due to such misuses as these. Many people work on the principle 'when all else fails, read the instructions', often with disastrous results.

Defective machinery and equipment

There often seems to be a lack of a sense of the importance of urgency, with the 'I'll do it when I get around to it' attitude leading to:

- failure to follow recommended maintenance and servicing schedules and instructions
- failure to service and clean machinery or office equipment
- failure to ensure that faulty machinery and equipment is serviced immediately — 'We have to get this batch out first'.

Deliberate ignition (arson)

The Association of British Insurers estimates that approximately 50 per cent of all direct fire losses are due to arson. The four main groups of arsonists are:

- vandals, who cause fire for a laugh or for kicks with a mindless disregard for property or life
- disturbed vandals, who cause fire as a form of rebellion against a society that, as they see it, has let them down
- employees or ex-employees who have grudges against a company or industry
- people who manufacture situations in which they may be seen to be 'heroes' and win commendations, such as the fire officer who is always first on the scene.

There is much that can be done to prevent arsonists. Even determined fire bugs *can* be deterred by ensuring that:

1. premises and restricted areas are inaccessible to unauthorized people
2. ensuring that waste materials are properly disposed of
3. using careful recruitment and selection techniques to ensure that you avoid an attack from within your own organization.

Contractors' unsafe acts and omissions

Contractors can be guilty of any of items 1 to 3 described above, but, because they do not own or directly work for the premises' owner or operator, they may not have the same degree of safety consciousness that your employees may have, so need regular monitoring.

The majority of fires started by contractors are the result of accidents occurring during hot work. For this reason, hot work should be supervised by a hot work permit scheme.

Supervising contractors is a vital part of management's responsibility towards your workforce and contractors.

Management failure

This is the biggest single human cause of such disasters and one that invariably incorporates the above main causes 1 to 5. Due often to the 'It won't happen here' attitude, mentioned earlier, no preventative action is taken, with the result that serious fire risks occur, presenting hazards to employees and others. This can be the result of ignorance, apathy, complacency, lethargy, lack of safety awareness or safety consciousness. These, in turn, are invariably due to the absence of *training* in fire safety and fire precautions procedures.

The importance of *training* in matters affecting the safety of people, premises and property in the case of fire cannot be stressed enough (particular attention to fire training is given in Chapter 29).

Some helpful observations

The following list includes some typical fire safety hazards that I have seen when conducting health and safety audits:

- access to fire doors and fire extinguishers blocked by structures, furniture, plants, trolleys, materials, work in progress
- fire extinguishers placed at the wrong end of a room, so that access to them would be *through* a fire
- as the last point, but also no means of escape at the end of a very long office, with windows with only the small top-flight opening
- inoperative fire doors which have not been tested for many years, either rusted, clogged with dirt or 'time-welded' in
- fire doors nailed up by employees
- padlocks and locks on escape-route gates rusted-up, never unlocked or serviced (locks on doors *must* be opened during working hours)
- egress from fire doors blocked and overgrown by weeds and shrubs (one company's fire escape route was completely overgrown by several years' growth of bushes and the iron gate was rusted-up, while another's fire escape was completely blocked by long-discarded carpet squares and other refurbishment waste and one company's head office had 'rearranged' its main reception office, completely blocking access to the main reception door and the route to another fire door would have been through any fire)
- pathways and steps away from fire doors overgrown with moss (very dangerous, especially in wet weather) or strewn with rubbish
- pathway away from fire door just rubble, with no firm surface laid
- no lights in fire escape stairwells
- emergency lighting not working
- no safety barrier on egress pathway outside fire door
- egress away from fire escape denied due to the erection of new buildings
- fire extinguishers not checked for several years
- fire extinguishers 'spent', that is, they have been used and then not serviced or refilled
- fire extinguishers wrongly sited or moved from their proper place
- fire doors propped or jammed open (an offence unless electronic/magnetic release systems are fitted, as in many hotels)
- fire extinguishers used to prop open fire doors (another offence)
- fire extinguishers in cabinets, under tables, on shelves or otherwise 'out of the way' in hidden corners
- fire alarms inoperative (never checked for years) — 'Don't know how to check it', 'Don't know where the key is' or 'The key for the control panel is broken'
- fire alarm not audible in parts of building

- fire alarm not connected through to security lodge
- holes and wide cracks in ceilings and broken ceiling tiles, which would permit the spread of smoke and flames in the event of a fire
- paper items placed on or over heaters in offices
- paper and boxes stored in a gas boiler room
- ordinary, domestic 'half hour' door on the same gas boiler room.

These items are just a sample of the things found and the risks posed are all fully avoidable if management takes action, is aware of safety and is *trained* in fire precautions. If you have any of these situations in *your* workplace, you need to attend to it urgently and conduct some remedial fire safety training.

If a fire occurs, even if it is only a small one, *always* ensure that a full and proper investigation is carried out to determine its true cause and how it can be prevented from recurring. If you have no full-time fire officer, call the fire brigade — they will be pleased to investigate and advise (even after you have put the fire out yourself) as they would rather spend an hour advising and preventing disasters than dealing with burned-down buildings and dead bodies.

Better still, examine your fire precautions, fire prevention procedures and fire-fighting equipment on a regular basis to assess their effectiveness. Examine your machinery, equipment, materials and working practices — including those in the office — to assess how you can prevent a fire or explosion.

NHS managers

Section 60 of the NHS Community Care Act 1990 removed Crown immunity for health authorities so they are now subject to the same requirements as industry. Managers in NHS establishments are therefore now as personally liable as managers in any other place of employment.

The consequences of fire

The consequences of both physical and human causes of fire are so extensive as to defy adequate description, but the following are the main ones:

- death and personal injury as a result of severe burns
- buildings destroyed, and businesses along with them
- expensive equipment damaged, and with it materials/products
- projects interrupted, with the associated feelings of frustration and inconvenience
- failure to meet objectives and completion dates
- loss of future orders
- damage to the environment
- loss of historic buildings.

Rather than have to deal with the consequences, though, work to prevent them happening. The vast majority of fires can be avoided by taking simple precautions, by adopting safe working practices and by providing adequate fire safety training to *all* management and staff.

Classifications of fires and how to extinguish them

Fire authorities speak of four classes of fire — A to D — plus a fifth, electrical.

- *Class A* These are free-burning solid combustible materials, such as, wood, paper, cardboard, cloth and other carbon compounds, which normally leave glowing embers.

They are extinguished by cooling, say by means of a jet or spray of cold water, but you *must* ensure that the fire is fully 'damped down' otherwise it may flare up again because there is some residual heat.

The main causes of class A fire risks are the building structure itself, furniture, wastepaper baskets, stationery stores, cleaner's rooms and waste disposal units.

- *Class B* These are flammable liquids and liquefiable solids, such as oils, paints, fats, petrol, paraffin and greases — that fall into two groups:

Group 1 — polar materials, such as alcohols/methylated spirits, that will mix with water
Group 2 — conventional hydrocarbon fuels, that will *not* mix with water. They are extinguished by using: group '1' — alcohol-resistant foam, and dry powder (not water-based or conventional foam extinguishers, as alcohol will mix with the water content of these media (note, though, that the use of water spray, water fog is limited to those who have the necessary equipment to produce these specialized methods of extinction — that is, the fire brigade or some fixed systems). For fires involving hydrocarbon fuels, extinguish them with carbon dioxide (CO_2 gas), dry powders or foam, water spray, water fog.

Class B danger areas include kitchens, boilerhouses, underground car parks, garages (to which separate legislation under local licensing legislation applies) and spirit stores.

- *Class C* These are flammable gases and liquefied gases, such as methane, propane and butane.

They are extinguished by cutting off the supply. Liquid petroleum gas will seek the lowest point and the explosion potential is enormous. In the event of spills, do not extinguish the flame but contain the conflagration to avoid spreading the fire.

With bottled gas, a skilled firefighter (eg fire brigade) can extinguish a bottled-gas flame by using a dry powder extinguisher directly on the outlet of the jet and then turning the supply off, but this should *never* be attempted by other people. The general advice is that it is *very* dangerous to try to extinguish a gas fire without turning the supply off.

Liquefied gases are extinguished by smothering, say by foam for deep spills, dry powder for shallow spills or by CO_2 gas for either. Water-spray containers can be used in order to cool them.

- *Class D* These are metal fires, based on burning metals, particularly the alkali metals, including sodium, potassium, caesium and lithium. The problem with metal fires generally is that they react violently to generally used firefighting media. Water and any foam media produce hydrogen, which, in turn, is an explosive gas, while CO_2 gas reacts violently with metal, and halon results in an even more violent reaction. Conventional dry powders are of little use on metal fires because their velocity scatters the burning material and the powders react with the burning metal.

They are, thus, extinguished by gently applying a suitable agent. This is an extinguisher with a low-velocity applicator (preventing scattering of the burning metal) containing special powders that have been developed for metal fires.

These should be on-site if dangerous metals are present. Powdered graphite, powdered talc, soda ash, limestone and dry sand can also be used to put out this kind of fire.

Extinguishing metal fires produces many problems even for experienced fire officers using special powders. Special training in extinguishing metal fires is therefore *essential* and no one having only a basic knowledge of firefighting procedures should be allowed to fight metal fires. *Never* use extinguishing agents containing water on metal fires, as doing this is very dangerous, nor CO_2 gas or conventional dry powders for the same reason.

- *Electrical* These are any burning/smoking electrical equipment or apparatus, including cable. It is imperative to *switch off the power source*. Fires involving electrical equipment occur in ventilating systems, computer rooms, control rooms, switchgear, lift motor rooms and so on.

  They are extinguished by using dry powder or CO_2 gas extinguishers. Where the electrical supply cannot be isolated and there is a risk of electric shock, non-conductive agents, such as CO_2 gas, halon or dry powder can be used, but any extinguishing agent will only extinguish flames and (with electricity left on) the burning/smoking may continue.

  Note that electrical fires are not a separate class of fire to the fire brigade because, when the electrical power is switched off at the mains, the type of fire becomes a fire of the material that is burning and the appropriate extinguishing agent for the material involved can be used. We treat it separately here, however, because, in most workplaces, when a fire occurs in electrical apparatus and equipment, the power source of that equipment may not be easily or quickly accessible and so using an extinguisher may be the quickest and most effective option.

For fires in or of public service *vehicles*, the recommended media are spray foam/AFFF spray; but for private vehicles, the recommended medium is dry powder, which causes no damage to paintwork or upholstery.

In view of the need to match the extinguishing agent to the class of fire, you should seek advice from manufacturers of extinguishers as to which extinguishing media and specialist extinguisher to select for any given situation.

Types of fire extinguisher

There are eight basic types of fire extinguisher, five of which are on the fire brigade's recognized list, plus three others in popular use. These are shown in Table 12.1.

Water extinguishers are powered by the release of CO_2 gas using a controlled discharge lever (to BS 5423, 1987). Some old-type (pre-1980) CO_2 water extinguishers with a plunger still exist. To stop the water jet of these, turn upside down and allow the gas to escape.

Halon (halogenated hydrocarbon) extinguishers use a lightweight vaporizing liquid and are also known as BCF (Bromochlorodifluoromethane) (see also the cautionary note regarding their use).

Foam provides a seal against reignition, but it is only effective if it is used in large quantities.

AFFF stands for aqueous film-forming foam, for use on any type of fire.

Table 12.1 Type of fire extinguishers

Type	Colour	Function	Types of fires used on
Water	Red	Cools	Combustibles (wood, paper, rags, etc.)
CO_2 gas	Black	Smothers	Any; good on electrical fires but see 'Some cautionary notes', below. Not effective on combustibles or in open air. Do *not* use large CO_2 gas extinguishers in very confined spaces
Halon	Green	Smothers	Any; excellent on electronic equipment; but *do not* use in large quantities if complete ventilation is not possible. Do not use on very high temperature fires. (See 'Special note concerning halon', below)
Dry powder	Blue	Smothers	Electrical, vehicle engines, kitchens, petrol, oils, but messy and effectiveness reduced in windy conditions. Also useful where water damage must be kept to a minimum
Foam	Cream	Smothers	Petrols, oils, aircraft
AFFF	Fawn	Smothers	Any; liquid mixture — messy
FFFP	Fawn	Smothers	
Multipurpose	Red	Smothers	Any
Fire blanket	Red holder	Smothers	Any, especially fat/oil fires

FFFP stands for film-forming fluoro-protein foam. This type of extinguisher should *not* be used on *electrical* fires, unless you know that the particular extinguisher has passed the electrical conductivity test (which will depend on its manufacturer). This type of extinguisher must be emptied and refilled every three months.

Fire blankets are made from fibreglass coated with silicone rubber to provide an impenetrable barrier. Simply place over the fire to smother it. Be sure not to beat the fire with a fire blanket or throw it. Check that any fire blanket is made to BS 6575 specifications.

Multipurpose fire extinguishers are powder ones.

Some cautionary notes

1. *Do not use water on any electrical fire*. To do so is to risk electrocution. Place all water-type extinguishers *away* from electrical apparatus, to prevent them being used unthinkingly or in panic.
2. Do not use *large* halon extinguishers in any confined space — say in a very small office, where there is insufficient means of fully venting the affected area, particularly where there are no large opening windows.
3. People must exercise care in using CO_2 gas as:

   • it can suffocate — its purpose being to smother fire — as the maximum a human being can absorb is a 9 per cent concentration, while the extinguisher is 34 per cent concentration
   • it produces dry ice, which can burn the skin if contact is prolonged

- it produces a loud pop, which can startle some.

Notwithstanding these, it is a highly recommended fire extinguishing agent and commended as an alternative to halon.

4. At present, there is no legal requirement for any colour-coding of fire extinguishers, which can cause problems of identification (especially in some large retail stores where they must also look attractive and match the decor). The European standards organization (CEN) has plans to make *all* fire extinguishers *red* in colour, with colour stripes to indicate their content and labels for instructions on safe use, which would certainly help a great deal.

5. When using and servicing a fire extinguisher, you must conform to the service and use requirements of BS 5423 (BS 6575 for fire blankets). Complying with these standards will be a defence in cases of mishap while non-compliance will mitigate against you.

Special note concerning halon

Halon 1211 is toxic and harmful to human beings, so if there are no wide-opening windows (just extractor fans, say, or only the small top flight of windows open), use either the smallest size or an alternative, such as a small CO_2 gas extinguisher.

The Home Office advice in its guide to the Fire Precautions (Places of Work) Regulations 1995 states:

> For environmental reasons it is recommended that the provision of halon extinguishers should be avoided where other suitable extinguishing media is available.

But further, there is an international agreement to phase out the production of halon. In future, the majority of halon extinguishers will have to be replaced with those containing other firefighting media, so that it will become more difficult (and more expensive) to replace the contents of fixed halon systems.

The 'safe' level of exposure to halon fumes is to a 4 to 5 per cent concentration in the atmosphere for a maximum of a minute. Thus, the maximum emission of halon must be at or below 4 per cent. There was an 85 per cent cut in the production of halon by 31 December 1992 and ICI has already taken the decision to close its last halon 1211 plant and completely stop production. The Montreal Protocol, an international agreement governing the phasing out of ozone-depleting substances, imposed a total ban on production after 31 December 1993, apart from 'essential uses'.

Essential uses of halon 1211 are defined by the United Nations Environment Programme (UNEP) as those where it will be impossible to implement alternative systems in the short term. The Ministry of Defence will be the main body concerned and essential uses should be met by the contents of a 'halon bank, once it has been established' (ICI Press Release, 19 June 1992).

The alternative to halon 1211 is halon 1301, which is a breathable gas at 5 to 7 per cent concentration, but it is only available in sprinkler room flooding systems. However, for reasons outlined earlier, its future is uncertain.

Summary

We have looked at the classes of fire and types of fire extinguishing media. Now let's combine the two in a simplified chart (see Fig. 12.2).

Class of fire	Water	Spray foam	CO_2 gas	Dry powder
Type A (combustibles)	√	√		√
Type B (flammable liquids)		√	√	√
Type C (flammable and liquefied gases)			√	√
Electrical			√	√
Vehicles		√		√

Note: Halon is not included as a recommended portable extinguisher.

Fig. 12.2 Which portable extinguisher to use

Fixed fire-protection systems

There are various types of fixed-system fire extinguishing equipment. They include:

- *high pressure optimized spray* (formerly known as water spray normal sprinkler system), droplet-sized for dispersal of heat and smoke
- *Water hose reel* extendable, wall mounted
- *halon 1301* a breathable gas in 5 to 7 per cent concentration, it gives room flooding and is a lightweight, vaporizing liquid
- *water fog* a lightweight alternative for sprinkler systems, using high pressure and small amounts of water, atomizing it into minute water droplets, sprayed at high speed from a self-contained system to fill a whole building; it cools and extinguishes and is an alternative to halon and CO_2 gas.

Sprinkler systems work by maintaining water pressure in pipes and holding this back by means of a glass bulb in a small frame. When heat expands the contents of the bulb, it breaks and permits the flow of water or halon spray. The colour of the bulb indicates the pre-set temperature at which it is activated.

Fixed fire-safety systems

There are also various types of fixed systems for protecting people and property in the event of fire, including:

- *smoke detectors* although not a statutory requirement at present, any fire officer will confirm the advisability and benefit of fitting them, but, this said, they can *become* legally required by virtue of trade-offs, that is, following Building Regulations *or* using fire-engineering solutions to overcome MOE problems; they can be cheap and easy to install (depending on the make) and they pay for themselves many times over; note that under Approved Document B of the 1991 Building Regulations, mains supply smoke detectors *must* be installed in all *new* homes
- *ionization smoke detectors*, which detect the products of combustion even before visible smoke is detectable
- *aspirating smoke detectors*, which detect fires that are just starting but are not yet visible to the human eye

- *monitored fire-detection loops*, which have control panels with liquid crystal or vacuum fluorescent displays
- *electronic/magnetic door-release units*, which automatically release doors in the event of fire being detected — these are used widely in large hotels and conference centres, but note that it is an *offence* to hold fire doors open with anything other than with this type of retainer/release system
- *alarm bells*, which ring loudly following activation of the alarm system either manually or by a fire-detection system
- *heat detectors*, which operate either by detecting the difference in temperature and rate of change between two semiconductor sensors or responding when a fixed top temperature is reached
- *letterplates*, which are flame-resistant with intumescent gaskets, to prevent the spread of smoke/flames through letter slots (letterboxes should be made of sheet metal and hung on the back of the door to catch any incendiary device introduced through the letter slot.

Fire certificates

Fire Precautions Act (section 1), Fire Precautions (Hotels and Boarding Houses) Order 1972 and Fire Precautions (Factories, Offices, Shops and Railway Premises) Order 1989 require an employer or keeper of premises to apply for a fire certificate in the following circumstances:

- any place of work where more than 20 people are at work on the ground or lower (such as basement) floors
- any place of work where more than 10 people are at work above ground level
- a building where highly inflammable or explosive substances are stored or used in or under the premises
- sleeping accommodation in a hotel or boarding house that accommodates:
  —more than six people (including staff and guests)
  —is above the first floor (that is, it is on the second floor or higher)
  —is below the ground floor
- places of entertainment
- licensed premises.

Note that this second circumstance was changed in 1988 to the aggregate of *all* persons at work on *all* floors above ground level, not the numbers on each floor. Thus, if you have, say, 3, 2, 4 and 2 employees, working on the first, second, third and fourth floors respectively (not the ground floor), the total is 11 above ground level and you need a fire certificate.

Also since 1988, 'at work' in both the first and second circumstances means not just those who are actually 'employed', but all those who are working in the premises.

All the above circumstances were further enhanced by the Fire Precautions (Places of Work) Regulations 1995, which took effect from 1 April 1995. There are no proposals in these Regulations to extend the list of premises that require a fire certificate.

Applications for fire certificates are to be made under the Fire Precautions (Application for Certificate) Regulations 1989 (SI 77).

By a 'place of work' is meant any place where people are 'at work', as defined in the terms of the HASWA (see Chapter 6). Visitors, contractors and customers are not counted as being persons 'at work' for the purposes of calculating the numbers counted for fire certificate applications, though persons on 'training for employment' schemes are (see Chapter 5 for how to determine who are employees). However, some fire authorities do not regard IT, YT or ET trainees as employees for the purposes of a fire certificate (despite the Regulations quoted in this chapter). This said, such a ruling does not absolve employers from affording adequate fire protection and complying with all the requirements of the FPA and supporting orders and Regulations.

Hitherto, many places of entertainment and clubs have not had fire certificates, *per se*, but have had the same standards contained in their public entertainment or club licences. Now, however, they have been brought fully into the scope of the Fire Precautions (Places of Work) Regulations 1995 (FPR 95).

The situation for joint-occupancy premises
To justify an independent fire certificate, a building must be either:

- totally separate and free of all connection with other adjacent buildings
- if part of a building is divided into sections or units, those sections or units must be completely separated by fire-resistant walls with their own fire escape route *and* providing total vertical separation up to the roof.

However, although there may be separation by fire-resisting walls with separate MOE, if any of the floors from differing occupancies overlap each other *without* an unbroken vertical line of fire separation, then the *whole* building, including these areas, will count as one for fire certification purposes.

In cases where buildings have been partitioned into smaller sections or units, each sharing communal fire-escape routes and/or are *not* separated by fire-resistant walls, then the whole is counted as one building for the purposes of a fire certificate. In such circumstances, it is the duty of the owner or operator of those premises to obtain a fire certificate and to provide a copy to the tenants of each section or unit.

However, if you are the occupier of a *section* of a joint-occupancy building, there is nothing to prevent you from applying for a fire certificate if such would assist you in complying with the law.

In the case of joint-occupancy premises, the owner or operator of the building(s) is responsible for maintaining fire-precautions standards as required by the certificate in the *communal* area, but each individual employer in the partitioned sections or units is responsible for providing and maintaining fire-precautions procedures and fire-fighting equipment within their *own* section and for maintaining MOE they may use that are also communal areas. However, each building is assessed individually and fire authorities can make either or both responsible for any aspect of fire safety.

The situation for single-occupancy buildings
The responsibility for maintaining premises in single-occupancy buildings will *always* be with the *occupier* (even if it is rented/leased), not the *owner*.

The contents of a fire certificate
A fire certificate will specify:

- the particular use or uses of the premises it covers
- the means of escape the premises are to have

- the means for ensuring that the MOE can be safely and effectively used at all times when the building is in use
- the measures to prevent the spread of fire, smoke and fumes
- the emergency lighting and direction signs required
- the means to be provided for first aid fire fighting by persons in the building
- the means for giving warning in the event of fire
- for factories, details of explosive or highly flammable substances stored or used on the premises.

A fire certificate may also specify the requirements for ensuring that the following standards of fire safety are maintained:

- maintenance of the MOE keeping them free from obstruction
- maintenance of other fire precautions specified in the certificate
- the training to be given to persons employed on the premises
- the maximum numbers of persons permitted to be on the premises, on each floor, at any one time
- any other fire precautions relevant to the building and its use.

Enforcement of FPR 95

The responsibility for enforcement of all EC Directives rests with national governments. In the case of the 'Framework' Directive (89/391/EEC) and the 'Workplace' Directive (89/654/EEC), this responsibility in the UK is divided as follows:

- for health and safety, *per se*: the Health and Safety Executive;
- for fire safety and fire precautions: the Home Office.

The responsibility for enforcement of the FPR 95, which arises out of the foregoing Directives, is delegated by the Home Office to the fire authority.

The legal requirements of FPR 95

These Regulations lay down minimum legal standards for fire precautions and fire safety as follows.

- *Fire doors* All internal and external fire doors must be made of solid, fire- and smoke-resisting material. They must give at least 30 minutes' protection in low- or medium-risk workplaces, 60 minutes' protection in high-risk workplaces.

Note that sliding and revolving exit doors are *not* fire doors, unless specifically designed or adapted and approved by the fire authority. If fitted, therefore, there must be an additional outward-opening fire door, normally adjacent to the revolving or sliding door.

The fire door part of any fire-resisting construction *must* give 30 minutes' protection and be fitted with a positive self-closing device and have a 'FIRE DOOR — KEEP SHUT' sign affixed (section 5(a) of FPR 95).

- *Direction* All fire doors, doors opening on to staircases or corridors and other doors affording exit from workplaces where more than 50 people are employed *must* open outwards.
- *Exit signs and lighting* Every door, window or other exit (other than the main exit), access room and egress route affording means of escape must have 'FIRE EXIT' notices affixed to them (section 5(a) of FPR 95). Artificial lighting must be provided from a mains or back-up generator supply during hours of darkness

(generally after 1800 and before 0800) or in areas that do not otherwise have natural or artificial light. Also, emergency lighting must be provided in case the artificial lighting powered from the mains fails (section 5(b) of FPR 95).

- *Lifts and hoists* The FPA requires that every lift or hoist be completely enclosed within fire-resisting material and doors that afford 30 minutes' protection. However, this is not always done in practice as the shaft could spread fire, so the various risks are assessed with regard to the whole of the building. Some lattice-style lift shafts in older buildings adjacent to accommodation stairways are one example.
- *Locks* Doors must *not* be locked or fastened so as to deny *immediate* use during working hours.
- *Keys* A key in the lock or glass case or a glass-release bolt are *not* permitted after 1 April 1995 (section 5.2(1) of Guidance to FPR 95). Where such exist, these must be removed and a suitable mechanism must be fitted, such as a push-bar door-opening mechanism.
- *Fire alarms* Fire alarms must be indicated (section 7(3)), and records maintained of types, numbers, locations and servicing of all alarm systems.
- *Equipment* Firefighting equipment appropriate to your situation must be provided, which takes account of: the size, design, construction and content of the workplace, the nature of the activity carried on there, and the fire risk assessment (section 6(1)). It must be readily accessible, maintained in good working order, clearly indicated and regularly serviced (section 6(3)). Signs made to BS 5499, parts 1 and 3, must be displayed to indicate the location and correct siting of such equipment (section 6(2)). Portable equipment must be immediately available for use, that is, access to it must not be blocked, and it must be serviceable for use (section 6(3)).
- *Clearways* All fire doors, access routes to them and egress routes away from them or from the building must be kept clear at all times. This includes the arrangement of the contents of working rooms, which must be laid out in such a way that MOE can be reached easily without there being any kind of obstruction.
- *Automatic systems* There must be an automatic fire-detection system fitted where the outbreak of fire is unlikely to be noticed before a life-threatening situation arises.
- *Waste* Although not included in FPR 95, all combustible waste should be disposed of daily in a safe manner and not generally left in workplaces, including offices. Waste should be stored in a safe place set aside for the purpose, well away from personnel and possible sources of ignition. The area you set aside for the temporary storage of combustible waste (only until disposal) must be separated from the rest of the workplace by a fire-resistant construction or in such a manner that any burning waste would cause the least possible risk to people in the workplace. Do remember also to protect combustible waste from vandals and arsonists.

Construction sites

A new code of practice, Fire Prevention on Construction Sites, has been issued by the LPC and FPA in conjunction with the National Contractors' Group and the Building Employers Confederation. While not included in FPR 95, this is a very important code, aimed at reducing the number of accidental and malicious fires occurring on UK construction sites. This code of practice covers the following points:

- compliance with the code of practice

- emergency procedures
- definitions
- design phase
- construction phase
- fire protection
- portable fire extinguishers
- emergency procedures
- site security arrangements
- temporary buildings
- electricity and gas supplies
- hot work
- waste materials
- plant
- storage of flammable liquids and liquid petroleum gas (LPG).

Planning for fire safety

When a fire occurs is too late to think about fire safety. There are five stages in planning for fire safety:

1. construction
2. occupancy
3. protection
4. firefighting
5. fire and emergency drills.

Construction

When a building is constructed, it must comply with both the FPA and Building Regulations 1991. These requirements take account of the building's intended use and the nature of the product and/or service of the approved use.

Occupation

Ask the following questions when initially occupying a building.

- Does the building conform to the requirements of the intended occupancy?
- Did the former occupants have a different product and/or service and thus your occupancy involves a change of use?
- What changes will you need to make?

Many companies have come unstuck by failing to ensure that correct and sufficient fire safety measures were implemented upon their occupation of a building (see 'Alterations to buildings', below).

Protection

Ask the following questions to find out if the existing fire-protection systems are adequate.

- Are all the measures necessary to protect against the start and spread of fire in place?
- Are all the ceilings and walls sealed to prevent the spread of smoke and flames?
- Do all fire doors provide a good seal and an effective 60 or 30 minutes' resistance to the spread of flames, smoke and gases (according to the assessed risk level)?
- Are all the fire doors constructed of solid materials with no ventilation grilles in them (unless made of intumescent materials that expand in heat)? It has been

known for fire doors to have ventilation grilles put in them, even at the construction stage.

- Do you have adequate MOE, including fire doors, egress routes (gangways, corridors, fire escape stairs), alternative means of escape?
- That very long office with a fire door at one end; is there an alternative means of escape at the opposite end? Can windows provide emergency escape routes? A window where only a small top flight opens is *not* an escape route!
- What means of raising the alarm do you have? Is it effective?

Firefighting

Ask yourself this question: are all the correct types of firefighting equipment (as advised earlier) in place, in the correct sizes and numbers?

Fire and emergency drills

Unless specified in a fire certificate, hitherto companies have not been pursued for *not* holding regular fire drills, but the fact that they had not done so would militate against them in the event of an injurious or fatal fire. However, from 1 April 1995, under section 11(6), it became *compulsory* to hold regular fire drills (once per year as a *minimum*, by law, but preferably twice per year) if:

- more than 20 persons work as employees in the whole building)
- more than 10 persons work as employees on all floors above and below ground level
- explosive or highly flammable materials are stored or used.

It would be sensible to hold fire drills more frequently than once a year if situations demand it, such as if there is a high turnover of trainees — IT/YT/ET, for example. Do remember the rules on multiple-occupancy premises, as it is the total numbers employed by *all* the premises' occupants, not the numbers employed by single employers, that count.

Fire drills are a vital part of *training*. See Chapter 30 for full information on the content of fire drills and how to conduct them.

Means of escape

It was mentioned earlier that fire authorities do not assess so much the *likelihood* of fire occurring as the *potential risk* of injury to, or death of, people in the event of a fire. The main principle of fire safety is that people must be able to get out. Thus, the UK's very strict standards of fire safety place great emphasis on the provision of *means of escape* (MOE) from a workplace. Persons must be able to proceed safely along a recognizable escape route, *by their own unaided efforts*, to a place of safety, regardless of where the fire may be.

Thus, it is not just the final exit to a place of safety that is of concern, but all of the route from a person's place of work to that place of safety that is considered. Just stand in the middle of a workplace — whether factory, busy office or well-stocked shop — and ask yourself the questions, What if a fire started here, or there, or there? What could be the possible consequences?

Means of escape must be arrived at after taking account of the following factors:

- the results of an assessment of the fire risks and fire hazards on the premises
- the fire-resisting construction

- the risk of fire and smoke spreading (see below)
- the surface finishes of the MOE (see below)
- the occupant capacity (see below)
- the exit capacity (see below)
- the main MOE from a workplace to a place of safety
- the distance of travel (DOT) required from the workplace to a place of safety (this will depend on the findings of the risk assessment, but, generally, the greater the risk, the shorter must be the DOT distance of travel)
- alternative means of escape from most situations, unless the distance of travel in one direction is no greater than those laid down in Home Office publications on distances of travel
- the location and nature of the fire doors in the escape route (see below)
- the signs directing people to the exits and exit signs on doors
- the location of the final exit or (if not possible) a place of relative safety (such as a protected escape route within the distance of travel)
- the lighting in escape routes (normal and emergency)
- the location of the place of safety away from the building
- the protection of the MOE from the risks of smoke and flames by fire-resisting construction
- the width of the MOE route, which should take account of the numbers employed, but, in any event, must not be less than 1.05 metres wide.
- the number of exits from each workroom or storey in the building, according to the numbers of employees; these must be of an adequate width.

The following are *not* acceptable as MOE and should not be designated as such (though they can be provided separately to the means of escape):

- lifts (except those designed for the safe evacuation of disabled persons)
- escalators
- ladders (except as the MOE from high-level plant, cranes or hoists and for use by only one or two able-bodied people), though they may not be totally excluded
- self-rescue and lowering devices (except in very isolated places and for use by one *trained* able-bodied person).

Escape lighting All escape routes should be provided with sufficient lighting to enable people to see their way out safely. This includes the provision of emergency escape lighting where there is a lack of natural daylight, including external escape routes. Larger premises should have self-contained lighting units which operate automatically in the event of an emergency, while in smaller workplaces, this lighting can be by battery-operated torches (including spare batteries) suitably located and known to employees.

A MOE *must not* have within it any of the following items, as to place them in the MOE would be to create hazards:

- portable heaters (of any kind) or heaters with unprotected naked flames or radiant bars
- fixed heaters that use gas cylinders as their power source
- oil-filled heaters or boilers
- cooking appliances
- stored furniture
- coat racks

- furniture, beds, laundry or cleaning equipment, and so on, temporarily stored there
- lighting that consists of naked flames
- gas boilers, pipes, meters and fittings (except those installed strictly in accordance with Gas Safety Regulations)
- gaming or vending machines
- electrical equipment (except normal and emergency lighting or fire alarm systems).

In areas devoid of natural light or where people work outside of normal hours, all MOE must afford lighting to provide 0.2 lux of light (roughly the amount of light produced by a candle). There should be no 'borrowed' light from outside.

These might seem like just common sense — of course MOE should never be obstructed by anything — yet many of these items have been found there during health and safety audits. To not keep them clear is illegal.

Fire-resisting construction

Many people do not appreciate that smoke and flames can find a way through almost anything and will always take the line of least resistance. It is vital to fire safety, therefore, to ensure that smoke and flames cannot spread to any MOE or other parts of a building in the event of fire by getting through either:

- materials that will burn and allow fire to progress
- imperfections in structures.

Routes that need to be protected from fire (eg MOE to a final exit) must be protected by a fire-resisting construction. This means that, in these situations, all walls, floors and ceilings that immediately enclose an escape route must have a fire resistance of:

- *at least* 30 minutes in medium/low-risk areas
- *at least* 60 minutes in high-risk areas.

This is not an unreasonable expectation when you think that the longest fire drill/ escape time could be three minutes, after which the fire brigade need time to get into the building to fight the fire and effect any rescue necessary.

Where the required minimum of 30 or 60 minutes' fire resistance is not possible (say, in older or architectural/historic buildings), then a reduction in the distance of travel must be sought or a means of automatic fire detection or suppression may be recommended.

Linked buildings *must* have a 60 minutes' separation wall between each section. A 60 minutes' resistance fire door is permitted, if needed, for fire exits only.

Flames and the spread of smoke

Flames and smoke can spread frighteningly easily. Remember, too, that fires produce flames and smoke but these themselves give off hot gases, which are often toxic (that is, they are poisonous and potentially lethal). Such gases can come from any burning material, but most come from man-made items produced from chemicals, such as polyvinylchloride (PVC) or foam cushioning. Smoke can travel at 7 metres per second, one breath can make you unconscious, three or four breaths are fatal. More people die as a result of inhaling smoke and toxic fumes from fires than from burning.

Flames, smoke and gases can pass through:

- holes and cracks in structures, such as ceiling tiles leading to a ceiling cavity
- gaps between sections of structures, such as small gaps between wall and ceiling joins (especially where partitioning has been installed)
- ductwork, pipework, chutes and trunking, especially those used for ventilation and air conditioning
- voids between horizontal or vertical structures, such as those between a ceiling and the floor above or gaps above partitioning walls leaving a void to the roof.

All such possible passages for flames, smoke and gases to travel through must be sealed up completely with fire/smoke-stopping or cavity barriers or fire dampers inside ductwork to prevent the spread of smoke — unless it is a ceiling void where fire-resisting walls have been constructed from floor to roof expressly to contain fire.

Compartmentation

An effective method for containing flames, smoke and gases is to divide premises into fire-containing compartments. Some compartments can contain fire for several hours. Compartmentation in MOE can both prevent fires spreading *and* provide safe escape routes. However, the benefit of compartmentation can be lost if even a small hole is present to allow flames, smoke and fumes to pass through, so cavity barriers are very important in compartments. In compartments, doors providing 30 or 60 minutes' protection from fire must be fitted and remain closed.

Compartmentation could have prevented losses of over £100 million in each of two Ministry of Defence warehouse fires.

Surface finishes

Many types of surface finishes (paint, wood and so on) are flammable and can be very dangerous in the event of fire. Remember the King's Cross tragedy in which many died? This was caused by individual carelessness, but the fire spread because flammable surface finishes were used in the passageways.

So many people just put up wallpaper or paint their walls with flammable gloss paint without considering the consequences should a fire occur. When constructing, refurbishing or decorating any surface in any workplace — whether it is a MOE or not — it is always sound policy to consider what type of surface you could use that would *not* burn and help fire to spread. Needless to say, this is vital in fire-resistant constructions.

There are three classes of surface finishes approved for preventing or limiting the spread of flames: 0, 1 and 3 (there is no 2).

- *Class 0* For use in all locations, circulation spaces and MOE. Examples are brickwork, blockwork, concrete, plasterboard, ceramic tiles, plaster, rendering on wood or metal laths, woodwool slab, thin vinyl and paper coverings on *inorganic* surfaces (but *not* heavy flock wallpapers) and some thermosetting plastics (thermosetting means they resist fire/melting in heat).
- *Class 1* For use in all rooms and places of assembly, but *not* MOE, fire-resisting constructions, stairways, corridors or entrance halls. Examples are *flame-*

retardant treated timber, hardboard, blockboard, particleboard (chipboard), heavy flock wallpapers, thermosetting plastics.

- *Class 3* For use in:
  —small rooms not exceeding 4 square metres in floor area
  —*parts* of the walls of larger rooms where the area of walls covered does not exceed half the floor area, but with a maximum of 20 square metres of wall area. Examples are timber, hardboard, blockboard, particleboard (chipboard), heavy flock wallpapers, thermosetting plastics and expanded polystyrene wall and ceiling linings (thermoplastics).

None of these is acceptable in any escape route or in rooms other than as specified above.

Fire doors and escape capacity

What size of fire door should you have — double or single? How many? What is the distance of travel from the workplace (or place of assembly, for example in entertainment) to the final exit? What width of escape route should you have? These questions are very important when establishing how you will ensure that all employees and others will be able to get out of a building quickly and safely in the event of a fire. If they are not asked, what is provided could be disastrously inappropriate. We don't want to be trying to push 10 000 people through a single door 1 metre wide; nor do we want to construct 2-metre wide corridors with double doors when only five people will ever be likely to need to escape through them.

The provision of doors and escape routes needs to be proportional to the numbers of people employed in the building (or in sections of the building) who would have to use any MOE and the exit capacity (size and evacuation time) of escape routes. Do remember that you must not only include employees in your calculations but also realistic figures for visitors, contractors, the public, customers and so on who may regularly use your premises. There must be a sufficient number of escape routes which must be wide enough for the number of occupants and not reducing in width (Regulations 5(1) and 5(2)).

In crowded conditions, about 40 persons will move through a gap of 525 millimetres in 1 minute. The measurement 525 millimetres is known as the 'unit of exit width'. Thus, at '2 units of exit width' of 1.05m (1050 millimetres) 40 persons per half minute or 80 per minute will pass through. However, any exit width wider than 1.05 metres tends to cause disorderly movement and any theoretical advantages extra width you think it might hold is lost, hence the standard door width is 1.05m. When calculating the number of fire escape routes and exits needed, you should always *add* to that number one exit of equal size to the largest exit, to allow for one exit being blocked off by fire (fire authorities will insist on this).

In Table 12.2, exit capacities are listed and this information may assist in determining how many escape routes and fire doors you need or what would be the maximum number of persons permitted to use a given exit.

Escape routes can start at any point in a building where employees or others may be present and may follow seatways, gangways, doorways, corridors and stairways until the final exit has been reached. You will either have to:

Table 12.2 Determining exit capacities for escape routes

Class of risk	Maximum evacuation time	Rate of flow of people per unit width	Exit capacity (expressed as people per unit width)		Maximum number of people for any exit (4 units)*
			1 unit	2 units	
Low	3 minutes	$40 \times 3 =$	120	240	480
Normal	$2\frac{1}{2}$ minutes	$40 \times 2\frac{1}{2} =$	100	200	400
High	2 minutes	$40 \times 2 =$	80	160	320

*The maximum permitted width of *any* fire door is 4 units of width, that is, 2.10 metres.

- determine the *maximum* number of persons permitted to use an escape route, according to the capacity (size and evacuation time) of the escape route
- provide an escape route of fire-resisting construction with sufficient capacity to ensure the speedy and safe evacuation of the numbers of persons likely to use it in the event of a fire.

Criteria for MOE

There are a number of criteria governing MOE. They are:

- escape routes *must always* lead to a place of safety (as defined earlier in this chapter)
- single escape routes which pass through an inner room (that is, an access room) must always be avoided. If this is not possible, there *must* be means of making people aware that there is a fire in an outer room.

Note that this is *not* permissible if the outer room to which the access room leads is a high fire risk area:

- there must be alternative MOE, that is, more than one escape route, from all parts of the workplace (except for small workplaces or some of low or normal fire risk). This may be a suitably adapted large window leading to a fire escape or directly to a place of safety
- each escape route must be independent of the other and lead away from a fire in order to escape
- *multiple escape routes* where there are two or more escape routes in different directions, the maximum distances which people should be expected to travel in order to escape are:
- high fire risk areas: up to 25 metres (allowing a maximum of 1 minute to escape)
- normal fire risk areas: up to 45 metres (allowing a maximum of 3 minutes to escape)
- low fire risk areas: up to 60 metres (allowing a maximum of 5 minutes to escape)
- *single escape routes* where there is only one escape route, that is, in one direction, the maximum distances which people should be expected to travel in order to escape are:
- high fire risk areas: up to 12 metres (allowing a maximum of 30 seconds to escape)
- normal fire risk areas: up to 25 metres (allowing a maximum of 1 minute to escape)
- low fire risk areas: up to 45 metres (allowing a maximum of 3 minutes to escape)

- rooms: maximum 18 metres
- sleeping accommodation: maximum 12 metres
- where a single escape route is from a 'dead end' and forms part of a longer escape route, the total distance travelled to a place of safety must not exceed those distances given for multiple escape routes (above)
- where a MOE is a corridor exceeding 30 metres in length, it must be sub-divided by close-fitting self-closing doors
- where a MOE is a corridor which leads in one direction only or serves sleeping accommodation, it must be made of fire-resisting construction and have self-closing fire doors.

Fire doors

Fire doors must be self-closing or fitted with magnetic/electronic auto-closing devices (fitted at the same level as the auto-closer) that automatically release and close the door when a fire alarm is sounded. Fire doors should be hung on *three* hinges and be of fire-resisting construction and offer 60 or 30 minutes' fire resistance according to the degree of risk (high, low or medium). Any vent grilles must be of intumescent material (not wood) and approved by the fire authority.

Fire doors *must* be kept closed at *all* times, *not* propped open. Fire extinguishers must never be used to prop open any door. Sometimes, in hot conditions, employees (even managers) are tempted to keep fire doors open, but this is dangerous and illegal. In such situations, where extra ventilation is to be needed, why not fit electro/magnetic auto-closers?

Stairways

As with exit doors and escape routes, stairways should be wide enough for the number of people expected to pass through them. They should normally be protected by fire-resisting partitions and fire-resisting self-closing doors, *unless* in small work-places with not more than two floors, where:

(a) there is a low fire risk and the distance of travel to a fire exit is:

- not more than 60 metres (where there are two or more exits) or
- not more than 45 metres (where there is only one exit).

(b) there is a low or normal fire risk and the existing stairway is additional to those needed for escape purposes; for example, a third stairway in a building which requires only two protected stairways.

Disabled people

Unless exempt, if you have 20 or more employees, you are obliged by the Disabled Persons (Employment) Acts 1944 and 1958 to employ sufficient disabled people as to make up a minimum of 3 per cent of the workforce. You must ensure that you provide adequate facilities for them, including access, egress and welfare facilities suitable for wheelchairs and those who walk with the aid of sticks, crutches and frames. There are similar considerations for those with sensory deprivations, such as deafness and blindness. And what of the people with learning disabilities whose thought processes may be different.

These considerations become even more important where evacuation in a fire or fire drill for disabled persons is concerned. They need to be safe-guarded to the same extent as anyone else but need particular kinds of facilities.

The code of practice that sets out general standards for the provision of fire safety for disabled persons in workplaces is given in BS 5588, part 8. These standards apply to all new buildings and to existing buildings that are refurbished. Occupiers of existing buildings may find the code difficult to comply with due to design or conservation problems, but, in that case, contact the local fire brigade as someone there will be pleased to give appropriate advice.

But what can you do to protect disabled people in case of fire? The answer to this depends on the nature of their impairment and, when designing fire safety facilities for the disabled, you need to take account of this.

- *Wheelchair users* Lifts used for evacuation *must* be specially designed and approved for the evacuation of disabled people, as per the code of practice; otherwise, they must *not* be used for evacuation. Also, you must not leave the disabled who use an approved lift to their own devices — they must, by law, be properly supervised by management. If no suitable lift exists and you have to rely on stairs, don't wait until a fire occurs to think about the problem, *train* some members of your staff in the safe lifting and carrying of disabled persons — perhaps involving the disabled themselves. They are unlikely to be embarrassed, but, rather, will be pleased to think that their needs are taken account of and will feel more secure knowing this. Contact with any of the bodies listed at the end of this chapter or the fire brigade to this end will pay dividends.
- *Impaired vision* Some people are blind or partially sighted. What about producing signs in extra-large print and with good, clear typefaces, as well as audible signals at fire exits to ensure that they move in the right direction. Don't forget to place signs conspicuously and to provide very good lighting in the MOE — very important. Also, do consider guidedogs and their owners. Dogs are creatures of habit and, apart from their training, familiarizing the dog and owner, and those without guidedogs, too, with the escape route is essential — you do it for your able-bodied employees, so why not those with impaired vision also? Finally, in your fire planning, do assign normal-sighted members of staff to assist the visually impaired and give them training. Let the blind and partially sighted know who those people are.
- *Hearing difficulties* The deaf or partially deaf will often not hear even the loudest fire alarm bell or siren, so install some clearly visible and identifiable visual alarm system where deaf people work, not forgetting to also do this for those areas they regularly visit. You may also consider providing vibrating pagers to alert those with hearing difficulties in the event of fire, especially in high-risk areas. With these, they do not hear but, rather, feel the alarm sounding.
- *Mentally or physically handicapped* The key with this important group of people is *supervision*. Ensure that they are constantly reassured and led to a place of safety. They should be adequately supervised at all times and, whether in a real or artificial situation, they must not be left unattended at any time. As with wheelchair-bound and deaf persons, you should provide training to assigned able-bodied persons and let the handicapped (and their supervisor) know who they are.

The less able-bodied

There is one group of people who may look and behave as if they are perfectly able-bodied, but who, nevertheless, have impairments that could be hazardous in the event of an evacuation. Have you considered:

- those who have had strokes and heart attacks

- those suffering from osteo- or rheumatoid arthritis
- the epileptic
- those with poor sight or hearing (though it is not bad enough for them to register as disabled).

Consider what assistance will be given to:

- those with broken limbs in plaster, perhaps walking with the aid of crutches or sticks
- the elderly, infirm and very young in nursing homes and nurseries
- heavily pregnant women — an emergency situation can have drastic consequences, even if these result solely from the element of fear.

All these groups require serious consideration, inclusion in the fire drill procedures and (very important) *training* of assigned staff in the care and assistance they can offer them in an emergency situation.

Alterations to buildings

If you, whether occupier or owner of your premises, wish to effect alterations to your buildings, you must inform the fire authority of your intentions *before* the alterations are made, not afterwards.

However, to save time, inconvenience and added expense, when you are drawing up plans you can incorporate changes you will make in the future so that these are included in the fire authority's assessment. They must be assessed as it is very expensive to make the changes only to have to correct them afterwards. These include:

- changes in/to structure, use, fire loading (types of materials), numbers of persons at risk (including any section of your building), surrounding area that affects the MOE (mostly applies where you have immediate neighbours) and scaffolding erected outside a fire door and items, such as pallets, piled by others in your MOE
- alterations in the decorations, furniture and so on
- changes or increased storage of highly flammable or explosive materials and oils.

Flammable liquids

Flammable liquids (petrol, oils, paraffin, solvents and so on) are a chief hazard in fire — if not at the causal stage, then certainly in the spreading of fire once it has started. The key to fire safety with flammable liquids is *control*. Statutory control of flammable liquids rests with two bodies:

- the HSE for substances with a flash-point below 55°C (131°F)
- the fire authority for substances with a flash-point below 22°C (71°F) (if petroleum based) (however, in some areas petroleum legislation is controlled by the local council, not the fire authority).

Responsibility for control of these substances in companies rests with the senior manager responsible for health and safety. Managers must have systems of controls for flammable liquids that ensure that their storage, handling and use is safe and without risks to health (HASWA, section 2(2)(b), and COSHH Regulations).

All highly inflammable, flammable and explosive substances *must* be held in a safe storage area with fire-resistant construction. The only flammable liquids that should ever be allowed in the workplace are those being used and at that time they must be kept by the workbench, with their lids on when they are not actually in use. Flammable substances should never be left in the workplace overnight, but returned to store in sealed containers.

The *maximum* quantity of flammable liquid that can be stored inside a building is 68 litres in fire-resistant construction. You can have up to three 68-litre storage bins/vessels in an external storage compound, but each bin/vessel must be separated by a minimum of 6 metres *and* you must apply for a licence from the local authority (see above regarding statutory control bodies for petroleum). The maximum quantity of liquid petroleum gas you are permitted to store is 450 kilograms.

Managing fire safety

Fires do not happen, they are caused. Similarly, fire safety will not just happen either. Like health and safety generally, it has to be *managed*. In order to achieve the aims of fire safety, every director, manager and supervisor must see fire safety as a *daily* part of their management duties because what was OK yesterday may not be OK today. Every member of management has a clear personal duty of care under both the HASWA and fire safety laws to protect their employees and others and their premises from fire. This duty has been further enhanced by FPR 95, effective 1 April 1995. Regardless of whether or not a fire certificate is in force, management *must* comply with these new Regulations.

Fire can strike at any time. It is part of fire safety management to set up fire precautions to prevent fires from occurring in the first place as well as to make provisions for fire safety in the event of fire. Prevention is far, far better than the 'cure' of reconstruction afterwards. After all, you cannot bring back the dead.

Fire risk assessments

The primary management tool in fire safety is the fire risk assessment. Before you can know what type and extent of fire precautions and fire safety provision you need to make, you must know what risks you are taking precautions for or protecting against. Written fire risk assessments are required for all employers who have five or more employees and these assessments should be submitted to the local fire authority (who may request them if not submitted to them).

The assessment of the level of risk will depend on the type of building and its complexity, its furnishings and fixtures, the work activities and manufacturing processes carried on, the materials used in manufacture, the substances used or being produced in manufacture, and the types of flammable or explosive substances that are used or produced. Assessments should be carried out on construction (the Building Regulations will assist greatly here) and fire risk reassessments will be required if any refurbishment, renovation or change of use of the premises (say from factory to shop or nursing home) is planned.

The overall assessments of risk will be guided by two important factors:

1. the probability that a fire or an explosion could occur (the fire *risk*)
2. the likely consequences of a fire or explosion in terms of injury, fatality and/or damage (the fire *hazard*).

All premises have one of three levels of risk classification; they are:

- high risk
- normal risk
- low risk.

High risk The following considerations will invariably lead to premises being considered to be in the 'high risk' category.

- For workplace and sleeping accommodation, ask the following questions:

  —Are the premises used for sleeping accommodation (including residential care, nursing homes, hospitals, hotels and hostels, boarding houses and schools, halls of residence, colleges and so on)?
  —Is the workplace also used for sleeping accommodation (as above)?
  —Are there permanently or temporarily disabled or physically impaired people present?
  —Will there be young children or elderly people present?
- What materials and substances are, will be or could be present. Ask the following questions:
  —Are solid materials that are highly combustible, flammable or highly inflammable, including man-made materials and those that give off toxic fumes and smoke if burning present?
  —Are flammable or highly flammable liquids, such as petrol, oils, paraffin, solvents, chemicals present?
  —Is dust present, including even such seemingly innocuous airborne dust as flour?

  Such materials can be found in shops, stockrooms, paint-spraying booths, heat treatment areas and in raw materials and finished goods in factories, warehouses and so on. They will also be found in leisure and sports centres, schools, kitchens and restaurants. Look at *every* material and substance and assess its ability to cause or aid the spread of fire.
- The nature of the construction and structure of your building. High-risk buildings will include all of the following:
  —inadequate fire-resisting separation and/or construction
  —vertical or horizontal openings, gaps, cracks or holes through which flames, smoke or gases could pass (see under Flames and the spread of smoke, page 79)
  —wooden floors and joists
  —wooden floors and joists soaked in flammable liquids
  —long and/or complicated escape routes, which could cause confusion and/or delay in reaching a final exit
  —flammable or smoke-producing surfaces on walls, ceilings, floors (see Class 3 finishes under Surface finishes, page 80)
  —surfaces coated in flammable paints and other decorations.
- Parts of the building that would present a greater risk of fire or explosion than other parts of the building (think how you can protect those other parts from those greater risks). Such dangers are presented by the following:
  —manufacturing processes (perhaps near to 'safe' offices)
  —parts where highly flammable liquids are used or stored
  —parts where naked flames are used
  —places where excessive heat is generated
  —parts where the storage, use and/or production of chemicals, violently reactive and explosive substances, and other gaseous or vaporizing substances occur

—large kitchens serving restaurants, hospitals, hostels and hotels
—central fuel storage facilities
—parts where there is upholstered furniture that gives off toxic fumes and smoke when it is burned
—storage and/or disposal areas for waste.

In your assessment of such situations where these risks exist, you must consider not only employees *but also*:

- visitors
- customers
- members of the public
- the neighbouring areas.

You should also consider:

- whether or not large numbers of people will be present
- the elderly
- disabled persons
- the deaf and/or blind
- children and young people
- those in isolated parts of your premises
- whether or not very small numbers of persons are present, thereby reducing the level of assistance available to those in need.

Ask yourself and your advisers the question 'What if . . .?' If the answer is not a reassuring one, you will have to take measures for fire safety and/or fire precautions.

Normal risk Premises classified as 'normal risk' can still present problems of fire risks and hazards but they may not be outside normal means of control. A 'normal' risk is one where:

- the outbreak of fire is likely to remain localized
- fire is likely to spread slowly
- the risk of any part of the structure burning is small
- the risk of burning or other materials producing large quantities of life-threatening smoke and gases is minimal
- the *nature* of the occupancy is not classified as 'high risk'.

Such 'normal risk' premises and the hazards in them would include workplaces of 'traditional' construction, that is, those with brick walls, timber floors and roof trusses and no undesirable features. The use of these buildings and the materials and substances in them are unlikely (but it is still not impossible) to present serious hazards to people in them. Such premises may include:

- shops (except those selling high-risk items)
- offices
- other places where large numbers of people are not likely to be present.

Low risk There is no such thing as a '*no*-risk' situation — wherever you have people, buildings and materials, there is hazard and risk — but the classification 'low risk' means simply that the risk of fire occurring or, if it does occur, the risk of flames, smoke and gases spreading, is negligible. Here, the level of risk is 'acceptable' when the usual standards of fire protection are applied. But, remember that a low-risk situation with *no* fire extinguishers is then a high-risk situation. Examples of buildings and materials regarded as of low risk are:

- workplaces used for heavy engineering (provided no highly inflammable or explosive substances are present)
- processes that are entirely 'wet' and/or involve the use of non-combustible materials.

Offices and shops are most unlikely to be classified as low risk, while sleeping accommodation (of any kind) will *never* be low risk.

Undertaking assessments You will need to have a systematic, methodical way of going about your fire risk assessments, otherwise you may either miss important areas or make false assumptions. Part of the purpose of assessments is not only to identify 'what' but 'what if?' Thus, you must assess the likelihood of fire and explosion in each area and ensure that *all* defects found in your assessments are identified and rectified. The following is a suggested method of undertaking assessments.

1. Take each building (if more than one) one by one.
2. Divide each building into sections and, in larger premises (such as supermarkets or large stores), subdivide these into subsections.
3. Assess the process. Is it manufacturing, processing, offices, warehousing, storage, sales (shop or trade counter), servicing repair/maintenance (in-house or public), entertainment or something else?
4. Assess the materials and substances present, whether used or produced in manufacture, maintenance, cleaning, degreasing and repair or hygiene and health protection or whether sold to the public. Do they include gases, dust, powders, liquids?
5. Assess what kind they are. Are they highly inflammable, flammable, toxic or likely to give off gases if burned?
6. Assess what the possibility is that the materials and/or substances assessed in step 4 which are used or produced can ignite or explode. (Remember that dust and powders can explode if they exist in the atmosphere in sufficient quantities — expressed as parts per million — and depending on their nature.)
7. Assess what the probable risk is to people if a fire occurs.
8. Assess what *could be* (not would be) the likely consequences of fire or explosion on people in the area and/or surrounding environment, for example, from flames, smoke, gaseous emissions from burning materials.

So far, you have assessed only the 'what' and 'what if?' Now you need to assess how you can eliminate or minimize the risks and how you can protect against those risks. Thus, the next steps are as follows.

9. Find out whether or not any dangerous material or substance used in production can be eliminated, perhaps by using an alternative-nature material or substance that is *non*-flammable or *non*-explosive.
10. Find out whether or not any material or substance used can be replaced by a less hazardous material or substance.
11. Find out what forms of protection you will need in order to provide full fire safety and fire precautions. These could include fire-resisting construction for the process and the building or section in which the hazard exists, MOE, firefighting equipment, including portable and fixed equipment, safety rules,

such as 'no smoking' and correct/safe handling and storage, direction signs to the MOE and exits.

12. Find out what fire and safety *training* and *information* you will need to give to those involved in or affected by hazardous areas. You will need to include in the training and information details of the hazards, how to prevent fires and explosions, what action to take in an emergency and personal responsibilities. (Although training is one of the *most* important aspects of fire safety, it is dealt with last as you will need to answer all the foregoing questions before you can know what the contents of your training programme need to be.)

Responsibility Fire-risk management and risk assessments cannot be left to a chance or haphazard distribution of duties. This important management activity must be delegated to a designated, suitably qualified and/or trained competent person in a similar manner as for the management of health and safety, which, if you are a small business, may mean the owner-manager (yourself?) — it should not be passed to a junior level. Your competent person should be made responsible for your emergency evacuation plan. These safety management duties should be written into the competent person's job description, otherwise the person concerned will not know precisely what is required of them and there will be no accountability (my book *The Employer's Survival Guide* provides guidance on the completion of job descriptions).

Aids to fire risk assessment Can you reasonably expect *one* person to conduct all the assessments entirely unaided? They may be very well qualified, but they will still need technical and professional back-up, the kind of help required varying depending on the nature of buildings, processes, materials, substances and occupations undertaken by your company. The assessor will need to:

● enlist the aid of the health and safety committee
● perhaps establish a subgroup specifically to conduct assessments
● consult with key members of staff with professional expertise
● discuss things with special interest groups, such as those directly affected by flammable and/or explosive materials and substances, disabled, deaf, and visually impaired people, and those with other sensory impairments
● seek specialist professional advice from external sources on specific materials and/or substances and their attendant risks.

You may consider calling in an external specialist health and safety professional with particular knowledge of fire safety to carry out your assessments on your behalf. This may prove a little more expensive, but it will have the added advantage of being independent and unbiased and leave your own managers to get on with their jobs rather than be compelled to suspend their normal duties to carry out risk assessments. Free advice is available from fire authorities, on request.

Whether conducted internally or by an external specialist, risk assessments are a compulsory feature of fire safety in the EC Directives covering fire safety and their supporting UK Regulations. Assessments have also become a standard feature of *all* recent EC and UK health, safety, welfare and hygiene legislation and will continue to be a central feature of all current and future Regulations. Assessments are here to stay as a *statutory* management activity.

After completion of risk assessments, you *must* consult with your relevant fire authority *before* you undertake any changes to your fire safety or fire precautions set-up (including engineering or construction ones).

A helpful check-list to use as a guide when carrying out risk assessments can be found in Appendix 5.

In addition to risk assessments, you are required by FPR 95 to have a systematic system of fire-safety management that includes established routines that cover employees and others from the start to the end of the working day in the workplace, including:

- firefighting procedures
- provisions for the safety of all the people in the workplace in the event of fire
- regular checks on *all* fire precautions and firefighting equipment, with what remedial action is to be taken.

Two EC Directives — the Framework Directive (89/391/EEC) and the Workplace Directive (89/654/EEC) — lay down stringent requirements for fire safety that are enacted and backed by the FPR 95. These Directives and Regulations were effective from 1 April 1995.

Summary As a fire-safety management overview and by way of a refresher, the new Regulations and Guidance Notes enforce all that we have discussed so far in this chapter (and matters of training covered in Chapter 29) and cover:

- full risk assessments
- fire detection and warning
- MOE
- maintenance of fire precautions
- supervision of construction and maintenance work
- firefighting equipment
- training in fire precautions
- emergency evacuation plans
- refuse storage.

Fire risk assessment worksheets the HSE have included worksheets in the Guidance to the Regulations, to assist you in carrying out your fire risk assessments. They are at Appendix B in the Regulations for larger workplaces and Appendix C for smaller workplaces and are intended to be cut out and (presumably) may be freely photo-copied.

Compliance timetable

1. *All* employers, regardless of size and including self-employed persons, *must* comply with all the following requirements from 1 April 1995:

- fire risk assessments (Reg. 4)
- fire safety information (Reg. 4)
- fire procedures information and training (Reg. 4)

2. For the following:

- MOE (Reg. 5)
- fire detection equipment (Reg. 7)
- fire alarms (Reg. 7)
  a. all premises already occupied by employers as at 31 March 1996 must comply with these requirements by not later than 1 April 1998
  b. all premises newly occupied by employers on or after 1 April 1996 must comply with these requirements *immediately* following occupation

c. all existing premises (or part of any existing premises) newly modified on or after 1 April 1995 must comply with all these requirements *immediately* following completion of those modifications.

Although existing workplace premises have until 31 March 1996 to comply with the requirements, the message for them is: 'Don't wait until 30 March 1996 to start updating work under FPR 95 — get cracking now'.

In Appendix 4, you will find an example of a fire precautions manual, which you can either adapt or use as a starting point for your own. The sample risk assessment (and reassessment) schedule in Appendix 5, mentioned earlier, may be inserted after the first page of the fire manual when completed.

Reassessments A risk assessment is a bit like an MOT certificate on your car — it merely certifies that the vehicle was safe on the day on which it was tested. As time goes by, further defects begin to creep in.

Fire-safety and fire-precautions systems and equipment will, likewise, steadily deteriorate or wear with time and so the original assessment will become quite out of date. You will therefore need to carry out risk reassessments regularly.

Is it necessary to reassess *everything* each time? Probably not, but, in initial assessments, you will need to determine the frequency of reassessments required for each section or subsection according to the level of risk (high, medium or low) determined in the original assessments. Obviously, high-risk areas or processes will need to be reassessed more frequently than low-risk areas.

Once you have established what your reassessment schedules should be, do make sure that they are carried out on the due dates — perhaps by making an entry in a diary, in a brought forward or computerized scheduling system or whatever, so that you are automatically reminded that a reassessment is 'due today'.

Emergency evacuation plans

A vital aspect of fire safety is an effective and efficient emergency evacuation plan (or fire drill). Under FPR 95, every employer, government department manager and manager of premises for public entertainment and accommodation will be required to review and produce suitable plans. It is not expected that standard fire drills (available in laminated plastic form, onto which firms can write their own basic information) will be suitable for any companies except very small businesses and offices.

You will need to include in the assessments your procedures for evacuating all employees, visitors and the public from your premises — taking into account the following:

* the structural design of buildings
* complexities of non-standard buildings
* manufacturing processes
* storage and warehousing systems
* materials and substances used or produced
* the layout of manufacturing areas and offices
* disabled and impaired persons using your premises
* the MOE.

Suggestions for what to include in fire drills are given in Chapter 29.

Firefighting procedures

In designing your firefighting procedures, you will need to take account of all the factors considered with regard to evacuating the premises listed above, plus the types of firefighting equipment you will need to have available immediately to hand (see pages 68–70), the back-up resources that would be needed in a fire of any size (a small in-company fire team and/or the fire brigade) and the safety of those assigned to firefighting duties.

- *First aid* The first item in your procedures will be the training of every member of staff, including trainees, in first aid firefighting. This will mean knowing what types of extinguisher there are, their location, how to identify them, what their *safe* uses are, how to use them effectively and (very important) what *not* to use them on (for example, not using water extinguishers on electrical fires). The extent of general instruction should be purely at the level of first aid firefighting and nothing else — a dead hero is of no value to anyone.
- *Fire teams* For larger premises and/or premises with highly flammable or explosive substances used or produced in manufacture, you may need to appoint fire teams. These will be those employees you can rely on to attend a fire at (or immediately after) the first aid stage. They should be given detailed training in fire safety, perhaps based on the relevant contents of this chapter, and have good practical instruction in the use of all types of extinguisher and the fire-detection and automatic systems that are installed.
- *Occupational fire brigades* There are also advantages in very large industrial sites having their own occupational fire brigade that is able to respond speedily to an emergency.
- *Fire marshals* It would be sensible to appoint fire marshals. They could possibly be leaders of fire teams, if you have them, and would take responsibility for ensuring that all persons are accounted for and all sections checked and passed as 'fire safe' before they are returned to. The fire marshal should also be the person to ensure that the fire brigade is called *in every instance* of a fire. When the fire brigade do attend a fire, only they should give the all clear and say it is safe to return.
- *Procedures* Whether you have only first aid firefighting, appoint fire teams, fire marshals or occupational fire brigades, there should be set procedures for their duties when the fire alarm is sounded and (for occupational fire brigades) fire-prevention procedures. These should be determined at the assessment and reassessment stages (see above).
- *Fire brigade* One thing you must include in your fire procedures is who is to call out the fire brigade. The responsibility should be placed in one particular department/job description (perhaps the most appropriate person is the recep-tionist). However, don't leave this job solely to this person and assume that the fire brigade have been called; ensure that a more senior person (your fire marshal, perhaps) checks that this has been done. The fire brigade will never castigate you for calling them out to a fire that has been extinguished by the time they get there; they would much rather check that it is completely out than have to attend an out of control, disaster situation, and they are always pleased to give advice on preventing recurrences.
- *Fire drills* Fire drills are detailed in Chapter 20 together with training because they are an important aspect of training. But, do ensure that you inform the fire brigade when you have a fire drill, so that they do not attend a false alarm

unnecessarily. (In certain situations they may like to be involved in practice drills, but that is a decision for them to make, not for you by default.)

Maintenance

A vital part of any system of health and safety and fire-safety management is maintenance. Under section 2(2)(a) of the HASWA, companies are already obliged to provide planned, preventative maintenance to all plant, machinery and equipment and to manage systems of work in order to ensure the health and safety at work of employees and others who may be affected by them. The systems of work required under the HASWA already include the need for fire precautions and firefighting equipment, but this has been further enforced under the FPR 95.

All sections of every workplace that incorporate a MOE *must* be adequately maintained to ensure their safe and effective use at all material times (that is, when people are at work). Also, all firefighting equipment, fire-detection systems and fire alarms systems (whether bell, siren or manual systems) must be maintained in efficient working order. No system of maintenance can possibly be effective unless it is founded on assessments and continual reassessments (these are covered above) as, if you have no assessments, you have no understanding of what is to be maintained, to what standard, with what effect or at what frequency.

Records

You *say* you have carried out servicing, maintenance and repair work on plant and equipment and fire-safety or fire-precautions apparatus, but, if an injurious fire or explosion does occur and you have kept no *records* of any work you have undertaken, can you *prove* that you have done the work? All your protestations in court will hold no sway: no records, no proof, no defence.

Detailed records of all assessments, planned preventative maintenance, service and repair work, training, reassessments, fire drills and everything else to do with fire safety and fire precautions are vital. You will need to keep these records, detailing literally everything that is done, for at least three years. The suggested fire precautions manual given in Appendix 4 will assist you in this respect.

Health and safety policies

Every employer with five or more employees, including directors and trainees, must draw up a health and safety policy and bring it to the attention of all employees and those relevant parts of it to others affected by or involved in the company's operations. 'Bring the policy to the attention' does not mean handing over a few pieces of paper; it means telling them what it is in a training or briefing session. It would also be wise to get them to sign, confirming that they have received the policy document and have been trained in its contents.

You will need to include in your policy a statement of your intent and arrangements for carrying out risk assessments in the workplace, covering everything in this chapter, adapted as relevant to your situation. Your statement of intent and arrangements should include provision for any remedial action that may be necessary.

Never assume that something is 'irrelevant' — assess it. If your assessment gives a nil return, you are on safer ground than if you had not assessed it at all.

Competent persons As with the Management of Health and Safety at Work Regulations 1992, FPR 95 also requires the appointment of a 'competent person' who will oversee the management of fire safety, fire precautions and the emergency evacuation plan (see Chapter 19 for advice on competent persons).

Compliance costs
One of the problems that all management needs to address is that of compliance costs. For this reason alone, fire risk assessments are very important. They inform you of the costs of compliance and help you to budget for the implementation of necessary changes in the future.

Estimates of compliance costs vary widely and actual costs will differ from company to company, but the Home Office has estimated costs of £200 to £300 for small businesses.

Estimates for large certifiable premises are for up to £10 000 to comply initially with the requirements for structural and other upgrading work (with a national cost of £44 million) and with an average expenditure of £4425 per annum per unit thereafter. Hotels and boarding houses may cost between £150 and £300 initially with a national compliance cost of £2.5 million.

The total national cost of installing upgraded lighting and alarm systems in uncertified premises is estimated by the Home Office at £90 million. Finally, there is an estimated average total national cost of £70 million per year for all larger businesses, to a projected national total present-discounted net cost of £1.7 billion.

Training
A key feature of the new Regulations and Guidance Notes is fire precautions training. This is covered at length in Chapter 20, which also includes discussion of fire/evacuation drills.

Penalties
Acts of Parliament are really 'statements of intent'; the courts then interpret them and set precedents that people then follow as standards. Justice Popperwell, in his report following the inquiry into the Bradford fire, laid down some important case-law that every employer and controller of premises must follow:

- the MOE must be fully maintained at all times
- firefighting equipment must be maintained and records kept
- people *must* be trained in fire safety and fire precautions
- in assessments, there must be plans of action, with time limits for their execution
- the fire certificate must be read and understood, especially by the person responsible for overall health and safety and those responsible for particular areas, with signatures recorded to that effect. (For this reason, fire authorities now send fire certificates by recorded delivery, then no one can plead ignorance; you will be deemed to know.)

Non-compliance with these points *will* lead to prosecution.

Penalties for non-compliance vary according to the nature of the offence. The original fines under the FPA 71 ranged from £50 for obstructing a fire officer in their duties and failure to comply with instructions (section 19(6)), through £100 for pretending to be an inspector, to £400 for any false declaration or record or other offence under the

Act. However, these penalties have been radically altered under the Criminal Justice Act 1991, which was effective from 1 October 1992.

Fines in magistrates' courts are now up to a maximum of £5000 for failure to obtain a fire certificate where one is required or for failure to observe the conditions of such a certificate, and the same fines will apply to company directors, managers or secretaries who consent or connive to perpetrate such offences. Following trial on indictment by a jury in a Crown Court, similar fines may be imposed, with the addition of up to two years' imprisonment.

For breaches of the FPA 71, magistrates' courts may impose fines of up to £5000 and/ or up to three months' imprisonment. Fines are for *each offence*, which explains some apparently high penalties, but, for more serious offences under the Act, if magistrates consider their powers inadequate for the gravity of the offence, they can refer cases on indictment to the Crown Court for *unlimited* fines and/or six months' imprisonment.

There is also the intention to introduce further legislation that will enable magistrates to impose fines of up to *£20 000* for *each* offence. Other health, safety, hygiene and environmental laws already carry such penalties in higher courts.

So, better safe than very sorry!

Sources of help

To help you, the following 'Employer's Action Check-List', reproduced from the HSE Guidance to FPR 95, will be useful in ensuring that you carry out your obligations.

Employer's action check-list
Here are the main action points for you to follow to comply with the Regulations.

- identify fire hazards
- identify any staff and other people who are especially at risk
- remove/reduce fire hazards and provide additional fire-safety measures if necessary
- record findings of the fire risk assessments and action points
- consider arrangements for people with disabilities
- prepare the emergency evacuation plan
- provide enough exits for everyone to get out in good time
- ensure that all escape routes and exits are available for use
- provide an appropriate means for giving warning in case of fire
- arrange the checking, testing and maintenance of fire-safety equipment
- keep appropriate records
- ensure your staff are adequately informed and trained
- include fire safety in your health and safety policy for the workplace.

When you need advice and guidance in this area, the following sources of help may be useful to you.

- Institute of Fire Safety, PO Box 687, Croydon CR99 5DD (tel: 0181 654 2582)
- Association of Fire Protection Engineers, MCF Complex, New Road, Kidderminster DY10 1AQ (tel: 01562 825863)

- The Fire Protection Association and Loss Prevention Council, both at 140 Aldersgate Street, London EC1A 4HY (tel: 0171 606 3757)
- Abundance Management Services, Abundance House, 17 St Michael's Crescent, Oldbury, West Midlands B69 4RT (tel: 0121 552 2073)
- Chubb Fire Limited, Chubb House, Sunbury-on-Thames, Middlesex TW16 7AR (tel: 01932 785588).

For information regarding how to provide adequately for disabled and sensorily impaired people, the following addresses might be helpful.

- Access Committee: for England, write to 35 Great Smith Street, London SW1P 3BJ; for Wales, write to Llys Ifor, Crescent Road, Caerphilly CF8 1XL
- Disability Scotland, Princes House, 5 Chandwick Place, Edinburgh EH2 4RG
- Joint Committee for Mobility for Disabled People, Woodcliffe House, 51a Cliff Road, Weston-Super-Mare BS22 9SE
- National Federation for the Blind (UK), Unit House, Smyth Street, Westgate, Wakefield, West Yorkshire WF1 1ER
- Royal National Institute for the Blind, 224 Great Portland Street, London W1N 6AA *or* 9 Viewfield Place, Stirling, Scotland
- Royal National Institute for Deaf People, 105 Gower Street, London WC1 *or* 9 Clairmont Gardens, Glasgow G3 7LW.

Grateful acknowledgements to Chubb Fire Limited for much technical information on fires and fire extinguisher media contributed to this chapter and used with their permission.

Footnote: Compliance timetables are subject to final ministerial approval.

Implementation of the 'Fire precautions (Places of Work) Regulations 1995' (FPR.95), referred to in Chapter 12—Fire Safety of 'The Health & Safety Survival Guide' has now been delayed to a date yet to be determined. Thus, the 'Compliance timetables' given on pages 91 and 92 will not be adhered to.

However, any employer following the advice and information given in Chapter 12 will still be assured of compliance with the Fire Precautions Act 1974 and the conditions of any Fire Certificate, though certain detail will not be legally enforceable at the present time.

This error is regretted, though the data was understood to be correct at the time of printing, based on advice and information received.

13

Noise

Skin diseases, bodily ailments and physical injuries can often be healed or overcome, but one unseen ailment is completely incurable — *deafness*.

We all suffer noise pollution — aircraft noise, cars, heavy metal rock music or 'ghetto blaster' radios. We may become so accustomed to noise as to fail to recognize it as 'noise', and be indifferent to its effects and unaware of its consequences. In September 1993, the HSE issued a warning about 'walkmans', that using them posed a risk of deafness. Deafness is a serious health problem. Sometimes people are innocent victims of imposed noise but often it is self-inflicted by being indifferent to natural laws. Over many years, employees may have been exposed to excessive noise, such as that from weaving-loom sheds, pneumatic drills, industrial hammers or power presses.

Legal protection for employees against noise has been extended and reinforced by the Noise at Work Regulations 1989, effective, in parallel with the COSHH Regulations, on 1 January 1990. They incorporate the EC Directive on 'protection of workers from . . . noise at work'.

The terminology

- *Exposed/exposure* In the legislation this means what employees are exposed to while at work (exposure *away* from the workplace is not considered).
- *dB* This stands for deciBell, the unit of measurement for noise. It is not absolute but relative, rather like a thermometer. As a temperature of 100°C is boiling point for water, so 90dB is the level at which a person with normal hearing would have to shout in order to be heard. The dB scale is logarithmic so that, for example, two machines each producing 85dB do not add up to 170dB but 88dB. The maximum unprotected exposure limit is 89dB, the pain threshold is 120dB.
- *dB(A)* Sound does not just have volume, it also has 'frequency' (this is what the 'A' stands for). You can have a low volume and a high frequency or a high volume and a low frequency or any combination of these. When the dB measurement is adjusted to allow for frequency, it is written as dB(A) and is really only measurable by instruments. A pneumatic drill will produce 110dB(A), which, over 5 minutes, is equivalent in effect to a typewriter producing 70dB(A) for 5 hours.
- $L_{ep,d}$ The important factor is not just volume and frequency but *how much* dB(A) a person is exposed to (that is, the daily personal noise exposure), averaged over a monitored period of time. This period is normally eight hours and the resulting figure is called a time-weighted average (TWA). Alternatively, you can use the

formula to *predict* what the average exposure over an eight-hour period *would* be. The mathematical calculations necessary to do this are very complicated, but are expressed as dB(A)L$_{ep,d}$ or L$_{ep,d}$ for short (you may also see it expressed as L$_{eq}$ but the former has superseded this notation). This is the only true measurement, and is obtainable only by using electronic instruments.

- *First action level* This is the first daily noise exposure level of 85dB(A) at which action is required (as described below).
- *Peak action level* A level of peak sound pressure of 200 pascals (1 pascal equals a pressure of one-pound weight to the square inch in the sound wave). It is roughly equal to a peak pressure of 140dB, is the sort of loud impulse from a cartridge tool or gun and is capable of causing instantaneous hearing damage.
- *Second action level* The second daily noise exposure level of 90dB(A), at and above which action is required (as described below).
- *Daily personal noise exposure* The level of daily personal noise exposure of an employee ascertained in accordance with Part 1 of the Regulations, *without* hearing protection being worn.

Assessments

Every employer is required to carry out assessments of noise in the workplace and to take all reasonable steps to eliminate or minimize the hazards and the risks involved. Noise is measured in deciBells (dBs), but actually measuring noise is quite complicated. If you follow the following guidelines, however, this should keep you within the law.

The problem

Ill-health resulting from exposure to hazardous substances is relatively easy to identify. You can see oils and chemicals, smell most gases, feel something touching the skin and be aware of the sickness or disease that results. With noise, you cannot see or feel it and any effects of noise are not felt immediately on hearing it — you do not know what is happening until it is too late.

Noise injuries take the forms of:

- tinnitus (ringing in the ears)
- vertigo (loss of balance due to fluid imbalance)
- perforated eardrum (timpanic membrane)
- serious damage to the inner ear (that is, to the cochlea, hammer, anvil or stirrup).

Some impact noises are measured in pascals and can cause instantaneous damage. Noise at work can also cause stress and communications problems.

The ear

The ear is a very complex organ. Its sensitive parts (in order from the outer to the inner ear) are: the timpanic membrane (eardrum), hammer, anvil, stirrup, oval window, semi-circular canal and cochlea (see Fig. 13.1). Each of these parts of the ear receive auditory sound waves and pass them on to the next until they reach the auditory nerves leading to the brain. The most delicate parts of the ear are the:

- *eardrum* a membrane at the end of the auditory canal that is the first receptor of sound waves and, though a small pinhole in this membrane may repair, larger ones will not

- *hammer, anvil and stirrup* small fishbone-like instruments that are extremely delicate and once damaged by breaking under the strain of excessive noise, they never repair themselves, though some people have had very expensive artificial inserts
- *cochlea* a spiral, snail-like tube filled with fluid, lined with about 16–20 000 small hair cells that vibrate and pass sound waves to the brain; if the hairs all wear out as a result of being bombarded by excessively high noise levels, they cannot transmit sound to the brain and the result is deafness
- *semi-circular canals* liquid-filled tubes that help us have balance: when the fluid moves too much one way or refuses to return to homeostasis, the result is loss of balance, called vertigo.

Objectives

If you follow the advice given in this chapter and comply with the Regulations, you should achieve the following objectives:

- identify those areas and machines where noise in excess of the permitted levels is emitted (the use of noise measurement instruments to do this is essential as this cannot be estimated by just listening to them yourself)
- obtain and collate all data on each area or machine and assess the likely ill-health effects of prolonged exposure to that noise
- identify workers likely to be exposed to those noise levels
- assess the likely exposure of each worker to excessive noise levels (what dB(A) and $L_{ep,d}$ levels and for how long; see under 'The terminology' below)
- determine the action required to eliminate exposure to excessive noise levels or minimize the risk of exposure
- provide information, training and instruction for all employees required to work where noise levels in excess of 89dB(A) exist.

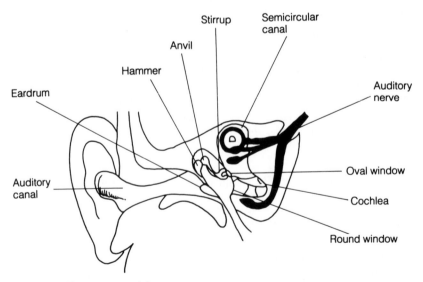

Fig. 13.1   The anatomy of the ear

Policy

You should include in your health and safety policy a section concerning your intent with regard to noise, its control and protection from it in the same manner as described in Chapter 7.

Delegation

While responsibility for ensuring that the policy is implemented is retained at director or owner-manager level, the duties concerning noise should be delegated to a competent person. Bearing in mind the high costs of measuring instruments, you may decide to contract an outside health and safety adviser to do this.

Assessments

The first duty under the Regulations is to conduct assessments of the noise problems you may have. If your workplace is very quiet, like an office or a storage warehouse, you just need to listen to assess whether or not you have a problem, but, once your noise level rises above certain levels, you must make formal assessments and follow procedures. The test is if you can be heard, without shouting, by a person with normal hearing 2 metres away from you. If not, you have a noise problem. Assessments are as follows:

First action level

If you discover that the exposure level in your workplace is at or above 85dB(A), then you must carry out assessments. The problem, is how do you know, without taking measurements, what the actual dB(A) is? You can only estimate, of course, and if you or an employee think it is higher than 84dB(A) using the 'shouting' test above, then you should carry out assessments.

You need not automatically issue protection at this level, but you may *advise* that it be used, and if your employees request protective wear, then you must provide it.

Peak action level

This refers to the 'pressure' on the ears of 200 pascals, one pascal equalling one pound per square inch. If your noise achieves the peak action level of 200 pascals, you must take preventative and/or protective measures.

Second action level

This is the level at and above which you *must* take action either to reduce the noise level or provide protection. There is no absolute requirement to reduce noise to below 85dB(A) or to protect from that level, but you *must* reduce the exposure level to below 90dB(A) TWA over an eight-hour period. This can be accomplished by taking one of three actions:

1. eliminate or reduce the noise level to below 90dB(A)
2. reduce the direct exposure by imposing a maximum time limit for exposure to it
3. provide ear protection that will reduce the exposure.

Maximum exposure limits

There are maximum levels of noise to which you may expose your employees without providing hearing protection. This is determined by the deciBell level and lengths of time spent in the noisy area. Each time the dB(A) exposure is increased by 3dB, the

Table 13.1 Determining maximum exposure limits

Exposure		Maximum time
Up to	89dB(A)	No limit
At/above	90dB(A)	8 hours
	93dB(A)	4 hours
	96dB(A)	2 hours
	99dB(A)	1 hour
	102dB(A)	$\frac{1}{2}$ hour
	105dB(A)	$\frac{1}{4}$ hour
	108dB(A)	$7\frac{1}{2}$ minutes

(how long should a person spend, unprotected, on a
pneumatic drill? — hardly worthwhile!)
Note: the deafening noise level of a personal attack
alarm is 103dB!

maximum exposure time is *halved* (remember dB scales are logarithmic), as shown in
Table 13.1.

How to eliminate or reduce the hazards

Having carried out your assessments and determined the noise levels of your working
area, the first action *must be*, to eliminate or reduce the level as much as possible
(section 6). Means of soundproofing vary:

- *barriers* silencers, metal-to-metal damping, brick screens, steel, plaster board,
  PVC or UPVC, half-inch Perspex or acoustic panels
- *sound absorption* various fibres, glass wool, polyurethane foam (these are
  provided in ear protectors — plugs or muffs — and can be incorporated into safety
  helmets where worn).

If these means do not reduce the noise level below 90dB(A), then you must do the
following.

- *Remove the risk* If the dB(A)$L_{ep,d}$ (or $L_{ep,d}$) level cannot be brought down below
  90, then you *must*, endeavour to eliminate or reduce the risk by removing the
  employee from the noise or the noise from the employee (section 7). Can the job
  be done by remote means? Can the employee take periods of time out of the noisy
  area?
- *Protect employees from the noise* If you cannot eliminate or reduce the noise level
  or remove it, you *must*, provide adequate protection against exposure for your
  employees. Just ear plugs may *not* be adequate protection. Forms of protection
  vary both in the type and degrees of insulation they provide and you must check
  how much they will reduce the noise level (section 8).
- *Identify zones* You must position signs in the areas where there is a noise problem,
  ensuring that they are clearly visible. There are two types:
  —warning signs — black muffs on a yellow background, usually at the entry
     point
  —mandatory signs — white muffs on a blue background, inside the area.
- *Ensure compliance* It is the duty of employers to ensure that the law and company
  policy are obeyed. It is not a simple matter of 'I told him'. It is the duty of the
  employee to cooperate and comply (section 7 of the HASWA), and section 10(2)
  does not mention the word 'reasonable'; therefore, *compliance* is reasonable.

Common objections Employees commonly raise objections to wearing protective gear. It is the duty of the employer to overcome these objections some of these and some suggested answers to them are as follows:

- 'I don't need them, I have become accustomed to the noise'
  'This is a dangerous belief.'
- 'I have already lost some hearing'
  'There is no need to lose more.'
- 'I can't hear fellow workers if I wear them'
  'You will hear much less if you are deaf; get close to the person and shout or move outside the area to talk.'
- 'They are uncomfortable/irritate my skin/make me sweat'
  'Keep the protectors clean or find a comfortable alternative.'
- 'The machines sound different when I wear them'
  'Control machines by observation rather than sound.'
- 'I can hurt my eardrums by inserting or removing the plugs too quickly'
  'An erroneous belief — earplugs cannot touch the eardrum.'
- 'I can get a hearing aid'
  'A hearing aid will not heal damaged hearing.'
- 'I will get an ear infection if I wear them'
  'Not if the plugs or muffs are kept clean or are exchanged regularly.'

Information and training

You must provide full information and training to your employees about:

- the nature of the noise problem — its location and levels
- the action you have taken to reduce and/or eliminate the noise
- the protective wear that is available and their duty to use it.

You should also provide them with reference points, letting them know to whom or where they should go for advice.

Summary

- Do you think you have a noise problem? If the answer is *yes*, carry out assessments.
- Having carried out assessments, is the noise above 89dB(A)? If the answer is *no*, take no action, but offer advice or provide hearing protection if requested.
  If the answer is *yes*, can you eliminate the noise? If the answer is *yes*, eliminate it.
  If the answer is *no*:
  —reduce the noise level as far as possible
  —inform affected employees, and keep them informed
  —provide ear protection and enforce its use.
- Have you reduced exposure? If the answer is *no*, evaluate and revise the plan. If the answer is *yes*, maintain periodic reviews and assessments.

The following action plan, based on the HSE's booklet *Introducing Noise at Work Regulations* (IND(G)75(L)), may prove useful here.

Action where $L_{ep,d}$ is (or is likely to be) at or above	*1st action level*¶	*2nd action level*¶
Reduce risk of hearing damage	*	*
Assess noise levels exposed to	*	*
Retain records of assessments	*	*
Reduce noise levels at noise source		*
Provide information, instruction and training to employees	*	*
Mark noise zones with notices		*
Provide ear protection:		
• to all who ask for it	*	
• to all who are exposed		*
• maintained and repaired	*	*
Ensure ear protection is used		*
Ensure all who enter zone use ear protection at all times[#]		*
Ensure equipment provided is:		
• used	*	*
• maintained	*	*
Employees' duties:		
• to use ear protection		*
• to use protective equipment	*	*
• to report any defects	*	*
Manufacturers'/suppliers' duties are: to provide information on noise levels likely to be generated	*	*

even for short duration
¶ first level — 85dB(A); second level 90dB(A) or 200 pascals.

Source: Introducing Noise at Work Regulations (HSE Booklet IND(G)75(L)).

14

Environmental protection

Environmental pollution is one of today's most topical problems, with serious concerns being expressed about rivers, the countryside, the sea, the atmosphere and the depletion of the ozone layer. One difficulty is that, while safety problems are tangible with physical consequences, pollution of the environment is often not immediately detectable and then it is too late. However, no company can now hide from its responsibilities to prevent its activities from harming people and the environment. Industry causes various kinds of pollution, both in its emissions and in some of the products it makes. The potential and actual harm to both environment and public has attracted the attention of legislators, as codes of practice have not proven to be enough.

The Environmental Protection Act 1990 is, thus, a highly topical piece of legislation, particularly as it brings tougher new environmental standards that will be set for industry and policed by a new inspectorate. The Act, in its 235 pages, is detailed, complex and extensive. What follows, therefore, is only a concise guide to its chief contents.

The Environmental Protection Act

This Act is designed to protect the environment from the many types of pollution emitted by industry. The Act came into force on 1 January 1991, to be implemented over six years.

The Act defines two important terms used widely under the Act:

- *environment*
  The 'environment' consists of all or any of the following media, namely, air, water and land; and the medium of air includes the air within buildings and . . . other natural or man-made structures above or below ground.
- *pollution of the environment*
  'Pollution of the environment' means pollution of the environment due to the release (into any environmental medium) of any process or substances which are capable of causing harm to man or any other living organisms supported by the environment.

These two definitions encompass just about anything affecting just about anyone, anywhere, with further definitions encompassing anyone who does or makes just about anything. In other words, you cannot escape.

The main duties of industry
The Act places a 'duty of care' on everyone in industry. This includes directors, managers and employees. Everyone at every level, without exception, must protect

the environment from their unsafe acts and omissions (and, thereby, their emissions into the environment) — 'emissions', in this context, being material, liquid and gaseous.

Waste on land The Act brought in new duties on you as a producer of waste, with responsibility for the control, safe storage and handling, management and disposal of waste.

The disposal of waste must be safe. The Act gives licensing powers to local authorities (see below) together with the responsibility to:

- monitor waste disposal
- prosecute those who cause unauthorized or harmful disposal of waste
- maintain disposal sites after their closure.

They also have a clearer role in recycling waste.

Statutory nuisance and air pollution Parts of the repealed Public Health Act 1936 have been brought into the 1990 Act. The definition of 'statutory nuisance' has been extended to include:

- buildings in states prejudicial to health or that are a nuisance
- smoke
- dust
- gases
- steam
- noxious odours
- effluvia emitted into the air from any business premises
- noise emitted from premises in a manner prejudicial to health
- accumulations of deposits
- animals kept in such a manner as to be prejudicial to health or a nuisance
- any other thing declared to be a nuisance.

Local authorities have powers to inspect areas around business premises and to take appropriate action to control and/or remedy any nuisance or thing prejudicial to health.

Litter control Litter louts are included, but are not the only targets of the Act. If a business causes or permits litter to be thrown, dropped or deposited in any place on land outside their own premises, including highways, public open spaces and educational establishments, they become liable under the Act. This includes responsibility for litter dropped outside your premises by employees, patrons and customers, such as outside dance halls, discos, fish and chip shops, take-aways and so on. You must provide bins.

Other sections of the Act deal with radioactive substances, genetically modified organisms, nature conservation, control of drugs, pollution at sea, straw and stubble burning and the import, use, supply and storage of specified dangerous substances. However, these are too complex and technical to be dealt with here.

Enforcement

The Act sets up Her Majesty's Inspectorate of Industrial Pollution (HMIIP), formed by merging the former Industrial Air Pollution, Controlled Waste, and Radiochemical Inspectorates. There is also the new Integrated Pollution Control System (IPCS), based with local authorities. The HMIIP and IPCS will jointly have powers of inspection, entry, enforcement through improvement and prohibition notices and/or prosecution. The High Court can also be called on to enforce orders served by the HMIIP and IPCS.

Penalties

Under the Act, both companies and individuals will be liable to prosecution. Where an offence has been committed by a corporate body, with the consent, connivance or neglect of the director(s), company secretary, manager(s), partners, cooperative members or other officer of the company, then those directors or others will be PERSONALLY liable.

Levels of punishment

Penalties for litter offences are between £400 and £1000 per offence. Penalties for offences under other sections of the Act are fines of up to £20 000 and/or imprisonment for up to two years per offence.

Magistrates' courts

Magistrates can inflict up to £5000 in fines and/or three months' imprisonment for each offence. However, if they feel that the offence(s) warrant punishments that it is above their powers to impose, they can refer the case to a higher court for sentence.

Higher courts

The following offences can attract higher fines and/or up to two years' imprisonment:

- failure to give notice of waste disposal activities
- failure to comply with the orders given by a local authority
- giving false statements
- making false record entries.

Parts of the Act equate to section 5 of the HASWA, so it must also be remembered that, under that Act, higher courts can impose *unlimited* fines for prosecutions brought under it.

15

Electricity at work

Governments often prefer self-regulation to legislation and, where possible, will encourage the setting up and observance of codes of practice. However, if self-regulation does not work, government then enforces the rules by passing Acts of Parliament or Regulations under those Acts. One typical case is the use of electricity at work, for which the Institution of Electrical Engineers (IEE) issued their own 'IEE Wiring Regulations', to which the Government gave backing. These Regulations have now become law and are incorporated into the Electricity at Work Regulations 1989, issued under the HASWA.

The purpose of these Regulations is to protect people from the risk of death or injury arising from the use of electricity at work. The previous Electricity Regulations of 1908 and 1944 (now repealed) had limited application to construction sites, factories, mines, quarries and electrical stations. The 1989 Regulations affect anyone who is at work in any workplace subject to the HASWA (see page 21 for the definition of 'at work'). There are still two ACOPs for mines and quarries.

The objectives of the Regulations

Electricity cannot be seen in the usual sense. It can be enjoyed when providing power for lighting, heating, cooking, driving machinery and so on, but, though not seen, it can be felt when it comes into contact with the body — often with serious, even fatal, consequences. These Regulations are designed to prevent hazards arising or avoid the exposure of people to the risks of hazards that could lead to death or injury from electrical causes. Compliance with these Regulations should save lives and protect health.

Who is responsible for implementing the Regulations?

A special duty of care is placed on all employers (directors and managers), employees and self-employed persons who in any way use or work with electricity. This particularly relates to matters concerning the use of electricity at work that are within the control of the employer (Regulation 3).

Only those persons who are adequately trained and qualified should be permitted to carry out work on electrical apparatus and installations (Regulation 16). They must also be given adequate information about the situations involving electricity in which they have to work. In this respect, directors and managers would be held liable for the consequences of permitting or causing an unqualified person to carry out any act for which they are not suitably qualified. Employees would be personally liable if such work was done on their own initiative and without the authority of their management. At the same time, by virtue of section 2(2) of the HASWA, an employer cannot issue instructions that unqualified persons must *not* undertake electrical work and then simply turn a blind eye while they act independently.

Assessments

Like the COSHH Regulations, the Noise at Work and other Regulations issued in compliance with EC Directives, the core of the Electricity at Work Regulations concerns assessments. Assessments are also a requirement of the Management of Health and Safety at Work Regulations 1992 (MHSW Regs), which became effective on 1 January 1993. As an employer, you are required to carry out assessments of *all* electrical installations, apparatus and equipment, even down to looking at fuses in electric plugs. The purpose of assessments is to determine the nature of work activities that utilize electricity and the nature and degree of risk involved in any electrical installation and/or work undertaken on them.

It may be that by virtue of a person's occupation in the vicinity of (not necessarily on) electrical installations, apparatus or equipment, there is a degree of risk to which that person is exposed. Assessments will determine those occupations.

Risk assessments
You, the employer, must assess and define all the foreseeable risks involved in the use of electricity at work and the measures that you propose to take to protect your employees and others who may be exposed to those risks.

The standards set by the Regulations

Systems and equipment
All electrical systems must be constructed and maintained so as to prevent danger from any conductor (Regulation 4).

- '*Systems*' include the source (such as a generator), provision, transmission, distribution and use of electricity, including all equipment in the system. The system also includes protective equipment and wear, which must be suitable for the intended use, well-maintained and properly used.
- '*Construction*' includes the design, installation, testing, commissioning, operation and maintenance for safety.
- '*Conductor*', in its broadest sense, is anything that is capable of carrying electrical current. It can include any metal casings and may apply to those conductors that are not part of the system, *per se*, but are within electrostatic or electromagnetic fields created by them.

The Regulations require a managed, planned preventative maintenance system, as for section 2(2)(a) of the HASWA. Electrical equipment should also be used in a safe manner, including, for example, fully uncoiling a cable (remember that electricity generates heat and heat can melt sheathing on cables and cause short-circuits — a common cause of fire).

Safe working limits
The strengths and capabilities — that is, safe working limits — of any system must not be exceeded in any way (Regulation 5). This applies not only to the load placed on a large electrical system, but to simple matters such as overloading of cables and too

highly rated fuses, frequent and common causes of fire, for example, putting a 5-amp cable on a 12-amp electric heater or a 13-amp fuse in a plug for a 1.5-amp electronic typewriter.

Effects of environmental conditions

All electrical equipment must be adequately protected from any adverse effects of the environment or other danger, such as the weather, wet, heat, dirt and dust, corrosive conditions, flammables or explosives (Regulation 6). Ask yourself, 'what if' — what would be the effect of a high-voltage electric cable placed outdoors, close to an acid tank or in a driveway used by lorries and fork-lift trucks?

Insulation

All conductors in a system must be either adequately insulated and protected (for example, in trunking) or sited so as to be 'safe by position', meaning that no one could touch it except intentionally (Regulation 7). But beware, what of service engineers carrying out maintenance — is any risk posed to them in obtaining access to positionally safe electrical systems?

Earthing

Charged conductors (or conductors which may foreseeably become charged) must be earthed so as to discharge electrical energy to earth or other suitable precautions taken to prevent danger (Regulation 8). Under Regulation 9, it is prohibited to have any device that breaks an earth conductor, except by a link or bar current transformer.

Connections

All electrical joints must be electrically and mechanically suitable for their intended use and installed so as to prevent danger. This would include simple things such as fitting power plugs (Regulation 10). Sticking two wires into a socket with matchsticks or joining two wires together with a clip or tape are definitely taboo (sadly, it is still known).

Protection

Sufficient suitably located means of protection from excess current due to overload, faults, short-circuits and so on must be fitted. These include fuses, circuit-breakers or cut-outs (Regulation 11). There are some specific points regarding these:

- *Fuses* are designed to protect electrically operated equipment and should always be used. They should always be of the correct rating, that is, not too high for the appliance used (for example, where a 13-amp fuse is fitted in a plug for a 2-amp radio, 1.5-amp computer or 1-amp shaver, the appliance is not protected).
- *Residual contact-breakers (RCBs)* are an excellent means of protection, fitted between the electric plug and the mains. They will cut out and break electrical contact in the event of an overload and are strongly recommended.

If a fuse blows or the RCB cuts out, it is telling you something. Don't do what a lady in a London office did and keep renewing fuses and only then complain (as she did after three months) 'the fuses keep blowing'. Get the apparatus or equipment checked.

Precautions

Any electrical equipment that is dead (redundant or being worked on) must be prevented from becoming electrically charged by isolating the electrical supply, locking it out and affixing suitable notices indicating that the system is locked out and must not be reconnected. All conductors should be proved dead before commencing any electrical engineering work by testing with suitable equipment (Regulation 13). It is recommended that the reversion to use of electrical circuits and apparatus that have been locked out should only be upon the obtaining of an authorized signature after electrical work has been completed and safety has been assured.

Working

Work on or near live conductors must be safe, that is, they must be insulated, unless it is reasonable that the conductor must be live, in which case suitable precautions need to be taken to protect those working on it (Regulation 14). There should be suitable locked out (as in Precautions above) and work permit systems within the management system (Regulation 13).

Working conditions

Adequate working space with means of access and egress must be provided, together with suitable lighting. There must be sufficient space for a worker to stand back from the conductor without this being hazardous (Regulation 15), that is, that they do not then step on to rubble, jumbled materials or face a sheer drop, for example.

Compliance with the standards

It is your duty as an employer to take steps to eliminate or minimize any risk identified in your assessments, so far as is reasonably practicable, and to comply with all the standards of electrical engineering laid down by the Regulations.

There is an absolute duty (with no defence) on directors, managers and employees and the self-employed to comply with the provisions of the Regulations that are under their control and employees have an additional duty to cooperate with their employer (Regulation 3).

The following Regulations are absolute: 4(4), 5, 8, 9, 10, 11, 12, 13, 14, 15 and 16.

There is the defence that 'all reasonable steps were taken and all due diligence exercised to avoid committing the offence' (Regulation 29), but see 'so far as is reasonably practicable' and 'who decides' on pages 21 and 22.

16

Working with lead

Considerable attention has been given to the effects of lead emissions into the atmosphere, particularly those due to vehicle exhaust fumes, prompting the changes to unleaded fuels. However, exhaust fumes are not the only source of lead contamination.

Many companies use lead in the manufacture of a wide range of products, some containing pure lead while, in others, the lead is diluted in compounds and mixes. Lead is classified as a hazardous substance with its own Regulations and is thus not included under the COSHH Regulations.

Although a hazardous substance, lead can be worked with quite safely if some simple rules are followed.

The Control of Lead at Work Regulations 1980

The Control of Lead at Work Regulations 1980 operates in a very similar way to the COSHH and Noise Regulations. The purpose of the Lead Regulations is to protect people at work from exposure to lead. They also have their own ACOP.

Assessments

The Work Place (Health, Safety and Welfare) Regulations 1992, effective from 1 January 1993, require detailed assessments to be carried out of all health and safety factors within your work areas in similar fashion to the COSHH and Noise Regulations. This requirement reinforces the Lead Regulations by which you, the employer, are required to carry out lead assessments. These should be repeated periodically to detect if there is any change. The purpose of lead assessments is to establish:

- what lead products are used in the manufacture of or in products supplied to customers
- what is the density of lead in the product
- what is the level of emission/vaporization of lead into the workplace
- what is the likely level of exposure for employees working on those lead products and those in the vicinity.

'But we don't have any lead here', you may say, but are you sure? Even if you don't *manufacture* lead, what substances do you use that *contain* lead? Any alloys, compounds of lead and substances or materials of which lead is a part, including lead strips on windows, are all included, so you will not know exactly what the situation is in your company until you have carried out your assessments.

Records

If you manufacture and/or use lead in the workplace, you must keep and maintain up-to-date records of this. These records must include details of:

- assessments
- air monitoring
- maintenance of plant and equipment
- medical surveillance
- biological tests
- medical treatment registers.

Protection

Emissions are measured over a set period of time (normally eight hours) and expressed as an average over that time, called a time-weighted average (TWA). If an emission (or vaporization) into the workplace is found to be at or above an eight-hour TWA of: 0.10 milligrams per cubic metre (0.10 mgpm^3) for tetraethyl lead, or 0.15 milligrams per cubic metre (0.15 mgpm^3) for all lead compounds other than tetraethyl, then certain precautions *must* be taken, as follows.

Employees who work with any lead substance or product *must*:

- wear impervious aprons to prevent them from wiping or rubbing their hands on their normal clothing (otherwise they may carry it home and contaminate food and young children)
- wear suitable protective gloves, unless the type of product worked, say, metallic-lead strips on windows, has a very low lead content and wearing gloves would prevent dexterity (note that barrier cream is ineffective as a protection against lead poisoning because lead is not absorbed through the skin and the cream will not prevent it being ingested from contaminated hands)
- *not* eat or drink in the workplace
- wash their hands before eating or drinking and must eat and drink in a suitable area (such as a canteen) away from the workplace
- avoid contact between gloved hands or unwashed/ungloved hands and the eyes or mouth
- practise a high standard of personal hygiene.

Also:

- smoking is strictly forbidden in areas where lead is worked — by those working with lead and those visiting or passing through the area
- where the lead worked is of a high density or where lead-welding is undertaken, suitable gloves and face masks must be worn.

Prohibitions

Under the Electric Accumulator Regulations 1925, those persons under 18 years of age are not permitted to be employed in work involving the melting, casting, burning, pasting, abrading or cutting of lead products. But they can be involved in washing, brushing and racking such products.

Under the Factories Act 1961, women and young people cannot be employed in operations involving:

- lead furnaces (for the reduction or treatment of zinc and lead ores)
- ashes containing lead
- desilvering
- melting scrap lead or zinc
- solder or alloys containing more than 10 per cent lead.

Information, training and instruction

You must provide all your employees who work with lead with adequate information, training and instruction regarding:

- the type of lead product being worked
- its consistency and use
- the safe methods for working with it
- the emissions or vaporizations from it into the workplace
- the protection and health precautions that you have determined are appropriate from your assessments (under either the Lead or Work Place Regulations or the COSHH (Amendment) Regulations 1991 and 1992).

Health surveillance

Under the Lead Regulations, all employees who work with lead must undergo regular health surveillance to assess the level of absorption of lead into their system, judged by the level of lead in the blood. This will consist mainly of blood tests and medical examinations. Such surveillance *must* be carried out by an appointed medical practitioner, approved by the Employment Medical Advisory Service (EMAS) or the HSE, not by a general medical practitioner. This approved medical practitioner may be your company doctor, but need not necessarily be so.

Lead poisoning

When lead is worked, it gives off emissions or vapour into the atmosphere that can be hazardous.

Lead cannot be absorbed through the skin; it is taken into the body via:

- inhalation (breathing)
- ingestion (eating).

While it is not harmful in very small doses and is unlikely to produce early skin problems, the effects of lead absorption can prove harmful in longer-term *cumulative* doses because it is stored in the body. Certain simple precautions are therefore necessary to prevent lead poisoning (see above).

Reporting

Finally, it should be noted that lead poisoning, where it occurs, is a notifiable disease. It should be notified to the HSE on Form F.41 and actioned under RIDDOR, as outlined in Chapter 14.

Records of all medical surveillances and any lead poisoning must be kept, including copies of HSE Forms F.41, and maintained for inspection when required.

17

Working with asbestos

Asbestos has been in use in the manufacture of a wide range of industrial and domestic products for many decades. It is only in recent years that the full implications of working with the substance have become fully understood as former employees of asbestos manufacturers and those using it in various processes have become ill or died as a result of lung diseases caused by exposure to it.

Various Regulations have been issued governing the manufacture and use of asbestos in products, of which three are currently in force: the Control of Asbestos at Work Regulations 1987, the Asbestos (Licensing) Regulations 1983 and the Asbestos (Prohibition) Regulations 1985. The purpose of these is to protect workers from the ill-health effects of asbestos.

The terminology

- *Action level* The level of emissions of asbestos in the workplace or external atmosphere at and above which action must be taken, as defined below.
- *Assessments* The detailed surveying or examination of the workplace to assess whether any asbestos is present, its type (if present) and the likelihood of exposure to it.

Types of asbestos

There are three main types of asbestos:

- 'blue' — crocidolite
- 'brown' — amosite
- 'white' — chrysotile or several of the fibrous and powdered varieties.

Blue and brown asbestos are carcinogenic substances, while white asbestos is relatively harmless, but it can cause problems to sufferers of asthma or people with bronchial problems.

The adverse effects of asbestos

No ill-health effects are felt immediately asbestos is inhaled, which gives a false sense of security to those who are ignorant of or complacent about what can happen. The problems are manifested 5 to 15 years later, with cancer of the lung, asbestosis (fibrosis of the lung) or mesothelioma (cancer of the pleura or peritoneum), the latter illness being caused mostly by blue asbestos, which is the more dangerous of the three main types. Only a very small amount of blue or brown asbestos is required to cause ill-health effects, with those resulting from exposure to blue asbestos being much more serious than those resulting from the other types.

Prohibitions

The following prohibitions are placed on asbestos products:

- the importing of crocidolite (blue asbestos) and amosite (brown asbestos)
- the supply and use of articles containing crocidolite or amosite for use at work
- asbestos spraying
- installations of new asbestos insulation.

Assessments

The Control of Asbestos at Work Regulations 1987 (known as the Asbestos Regulations) require assessments of asbestos substances to be carried out in all workplaces. This is now reinforced by the MHSW Regulations and the Workplace (Health and Safety and Welfare) Regulations 1992, issued to implement the EC Framework Directive, effective from 1 January 1993.

Under the Asbestos Regulations, before your employees start on any work that involves asbestos, you, the employer, must carry out an assessment of:

- the type and extent of the asbestos
- the likely exposure of employees or others who may be affected by it.

This assessment must determine the nature and degree of exposure and the steps that will be necessary to afford protection to both employees and others who may be affected by the presence of asbestos from the risks of contamination by it. Also, under the Regulations, a programme of continuous monitoring in the workplace and periodic reassessments must take place thereafter. (See Chapter 18 for detailed advice on how to carry out assessments.)

Action to take as a result of assessments

If blue or brown asbestos is assessed to be present at an action level, the enforcing authority (the HSE or an environmental health officer) must be notified at least 28 days before work is to take place there. The three action levels are:

- *level 1* exposure to asbestos consisting of or containing crocidolite or amosite of 48 fibre-hours per millilitre of air
- *level 2* exposure to asbestos containing other types including chrysotile, but *not* crocidolite or amosite, of 96 fibre-hours per millilitre of air
- *level 3* exposure to *both* types, at a proportionate number of fibre-hours per millilitre of air.

Any work involving removing asbestos or demolishing or refurbishing buildings where blue or brown asbestos is known to be present *must* be carried out by HSE-approved contractors who will have specialist apparatus, including decontamination facilities.

The enforcing authority will advise on the appropriate action to be taken and may require that a licence be issued before they authorize any work involving asbestos, depending on the nature of the substance and the exposure level.

Contractors Often, companies undertake demolition or installation work on sites not owned by them. If you are a contractor with your own employees working on sites not in your control, you should include a clear statement in your health and safety policy statement detailing the action that management and employees must take on discovering asbestos on sites.

Where asbestos is discovered in any workplace (including on a site), work *must* stop *immediately*, an assessment must be made (as above) and the appropriate advice sought from the enforcing authority (the HSE or an environmental health officer).

Cleanliness is essential where work involves the presence or use of asbestos. Employees who encounter asbestos and work with it *must* wear protective wear and/ or equipment, regularly change and clean outer clothing and maintain high levels of personal cleanliness.

Information, training and instruction

All employees required to work with asbestos must receive adequate information about the different types of asbestos, how to identify them and the risks involved. They must also receive training and instruction in what to do on discovering asbestos, precautions, protection and decontamination procedures.

18

Health and safety management for policy implementation and accident prevention

As said elsewhere in this book, accidents do not happen, they are caused. Good health and safety policies aimed at accident prevention, similarly, will not just happen, they must be *managed*. Health and safety should be seen to be integral parts of the management programme and not 'bolt-on' components or afterthoughts.

The costs of failing to manage health and safety effectively are high. In the HSE's booklet HS(G)65, *Successful Health and Safety Management*, the Chief Inspector of Factories lists those costs as being:

- 30 million days lost each year as a result of work-related injuries and ill-health
- a two-thirds real terms increase in employer's liability insurance (ELI) premiums
- a doubling of ELI claims on this insurance since 1985
- uninsured losses from accidents costing between 6 and 27 times the costs of the insurance premiums

all making the difference between profit and loss, especially in times when profit margins are squeezed.

Instilling a health and safety culture into your organization can be an uphill struggle. This is not helped by the veritable conveyor belt of new legal requirements for assessments, audits, policies, planning and minimum standards, all of which make it increasingly hard work just fulfilling your *minimum* administrative responsibilities.

In reality, the whole subject matter of this guide is the successful management of health and safety and, it is hoped, by conveying the essential elements of the legislation concisely and removing the gobbledegook in this area your life is made easier.

Sound company policy on the management of health and safety, taking full account of every aspect, is a vital part of good human resource management. If the advice given in this chapter is followed, it will assist you in effecting good management into health and safety and avoiding accidents, injuries and ill-health effects, such as those discussed in earlier chapters.

The terminology

- *Risk assessment* A systematic, detailed, wide-ranging examination:
  —by an employer of the risks to which their employees may be exposed while they are at work
  —by a self-employed person of the risks to which they may be exposed while at work
  —by both an employer and a self-employed person of the risks to those not in their employment who may be affected by their acts and/or omissions and by self-employed persons working for them.
- *Preventative and protective measures* The actions and provisions identified from assessments as being necessary to comply with any legal requirements and prohibitions.
- *Hazard* A condition that exists or could exist in the long or the short term and which could cause injury or ill-health effects to people (this could also include the possibility of damage to property). This includes the condition of machinery, hazardous substances, systems of work, the organization of work, the workplace and even workers themselves.
- *Risk* The likelihood or probability that a hazard could arise and the possible severity of the consequences in a given situation. The HSE expect both employers and the self-employed to consult the HSE's Guidance Notes, manuals, suppliers' information and so on to ensure they are familiar with the risks and hazards in their work situations. Remember, there are *no* laws that say you must carry out work to manufacture goods, but there *are* laws that say they must be made safely.
- *Extent of the risk* The number of people who might be exposed to or affected by a risk.
- *Reasonably practicable* Costs v risks, that is, balancing the assessed cost of protecting against exposure to a given risk with the probability of that risk arising:
  —if something is possible, it is practicable
  —if something is possible and the cost of eliminating the risk is low in relation to the level of that risk, then it *is* reasonably practicable
  —if something is possible, but the cost of eliminating the risk is excessive in relation to the level of risk, it is *not* reasonably practicable, but an alternative means of doing the job or alternative substances should be sought, preferably before embarking on the risky alternative.
- *Ergonomics* This is the study of the application of human biology and engineering to the relationship between workers and their environment. In health and safety, this means designing and adapting machinery, equipment, protective wear and systems of work to suit physical characteristics, including height, weight, stamina, gender.

EC Directives and UK Regulations

A number of European Community (EC) Directives on health and safety, issued by the European Commission, came into effect on 1 January 1993, placing obligations for implementation on all EC member states and upon managements in industry throughout the EC. These Directives were implemented in the UK by a number of supporting UK Regulations. These Directives (EC reference in brackets) and Regulations are as listed in Table 18.1.

Table 18.1   EC Directives and their corresponding UK Regulations

EC Directive	UK implementing Regulation
Framework Directive (89/319/EEC)	Management of Health and Safety at Work Regulations 1992 Fire Precautions (Places of Work) Regulations 1993

These are the 'umbrella' EC Directive and UK Regulations to the following subsidiary Directives and Regulations

EC Directive	UK implementing Regulation
Workplace Directive (89/654/EEC)	Workplace (Health, Safety and Welfare) Regulations 1992 Fire Precautions (Places of Work) Regulations 1993
The Use by Workers of Personal Protective Equipment Directive (89/656/EEC)	Personal Protective Equipment at Work (PPE) Regulations 1992
Work with Display Screen Equipment Directive (90/270/EEC)	Health and Safety (Display Screen Equipment) Regulations 1992
Manual Handling of Loads Directive (89/655/EEC)	Manual Handling Operations Regulations 1992
Use of Work Equipment Directive (90/654/EEC)	Provision and Use of Work Equipment Regulations 1992

Each of these UK Regulations has an ACOP to guide management as to how to enable the full implementation of the Directives and Regulations to take place in their organizations. It is the UK Regulations themselves that management must obey, not the EC Directives *per se*.

The new laws all have important implications for the management of health and safety. However, to include every aspect in one chapter would be too unwieldy, so here, our discussion is concentrated on two broad subjects:

1. the philosophy and a general approach to health and safety management
2. the EC Framework Directive, implemented in the UK by the Management of Health and Safety at Work Regulations 1992 (MHSW Regulations).

Other subsidiary EC Directives and UK Regulations also pertinent to the management of health and safety are dealt with in later chapters under their respective subject headings.

Other UK health and safety laws
Sections 2(1), 2(2), 3(1) and 3(2) of the HASWA and relevant subsections state that it is the *duty* of employers and every manager to safeguard the health and safety of their employees and others who may be affected by their unsafe acts or omissions. Similarly, sections 7 and 8 of the HASWA lay down the *duties* of employees towards themselves and others who may be affected by their unsafe acts or omissions.

There are many other pieces of legislation that directly impose duties on every manager and employee, the main ones being the:

- Fire Precautions Act 1971 and supporting Fire Precautions Orders
- Fire Precautions (Places of Work) Regulations 1995

- Control of Substances Hazardous to Health Regulations 1988, as amended in 1990, 1991 and 1992
- Reporting of Industrial Diseases and Dangerous Occurrences Regulations (RIDDOR) 1986 (as amended).

There are many others, dealing with specific issues such as lead, asbestos and abrasive wheels.

Philosophy and general approach

In order to achieve the aims of your company's health and safety policy and to achieve acceptable levels of accident prevention, every manager must see health and safety as a management function, that is, as a daily part of their management duties, written into the management job description. Health and safety is not something we do providing there is time, but, rather, is a priority; nor is it something we do when conditions are good but which we avoid on 'rainy days'.

What is an accident?

A definition given in *Safety Practitioner* (November 1985) was:

> An accident is some concrete happening which intervenes or obtrudes itself upon the normal course of events. It has the ordinary everyday meaning of an unlooked for mishap which is not expected or designed by the sufferer.

As an intruding or obtruding event, it thrusts itself on us without our consent or welcome. Being unlooked for, it is something we do not expect. As a mishap, it has undesirable consequences — injury, ill-health or even death. How, therefore, can we prevent this thrusting, unwelcome, unexpected intrusion and its unwanted results? Only by accident prevention. But how do we achieve accident prevention? Only by good management of health and safety. So where do we start?

The vicious circle

Studies of accidents over many years have found that there is a self-perpetuating cycle of events that operate causes and effects in accidents. The cycle can begin or be perpetuated at almost any point, but, for our purposes, we shall begin at 'Negligence; human error' (see Fig. 18.1):

- a person is negligent, commits a fault or a mistake
- this leads either to an unsafe act or unsafe omission (something someone did wrong or failed to do in the right way) or to an unsafe condition, then
- any or all of these three lead to the creation of a hazard, which in turn leads to
- a dangerous occurrence.

If no one is hurt and no damage results, this occurrence is termed an 'incident', or near miss, but if injury or damage occur, the occurrence is termed an accident, with all its attendant consequences. We can represent this 'vicious circle' as shown in Fig. 18.1.

To prevent accidents, we need to break this vicious circle. This can only be done at two places in the cycle: at 'Negligence; human error' or at the 'Hazard' stage.

- *Negligence and/or human error* can only be remedied or prevented from arising by education and training in health and safety, that is, the provision of infor- mation, instruction, training and safety supervision, as required by section 2(2)(c) of the HASWA, the MHSW Regulations and numerous other Regulations, both well-established and recent. Too often, health and safety is regarded as common

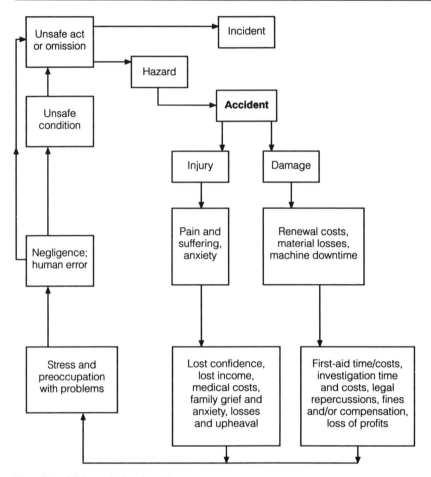

Fig. 18.1   Vicious circle of accidents

sense, but workers cannot have common sense about something they know little of. This is when they, and others, pay the price in injuries. A useful mnemonic (memory aid) to encourage health and safety consciousness in workers' minds is KAFE:

—**K** = knowledge

—**A** = attention or alertness

—**F** = foresight or forethought

—**E** = example.

- *Hazards* can be eliminated, thus preventing them from becoming accidents, by conducting regular health and safety audits and inspections. All employees should be encouraged to exercise health and safety awareness in the workplace as they look out for and report all hazards to their management. Another useful mnemonic to help workers to act when hazards are discovered and cannot be immediately remedied is GWR:

—**G** = guard the hazard

—**W** = warn against the hazard
—**R** = report the hazard to management.

Managing health and safety

The Management of Health and Safety at Work (MHSW) Regulations 1992 lay down a very broad scope of management duties in order to achieve improvements in health and safety. In our management of health and safety as a means of accident prevention, we can make a structured, multipronged attack on that vicious circle by using the following:

- risk assessments (Regulation 3)
- prevention, elimination and protection (Regulation 3)
- health and safety arrangements (Regulation 4)
- audits, inspections and hazard checks
- fire prevention and fire precautions
- information, instruction and training (Regulations 8 and 11)
- investigation and reporting of accidents and incidents
- health surveillance (Regulation 5)
- health and safety assistance (Regulation 6)
- emergency procedures and procedures for danger areas (Regulation 7)
- responsibilities to non-employees (other employers) (Regulation 10)
- responsibilities to non-employees (temporary workers) (Regulation 13)
- employees' duties (Regulation 12)
- cooperation with safety representatives (Regulation 17)
- multiple-occupancy premises (Regulation 9).

We shall relate each of these action points to the relevant Regulation in the MHSW Regulations.

Risk assessments

For many years, inspections have been carried out at intervals by the HSE, environmental health officers (EHOs) and fire officers. The theme and emphasis in all the EC Directives and 1992 implementing UK Regulations is *self-assessment*. Risk assessments must be written, except for the simplest of cases, and in them management is required to:

- assess the risks in their own workplaces to which workers and others affected by their operations may be exposed (this, perhaps, is common sense as they who create the risks know best how to eliminate or manage them)
- determine the measures necessary to achieve the standards of health and safety required or to comply with prohibitions imposed by law
- compile and maintain written records of those assessments and of any reassessments that are subsequently carried out
- make them available to the HSE, EHO or fire authority on request
- take the necessary steps to implement all necessary remedial action.

By 'prohibitions' is meant those things that it is prohibited by law for an employer or manager to do or allow to exist, not 'prohibition notices' (though you do have to comply with these also).

Fire authorities will require the presentation of assessments to them automatically, with the proviso that no action is taken on assessment findings until they have reviewed and approved them.

Objectives The purpose of risk assessments is to:

- determine risks to which employees and others may become exposed
- identify the measures that will be needed to comply with legal requirements and prohibitions affecting work activities
- provide retraceable data for subsequent reassessments or as proof or evidence in the event of an alleged breach of Regulations.

Who should carry out assessments? Regulation 3(1) requires all employers to carry out assessments of the risks to the health and safety of workers and others who may be affected by work undertaken within their operations. In the case of self-employed persons, they should assess the risks to their own health and safety and that of others who may be affected by their work activities (Regulation 3(2)).

'Suitable' and 'sufficient' Risk assessments must be both 'suitable' and 'sufficient', that is, they should:

- identify any significant risks arising out of given situations in the workplace
- enable the measures to be taken to comply with all relevant legal requirements to be identified
- be appropriate to the nature of the various jobs in the workplace, with provision for the assessments to be valid for a reasonable period of time, bearing in mind possible changes
- identify particular groups of workers particularly at risk, such as those working with hazardous substances, the partially sighted, lone workers, the deaf, epileptics (including the possible effects of visual display equipment on them — see also Chapter 19).

Where work activities are complex, detailed and subject to frequent change, your risk assessments will need to be broad-ranging in their application, with built-in arrangements for the control of those changes as and when they arise.

Disabled persons Do remember to include in your risk assessments, ensuring that they are also 'suitable' and 'sufficient', the provision of adequate facilities for disabled persons and the effect of your health and safety measures on them. Can a disabled person reasonably comply with your requirements? If not, how can you make them suitable for them? Also, are there any particular jobs that would expose disabled persons to risks by virtue of their disability?

Review and revision Nothing ever stands still or remains the same, so you should build in a system for reviewing your assessments and modifying the requirements to meet standards, as necessary. As with your health and safety policy, so with assessments; you should programme-in dates when your assessments will be reviewed and revised. These reviews will take account of changes in:

- technology
- machinery and equipment
- legal requirements
- products and raw materials
- personnel.

In addition to programmed reviews, you should also review and revise your assessments when, at any time, you suspect that they are no longer valid or when there has been a significant change in the work activities, for whatever reason, such as if you cease making or using particular substances.

How should you carry out your risk assessments? There are no hard and fast rules on methods of assessment as these will be dictated by your particular situation, including the nature of the hazards and risks in your workplace. However, the following general principles will help:

- categorize the main groups under which you will carry out your assessments — this will ensure your assessments are conducted in a systematic way and assist in recording your results. Some risk categories you might include are:

—manual handling	—mechanical handling
—working environment	—electrical safety
—chemicals	—radiation (ionizing and non-ionizing)
—upper limb disorders	—repetitive strain injury
—noise	—bacterial/microbiological
—visual display units	—machinery
—lead	—asbestos
—vehicle movements and marshalling	

(a number of these will have been covered by particular Acts or Regulations and they should be referred to for detailed guidance)

- make sure that you cover *all* hazards and risks:
  - —first, identify *all* the hazards in the workplace (if no hazards exist, there are no risks)
  - —then, determine *where* the risks of exposure of employees and others to those risks exist
  - —determine the *level* of those risks (low, moderate, substantial or high)
  - —find out what *Acts or Regulations apply* to those hazards and risks
  - —find out if there are any *existing controls* or precautionary measures for some risks, and, if there are, whether or not they are working, how effective they are and if there are residual risks from those control measures
  - —establish a *plan of action*, which enables you to carry out your assessments in a methodical manner, ensuring that nothing is missed, for example you could organize this by groups of hazard types, types of raw material, operation by operation or department by department
- assess actual ways in which operations and activities are conducted in the workplace, so that you can determine:
  - —variations from laid-down procedures, whereby risks can be brought in by workers unnoticed
  - —what non-routine activities may present risks, such as vehicle movement, loading and unloading, maintenance operations, changing production schedules, interruptions to operations
- ensure that *all* groups of employees and others who are affected by the company's operations are included in your assessments (remember to include small, non-production groups, such as clerical/secretarial and security staff, maintenance staff, visitors).

How much detail should you include in your risk assessments? This will be determined by the level of risk, whether it is:

- *high risk* — possibly cause serious/major injury or death — high level of detail
- *medium risk* — minor injuries could possibly result — medium level of detail
- *low risk* — negligible injuries likely — minimum level of detail.

A first, rough risk assessment may be appropriate to determine particular areas where high, medium and low risks exist. Then go into detail with each risk area, first detailing those risks covered by legislation (such as the COSHH Regulations, Regulations for asbestos, lead, carcinogens). Finally, deal with other specific areas not covered by particular legislation.

What about companies with multilocation operations? Where companies have several locations, whether factories or administrative centres, it will be helpful and cost-effective to design a common assessment proforma to alleviate unnecessary duplication. This can then be used across the whole organization. These should be broad in scope and application, but capable of local adaptation to particular work activities.

Existing assessments If you have already carried out risk assessments under existing legislation, such as COSHH, asbestos, lead, electricity, noise, you do not need to reassess those areas. However, you should review those assessments to determine whether modification is necessary.

Recording As with health and safety policies, if five or more persons (including directors or owner-managers) are employed, your assessments must be recorded in writing, reflecting the high, medium or low detail of the assessments (as above). Larger organizations may record the findings of assessments electronically, but with the proviso that data must be easily and readily retrievable. You should record all significant findings under these main headings:

- hazards
- risks
- existing control measures
- those affected by the assessment
- action required.

The amount of detail in your records should be sufficient to convince an inspector, fire officer, competent person or safety representative that your risk assessments are suitable, sufficient and capable of review.

Examination of records Obviously, managers and specialists will need access to the records of assessments; but they may also be required by fire officers, HSE inspectors, EHOs, safety representatives or the company's competent person(s). It is quite possible that the relevant authorities will ask to see your assessments to agree with you the action you intend to take, especially concerning fire safety assessments which the fire authorities may ask you to produce to them.

Prevention, elimination and protection

There is a link here with the requirements of the PPE Regulations. Your health and safety policy must include measures you will take to prevent risks from arising or to deal with risks where they may arise. The ACOP to the MHSW Regulations expects you to avoid the creation of risks altogether by, for example, deciding not to use a substance to which employees may be exposed and seeking a non-hazardous alternative.

Elimination of risks The first endeavour of management should be to eliminate identified risks and prevent exposure to those risks, rather than guard or warn against them. This means:

- tackling hazards at source by applying remedial measures, such as seeking alternative substances
- complete enclosure of hazardous substances
- guarding against hazards or treating slippery surfaces.

Elimination of risks may be achieved by incorporating improved technology and technical progress.

Adaptation Sometimes risks can be present because the design of workstations and the construction or siting of machinery is not suited to individual ergonomics (see below). Your assessments should consider what can be done to adapt to individual needs, *not* how individuals can be adapted to the work.

Protection against risks Only after elimination has been ruled out as impracticable or it is not possible to prevent exposure to them, protection against those risks must be afforded by the provision of PPE. You should determine what protective equipment and/or wear is needed to protect employees and others who may be exposed to those risks. However, you should still seek to progressively reduce the levels of risk. Both elimination and protection should be considered and determined in the detail of your assessments.

Ergonomics The application of ergonomics is a further means of avoiding exposure to risks, for example, by adapting the work and its organization to the individual. This includes the selection and adaptation of work equipment and the work methods employed. You should also take full advantage of technological and technical progress to improve the safety of working methods.

Priorities What do you tackle first? As with any management activity, including training, it will be most profitable to pay attention first to those areas that will yield the greatest benefits. The 80:20 principle usually holds true, that is, that 80 per cent of problems are found in 20 per cent of the area. You should seek to give priority action to those areas where greatest benefit can be achieved in the shortest time — and possibly save the company money into the bargain. For example, attending first to protection of the *whole* workplace may be most appropriate, unless there is a very small working group at serious and potentially costly risk to a particular hazard. Priorities may be particular, high-risk areas, hazardous substances, departments where the greatest number of accidents occur or where health and safety problems have financial implications.

Health and safety arrangements

Policy Your health and safety policy (see Chapter 7) needs to be implemented at all levels throughout your organization; any subsidiary location's health and safety policy must be adhered to within respective units. It is important that your policy documents are kept up to date and so regular reviews of policy must be undertaken. Central policies need to be amended regularly in the light of developments in plant, machinery, processes and substances, as well as in legislation, while the subsidiary's policies need to reflect changes in the main policy. Your central health and safety coordinator needs to be informed of any problems in implementing the overall company policy, so that necessary assistance can be given or suitable amendments made.

A vital part of *any* health and safety policy is the arrangements for putting that policy into effect. The MHSW Regulations advocate some established management principles:

planning, organisation, control, monitoring and review.

Because health and safety is an important management activity, we shall extend this list, including these *and* other important management skills, as follows:

- analysing
- planning
- objectives
- organizing
- controlling
- monitoring
- reviewing
- responsibility
- competent persons
- coordinators of shared premises
- health and safety discussion.

Analysing Before you can undertake any management activity, including health and safety, it is essential to *analyse* your tasks and what action you need to take. Your analyses could cover:

- what substances or materials are used and/or made
- what processes are undertaken
- what types of machinery and equipment are employed
- what hazards arise from those products and processes
- what facilities and organization are available to you to implement your health and safety policy
- what areas of improvement there are
- in view of the above, how valid your health and safety policy is.

Having analysed your overall situation, you will then be ready to formulate your planning strategy.

Planning It is important that you plan your risk assessments and the management of health and safety generally to ensure that your activities are conducted in a systematic and methodic manner. Poor planning, including the absence of pre-prepared assessment check-lists, will cause the risk assessments to be incomplete. Your plan should address all risks concerning machinery, equipment, substances, processes and facilities and include:

- the identification of priorities
- the setting of objectives
- the costings for putting your plan into effect, including changes that you have identified as necessary.

Objectives The setting of objectives is important in any activity, but nowhere more critical than in health and safety. If you do not have an objective, any road will get you there, in other words, if we have no objectives in health and safety management, then we cannot be sure of achieving anything. Your objectives should be neither too modest nor too ambitious, but they should always be realistic.

Organizing Your plan needs good organization with a structure that has clearly defined responsibilities, facilitates progressive development in health and safety and achieves minimum and desired standards. You will need to:

- identify the ways in which your objectives are to be achieved
- define procedures for dealing with emergency situations
- set up communications systems between management and employees
- establish ways to protect non-employees.

Controlling Control mechanisms are very important to ensure that your plan is fully activated. Those managers in your organization with direct responsibility for health and safety should exercise those controls to ensure that the decisions taken and included in the plan are implemented. Your control mechanisms should include such things as:

- ensuring that all necessary resources are made available
- ensuring that all managers and employees know their responsibilities and objectives
- that there are regular assessments of the effectiveness of your policy
- finding ways in which you can motivate employees to adhere to your policy requirements and achieve objectives.

Monitoring Regular checks on progress are very important to ensure that there is progressive improvement in your health and safety management with the achievement of stated objectives. You will need to appoint responsible persons trained in health and safety to monitor standards and progress.

Reviewing Nothing ever stands still, everything is constantly changing. You will need to review both your plan and your strategy regularly to ensure that your plan and objectives are kept up to date. Periodic reviews should include:

- changes in product ranges, processes, methods and machinery
- updates in literature and new technology
- changes in legislation that may impose unscheduled reviews
- summaries of accident records and investigation reports to assess what predominant accidents and injuries require intervention
- a review of health and safety committee meetings to determine how your policy and assessments are being implemented.

Responsibility *Every* member of management at *every* level must know their specific responsibilities and accountabilities for health and safety (and food safety and hygiene where appropriate). Each senior manager, middle manager and supervisor should be made personally accountable for health and safety matters within their spheres of operation, but they may also delegate health and safety duties to subordinates via either written instructions or including them in job descriptions. For the very small organization, it is often down to the director or owner-manager.

Competent persons The MHSW Regulations now require that 'competent persons' be appointed with responsibility for health and safety within your organization (Regulation 6). See also Health and safety assistance, later in this chapter.

Health and safety coordinator Where there is no 'resident' competent person, but the services of an external adviser are employed, it is suggested that you should appoint a mature and responsible person within your establishment as health and safety coordinator, though this is not a legal requirement, except in multiple-occupancy premises.

This person need not be a qualified safety practitioner, but should have enthusiasm for health and safety and display a degree of safety awareness and consciousness (see Information, instruction and training, below). The duty of a health and safety coordinator should be just that, to 'coordinate', that is, to ensure that all necessary health and safety action is taken (not necessarily taking it themselves), ensuring that all necessary health and safety resources, advice and guidance are organized.

In addition to their direct accountability to their managers, health and safety coordinators will have a functional relationship with any central health and safety coordinator at head offices (if appropriate) and with the local HSE or EHO.

Health and safety discussion One of the themes of the HASWA is the involvement of the workforce in health and safety. Management is strongly encouraged to facilitate the establishment of a health and safety committee (see Chapter 7). If no committee exists because none is legally required or (as in very small businesses) is inappropriate, health and safety should be included on the agenda of management meetings. Discussions on health and safety (whether in committee or management meeting) should be so ordered to ensure that all matters pertaining to health, safety, welfare and hygiene can be aired, plans of action determined and problems resolved, but it is suggested that the item 'any other business' should be excluded to avoid your health and safety forum drifting away from this subject into 'any old business'.

Multiple-occupancy premises Regulation 9 requires that where more than one employer occupies premises, there must be cooperation between those employers (see Multiple-occupancy premises, later in this chapter).

Audits, inspections and hazard checks

An essential aspect of continuing good health and safety management is the conduct of regular audits, inspections and hazard checks. These are separate from the risk assessments discussed above, but a valuable extension of and support for them.

You should arrange for comprehensive health and safety audits to be carried out by your own in-house or external specialist health and safety practitioners on a frequent, but irregular, basis. Additionally, individual departmental/functional managers should be given the responsibility of personally conducting inspections within their spheres of responsibility not less than once a month to ensure that *all* health and safety requirements are being met.

Audits and inspections Carry out regular, detailed checks of the workplace. In addition to fire manual audits, as outlined under Fire prevention and precautions, below, certain important routines concerning fire safety and precautions are included in the health and safety audit.

A health and safety audit should be carried out every six months and be detailed. It is called an 'audit' because it is the same process as an accountant/auditor carries out when auditing a firm's accounts to assess its financial status. Important items to check include the following.

- Are all statutory documentation and other minimum requirements complied with and up to date?
  —Is the employer's liability insurance in force?
  —Have correct signs and posters been displayed?
  —Has the accident book (DSS Form BI 510) been maintained?
  —Have checking-in/out registers been set up and used?
  —Is the first-aid box maintained to standard?
  —Have test certificates been maintained and are they correct?
- Are all fire doors freely accessible and kept operable and free of obstruction at all times?
- Are all emergency egress routes clear and free from all hazardous obstacles (such as overgrowth, discarded materials, boxes)? (Ensure that nothing is placed in the way of fire escapes/exits, even temporarily.)
- Are the surfaces of all routes to and away from fire exits safe (are they free of ice in winter, moss, dirt and rubbish)?
- Check the accident book — are particular types of injury occurring regularly, thus indicating the need for accident prevention action in that area?
- What is the level of knowledge of health and safety among employees, especially trainees? (Checks on log books and brief questions will quickly indicate what this is. Experience tells us not to assume that because they have been taught, they know.)
- Is adequate and correct firefighting equipment in place?
- Are all fire extinguishers serviced and in-date (that is, checked less than a year ago)? If out of date, contact your service contractor.
- Has a fire drill taken place in the last six months or as frequently as required by your fire certificate?
- Does the fire alarm work? Can it be heard by *everyone*?
- What arrangements have been made for the deaf? (say, flashing lights?)
- Is the evacuation procedure clearly known and posters displayed?
- What is the standard of manual handling? Is there a need for training in kinetic handling?
- If you have tools, machinery, ladders, scaffolding, electrical equipment and apparatus, are they all in a safe condition, stored correctly and test certificates maintained?
- Are all lights working efficiently, and diffusers fitted?
- Are all employees, including trainees, fully trained in fire precautions, fire drill and firefighting procedures?
- Does all visual display equipment — including workstations, VDUs and working environments — comply with the Health and Safety (Display Screen Equipment) Regulations 1992? (See Chapter 19.)
- Are all manual handling operations carried out safely, at least to the standard required by the Health and Safety (Manual Handling of Loads) Regulations 1992? (See Chapter 23.)
- Are all your fork-lift truck and power truck drivers trained to the standards of the MOTEC/Joint Council of Industry Training Boards requirements, per Regulations?

- Are all the people you require to mount abrasive (grinding and cutting) wheels trained according to the Abrasive Wheels Regulations 1970 and is a register maintained?
- Do you hold inspection/test certificates for all power presses (if used) and are there hand-over certificates from one shift to another as required by the Power Presses Regulations 1965 (amended 1972)?

This is not an exhaustive check-list but includes most of those elements required by law.

Compile a report and action list from your audit findings and issue the relevant sections to each responsible person. Again, in very small businesses, this is down to the director or owner-manager.

For monthly inspections, ask, have the observations raised in the annual and biannual audits been acted upon, especially those concerning high- and medium-risk hazards?

For weekly inspections, responsible members of staff should conduct them by walking through each area (including outside) with safety awareness in mind (see Information, instruction and training, below), but not on the same day each week. They should:

- note all existing or potential hazards and the degree of risk presented by them
- check what action has been taken as a result of the health and safety audit/ inspection report
- pass the list of actions needed to those responsible, ensuring that priority interventions are taken swiftly when situations that immediately threaten the health or safety of employees and others arise, following this up to ensure that action has been taken.

If immediate remedial action is not possible, the offending area/item should be adequately guarded, warning notices placed and action taken as soon as practicable.

Hazard-spotting via weekly inspections will not itself suffice, but it is valuable as an interim check between health and safety audits and inspections.

Fire prevention and precautions

Fire can strike at any time. It should be a function of health and safety management to prevent the occurrence of fires and the consequential injuries they cause to employees. Managers are responsible for ensuring that the requirements of the Fire Precautions Act 1971 and of a fire certificate (if one is in force) are complied with (see Risk assessments and Audits, inspections and hazard checks, above). Visitors, customers (except in shops) and contractors must also be informed of your fire drill procedures to be followed should a fire or other emergency occur during their visit.

These requirements call for regular checks on all fire precaution measures and firefighting equipment, with remedial action taken where appropriate. A fire officer will always be impressed to see a fire precautions manual in use in this respect. A suggested fire precautions manual, with self-explanatory sections, is included in Appendix 4 to assist you in carrying out your legal duties.

To manage fire safety and fire precautions effectively, managers (or their deputies) *must* make all the annual, biannual, quarterly, monthly, weekly and daily checks, as appropriate, and record any consequential action taken and sign it. The duty of maintaining your fire precautions manual should be delegated to a responsible person who has received training in fire safety and management (your local fire officer will be glad to advise on cost-effective courses available within the fire service).

Information, instruction and training

Under section 2(2)(c) of the HASWA, various Regulations, the Fire Precautions Act and Fire Precautions Orders, the Food Safety Act, plus the more recent EC Directives, all employees, including trainees and those on government-sponsored employment and training schemes, *must* be given information, instruction and training in every aspect of health, safety, welfare, hygiene, fire precautions and the COSHH Regulations, as they affect them (section 2(2)(c) of the HASWA, Fire Precautions Act, COSHH Regulations and so on). All employees, including trainees, must be given written information, supported by verbal training and instruction in:

- your company's health and safety policy — what it says and how it affects their particular departments/areas and their specific occupations and skills
- the duties of every manager and employee, including trainees, under the law and company policy
- the rights to protection of employees under the law and your health and safety policy
- your fire safety procedures, including fire drills
- your precautionary measures, including firefighting equipment in use within your establishment and how to identify various items (see Chapter 12)
- which types of fire extinguisher to use on various types of fire
- which types of fire extinguisher *not* to use on particular types of fire (such as water on electrical fires, halon (banned from 1996) in confined spaces and poorly ventilated rooms, CO_2 gas in the open air)
- electrical safety, including cabling and use of extension leads
- who the first aider(s) is (are)
- the accident-reporting procedure (its importance to employees and the company).

The foregoing items are not in order of importance; all are *equally* important.

Occupational health and safety Every employee, including trainees, must be given health and safety training in their occupations and skills including laws, EC Directives and UK Regulations relating to them, such as the following:

- health and safety consciousness and awareness, that is:
  —*consciousness* 'thinking safety' about their jobs to avoid creating hazards and the consequences of their own unsafe acts and omissions
  —*awareness* 'watching out for safety' in the workplace — noticing and rectifying or reporting unsafe conditions that exist and present hazards to the health, safety and/or hygiene of employees and others (see The vicious circle, earlier in this chapter)
- the use of visual display units (VDUs) and visual display terminals (VDTs), including the recent EC Directive
- construction Regulations
- woodworking (carpentry and joinery) Regulations
- catering — food safety and hygiene, including the Food Safety Act 1990 and Food Hygiene (Amendment) Regulations 1990 and 1991
- dangerous machinery — the rules for safe operation and concerning prohibition or training, supervision and authorization

- engineering — rules for safety
- personal protective equipment and clothing (PPE), including the 1992 Regulations
- correct (kinetic) lifting methods — 34 per cent of injuries in 1991/92 were caused during manual handling operations
- good housekeeping.

A trained workforce will be assured that their managers consider health and safety to be of importance and a priority. Experience has shown training to be a source of motivation and a morale booster.

For some hints on the training and development of employees, including that in health and safety, see Chapter 6 of my book *The Employer's Survival Guide.*

Investigation and reporting of accidents and incidents

The MHSW Regulations do not impose requirements for accident investigation and reporting *per se* as they are incorporated in the Reporting of Industrial Diseases and Dangerous Occurrences Regulations 1985 (RIDDOR). These Regulations require that all industrial diseases, dangerous occurrences such as fire or explosion, injuries resulting in an overnight hospital stay and/or absence from work of four days or more (not counting the day of the accident but including any subsequent days that would not have been working days, including Saturdays and Sundays), must be reported to the HSE or EHO.

An accident-reporting procedure should be designed and followed in all situations where an accident occurs. Every injury, no matter how slight (unless a very minor cut or scratch), should be recorded on Department of Social Security (DSS) Accident Book DSS Form BI 510. This is important not only for your company records and should information be needed at some later date in the event of inquiry or compensation claim, but for the person suffering the injury in the event of any entitlement to state industrial injury benefit.

Too often, accidents and injuries are recorded in accident books and forgotten about, with the result that no remedial action is taken. Also, incidents often occur but are not reviewed to assess their potential for accidents. It is a vital part of the management of health and safety to require that all accidents must be investigated to prevent them from occurring again. Also, serious, non-injurious incidents should be investigated to prevent them being repeated as injurious accidents.

Every potentially serious incident or dangerous occurrence that does *not* result in injury or damage, but *could* have had serious consequences, and every injury more serious than a minor cut or scratch, should be investigated, and your company's accident investigation and report form completed. The completed report form should be forwarded to your company's health and safety coordinator, with details of the action taken.

Some may say, 'Why investigate if no one has been injured or no damage caused?', but an important principle of accident prevention is that incidents should be prevented from occurring again in case next time they are injurious accidents. A few minutes investigating an accident *now* may prevent many hours of investigation and grief at some later date.

A suggestion (only) for a company accident investigation and report form is given in Appendix 10, incorporating all that you need to fulfil all legal and, hopefully, internal needs.

Every serious injury that results (or may result) in absence of four days or more or an overnight hospital stay should be notified immediately to the company's competent person for investigation, report and recommendations to prevent it recurring. Where no competent person is appointed in-house, the occurrence should be reported to your health and safety coordinator who can decide on how to carry out an investigation, possibly engaging an external safety practitioner to do this. (See Health and safety assistance, below, concerning competent people.)

Additionally, for every 'reportable' accident (that is, one resulting in absence from work of four or more days — called a 'more than 3-days' accident' by the HSE), every death due to industrial accident and every dangerous occurrence (as given in the RIDDOR), a HSE Report Form F2508 *must*, by law, be completed and forwarded to the HSE or EHO, as appropriate, within seven days of the occurrence. In cases of notifiable diseases, the report must be on HSE Report Form F2508A. Any death or dangerous occurrence must be notified by telephone and followed up by HSE forms mentioned within seven days.

Notifiable infectious diseases If any employee (or non-employee working on your premises) suffers from a disease that is notifiable under the HASWA or for food handlers under Regulation 13 of the Food Hygiene (General) Regulations 1970 (see below), this must be reported to the local HSE or EHO on HSE Report Form F2508A (as distinct from F2508).

Industrial diseases Notifiable industrial diseases under the HASWA include rubella (german measles), typhoid, food poisoning, severe diarrhoea, hepatitis, meningitis, polio, impetigo or other serious skin infections, scabies, ringworm and athlete's foot. Smallpox and scarlet fever are also notifiable diseases, and under Schedule 5 of the Factories Act 1961, the manufacture, cleaning or repair of clothing is forbidden on any premises where there is anyone suffering from these diseases. However, as these diseases have been virtually eradicated, this has only limited relevance.

Notifiable diseases for food handlers include typhoid, paratyphoid and other salmonella infections, amoebic or bacillary dysentery, or staphylococcal infections (septic cuts, boils, spots/acne, burns, throat or nasal infections) as these are likely to cause food poisoning.

You should periodically review your accident book (DSS Form BI 510) and HSE Report Forms F2508 and F2508A to assess what types of accidents/injuries and ill-health effects are experienced in the workplace. Your analysis should summarize accidents as follows:

• the types and numbers of accidents that have occurred over given periods
• the types of injury resulting from those accidents
• the types of ill-health effects suffered
• the departments or areas in which those accidents occur.

From these analyses, you will be able to highlight any prevalent types of accidents and injuries and identify accident-prone departments or areas. Where you discover high incidences of particular types of injury or groups of similar injuries, this will indicate the need for intervention in any or all of several ways:

• modifications to engineer out hazards or the risks of exposure of employees to those hazards

- training or retraining to prevent recurrences of injury types
- provision of PPE or improvements/modifications to existing PPE
- improved levels or quality of supervision.

This will help you to determine the appropriate accident prevention measures to be taken, including the provision of health and safety training. For example, a high incidence of back injuries from manual handling will indicate a need for training in how to handle heavy things safely. See also Chapter 7 (Duties of employers).

Health surveillance

The principles of health surveillance are already established in several existing UK Regulations, including, for example, COSHH and those concerned with lead, asbestos and other carcinogenic substances (see also Chapters 10, 16 and 17). The MHSW Regulations, Regulation 5, reinforce the requirements for health surveillance established in those Regulations.

Objectives In many instances of disease and ill-health effects in the past, by the time employees were found to be suffering from them it was too late. The objectives of health surveillance are to:

- identify individuals who may be at risk of infection
- determine methods of protecting them from exposure
- detect symptoms of disease and ill-health at an early stage, before they take an irreversible hold on the sufferer
- check whether control measures to prevent adverse health conditions are effective
- provide feedback on the accuracy of your assessments.

Your risk assessments should identify those situations and circumstances in which health surveillance will be required by existing Regulations (as above), but also where:

- identifiable diseases or ill-health effects are known to result from the type of work undertaken
- there are valid techniques available to detect indications of those diseases or ill-health effects
- the likelihood of that disease or ill-health effect occurring exists under specific working conditions
- health surveillance can enhance the protection of affected employees.

What is included in health surveillance? Where it is assessed that an individual employee or group of employees are exposed to a substance or substances that present a risk of identifiable diseases and/or ill-health effects, you should include the following features in your health surveillance:

- the inspection of conditions likely to lead to infection with an identifiable disease or cause ill-health effects. Such inspection must be carried out by competent persons within the limits of their qualifications and experience
- health checks and clinical examination of affected employees by an Employment Medical Advisory Service-appointed occupational medical adviser or health nurse, possibly within your local Occupational Health Service, which may include assessments of biological, physiological and/or psychological effects of substances by suitably qualified practitioners
- the measurements and assessment of biological agents in the workplace or their metabolites in tissues, secreta, excreta, expired air or combination of these in exposed employees.

Records It is important that you maintain adequate health surveillance records. An example of a health surveillance record form is given in Appendix 3, which can be usefully adapted to other health surveillance needs.

Note that monitoring records that have a general application must be kept for a minimum of 5 years, while health surveillance records relating to named individuals must be kept for a minimum of 30 years. Should a company close or relocate out of the area, these records must be handed over to the local HSE or EHO (see Chapter 10).

Health and safety assistance

Every employer is now required to employ the services of a specialist health and safety adviser, called a 'competent person' (Regulation 6). The HSE's Guidance Notes state that 'Audits should be conducted by competent people independent of the area of activity being audited'. You may appoint one competent person who will take care of your overall health and safety requirements or, in highly technical or specialized activities, you may appoint several specialists to look after specific aspects of health and safety.

Internal or external? The appointment of a competent person is an absolute requirement of the MHSW Regulations (see Who is competent?, below). If you do not have a suitably qualified and experienced person or persons within your organization, the Regulations state that you should employ the services of a suitably qualified and experienced external adviser as your 'competent person'.

Sole traders and partnerships Where self-employed persons or at least one of the partners in a partnership have sufficient skills, knowledge and experience in health and safety, they may appoint *themselves* as the 'competent person', providing they are confident that they can undertake the tasks required. If they do *not* have sufficient competence, then they should either acquire that competence themselves or employ the services of an external adviser.

Who is a 'competent person'? While there are no specific qualifications laid down for this role, there being a wide range of types and sources of qualification with varying applications, the Regulations stipulate that they must possess sufficient training, experience, knowledge and 'other qualities' in the sphere(s) of health and safety in which they will operate, to enable them to carry out their appointed tasks and assist you in implementing your policy.

The following general guide may help you to ensure that a 'competent person' is actually suitable:

- they should be able to demonstrate sufficient knowledge and understanding of:
  —relevant, current best practice in health and safety
  —your industry, products and processes
  —risk assessments
  —accident prevention
  —current health and safety law and its applications
  and have an appreciation of the limitations in their ability but a willingness to enhance those qualifications and experience
- they should also be able to apply that knowledge and understanding to the work you wish them to undertake, including:
  —identifying health and safety problems and the need for remedial action
  —determining action plans to resolve those problems

—implementing those action plans
—evaluating the effectiveness of those plans
—promoting health, safety and welfare standards
—communicating health, safety and welfare practices
and, where you have complex and highly technical situations in your operation, you should ensure that your competent persons have the specific skills and knowledge that are needed and are able to apply them to those situations (such persons may be qualified specialists with membership of a professional body at a level that is appropriate to the task to be undertaken).

Information for competent persons It is not enough to expect that your competent person, by virtue of their qualifications and experience, knows all that they need to know about your particular situation. They should, therefore, be given sufficient information to enable them to act confidently on your behalf. This information should include details of:

• all factors known to affect, or suspected by you to affect, the health, safety and welfare of employees and others who may be affected by your operations, including visitors and contractors
• the risks identified in risk assessments (if undertaken)
• any preventative or protective measures taken in respect of risk assessments
• your emergency evacuation procedures and procedures for danger areas and those in charge of procedures (as outlined below)
• the likely risks arising from any shared workplaces
• details of those employed on fixed-term contracts or temporary staff employed via employment businesses.

If you have an externally appointed specialist adviser as your competent person, Regulation 6 requires that you should specifically inform them *particularly* of the above items, though other items are important, too.

Coordinating competent persons Where you have more than one competent person, whether internally or externally appointed, it is important that their roles be effectively coordinated by the person within your organization who is responsible for managing health and safety. This will ensure that common standards prevail and that there is cooperation between them, avoiding problems arising out of possibly overlapping or complementary roles.

Emergency procedures and procedures for danger areas
The requirement to have emergency evacuation procedures is already incorporated in the Fire Precautions Act 1971 and will be contained in a fire certificate, where one is in force. However, Regulation 7 now expands on this requirement and demands that procedures be established for every danger area and for eventualities of serious or imminent danger arising in the workplace.

What is a 'danger area'? It is any working environment that must be entered by an employee or authorized visitor and where the level of risk is unacceptable without special precautions being taken (MHSW 1992 ACOP). Included in this category will be a situation where a minor alteration or an emergency may convert a 'normal' working environment into a danger area. Danger areas will logically include, for example:

• chemicals and flammables storage compounds

- the presence in the workplace of hazardous substances (as given in the Chemicals (Hazard Information and Packaging) Regulations 1993, such as ammonia and phenol; see Chapter 10)
- areas where work activities involve the potential for fire and/or explosion should a mishap occur
- maintenance work or machinery adjustment.

These procedures must include evacuation and action to minimize injury or damage, with a named person nominated to implement those procedures, especially where they relate to the evacuation of people from the workplace.

Restricted access Including this in your procedures for danger areas should ensure that no unauthorized person enters any restricted access area, that is, any place where there is a known hazard and where only trained and competent persons are permitted to work or to enter, such as boilerhouses, chemical compounds, power press workshops, engineering workshops, X-ray departments and others using radio-activity.

Written procedures Under Regulation 4(2), your procedures must be written down and must set out the prescribed actions by employees in the event of any emergency (including any practice drills).

Instruction As with section 2(2)(c) of the HASWA, so with Regulation 7 of the MHSW Regulations: you must provide adequate and specific instruction in health and safety, with suitable warnings posted, where there are known danger areas. This instruction should be a combination of verbal presentation and written instructions.

Information You must provide information concerning restricted access or danger areas, with appropriate evacuation procedures, to persons who work in them or may be required to enter them for legitimate purposes. This information should include details of:

- the nature of the hazards that have been identified
- the measures that have been taken to protect them from hazards
- the procedures for an emergency shut-down
- the emergency evacuation procedures, including total evacuation and the egress routes to places of safety
- their duties in the event that they are exposed to serious, imminent and unavoidable danger, including stopping work immediately and following emergency shut-down and evacuation procedures.

'Unauthorized' persons should also be informed that risks exist in restricted access areas.

Emergency evacuation procedures These must:

- identify foreseeable events, such as fires, explosions, bomb alerts, spillages or leaks of chemicals and other substances
- require affected persons to be prevented from re-entering the premises or returning to work where the risk of exposure to danger exists until the emergency is declared over
- ensure that all people, including non-employees, known to be in the premises are accounted for

- reflect the requirements for emergency procedures laid down in health and safety Regulations, not being specified in this Regulation
- include the role and responsibilities of your competent person (see below)
- contain procedures for ensuring that, when an emergency is over, no danger still remains; this may include obtaining the expert advice of emergency services or HSE inspectors.

Places of safety Suitable places of safety must be identified and groups of individuals designated to them in your procedures, according to where they work. Places of safety must be:

- away from affected building(s)
- away from traffic routes (other than car parks)
- away from emergency access and egress routes, including electricity and/or gas substations.

Alternative places of safety should also be designated, in the event that primary places of safety become threatened by an emergency or those emergency vehicles attending it.

Traffic routes It is suggested that your procedure should include the prevention of vehicles entering or leaving your premises, except for authorized emergency vehicles, such as police, ambulance, fire brigade and those of HSE inspectors. People evacuated from the premises should also be prevented from wandering into traffic routes as they may present a danger to themselves and drivers; they should remain in their designated places of safety. Thus, egress routes to places of safety should not pass across traffic routes likely to be used by emergency vehicles.

Competent persons As under Health and safety above, you will also be required to appoint a competent person to undertake the implementation and supervision of your procedures. That competent person must receive adequate information, instruction and training and/or be suitably qualified to undertake their duties.

Responsibilities to non-employees (other employers)

Under section 3 of the HASWA, all employers and self-employed persons have a clear duty of care to safeguard the health, safety and welfare of persons who are not in their employment, a duty further enhanced by Regulation 10 of the MHSW Regulations, with some overlap with Regulation 9 (see Multiple-occupancy premises, later in this chapter).

You should inform:

- employers from an outside undertaking who work in your premises (such as contractors, subcontractors, specialist consultancies)
- the employees of those other employers
- self-employed people working on your premises
- employees of employment businesses working on your premises (see Responsibilities to non-employees (temporary workers) below

of:

- the risks to their health and safety arising from or in connection with your business and to which they may be exposed

- the measures you have taken, or will take, to comply with the requirements and/ or prohibitions imposed by health and safety laws to protect those non-employees from exposure to those risks
- the identity of the competent person responsible for emergency evacuation procedures and procedures for danger areas and the details of how you are complying with those procedures.

This information should also extend to visitors to your premises and those who may carry out work in your workplace.

When considering visitors or contractors working on your premises, you should take into account risks presented to your permanent employees by those people, such as from the tools, equipment and substances that they may bring with them. You should ask for (and they must provide under section 3 of the HASWA) full information regarding all such risks.

Under Regulation 10(3), your contractors, other employers and self-employed people working on your premises are responsible for informing their own employees of health and safety requirements while working on your premises and for supervising those employees, but you are responsible for making *sure* that they do this.

Responsibilities to non-employees (temporary workers) (Regulation 13)
If you employ people who are:

- on fixed-term contracts
- employees of an employment business

then you must provide both categories of employees, and the employer carrying on any employment business supplying you with temporary workers, with all the information required by the foregoing section and, in addition, details of:

- any special occupational qualifications and/or skills required in order to carry out the prescribed tasks safely and without causing risks to health
- any health surveillance that may be required by virtue of any Regulations affecting the work being undertaken.

An 'employment business' is an agency which employs and pays its own staff for the purpose of supplying them to other employers for temporary work, for a fee; not to be confused with 'employment agencies'.

The duty to provide information to employees of an employment business applies equally to the employer *and* the host employer in the workplace where that temporary worker is placed. There is, furthermore, a duty for:

- employees of an employment business
- the proprietor/manager of that employment business
- fixed-term contract employees

to fulfil all relevant health and safety requirements and for the host employer to ensure that they do, in fact, fulfil all health and safety requirements.

In short, *they* are responsible for *doing* it and *you* are responsible for *ensuring* that they do it.

Employees' duties (Regulation 12)
The duties of employees are laid down under section 7(a) and 7(b) of the HASWA (see Chapter 9), and these are to:

- safeguard the health, safety and welfare of themselves and others who may be affected by their acts or omissions at work (section 7(a))
- cooperate with their employer to enable them to fulfil their obligations under health and safety law (section 7(b)) — this duty includes complying with company policy, rules and regulations.

The MHSW Regulations (Regulation 12) enhance these duties by applying more detail to them, that is, stating that employees are to:

- behave as taught by any training and instruction given by the employer
- use any machinery, equipment, dangerous substance, transport equipment, means of production or any safety device provided in a safe manner, as taught
- observe written instructions given concerning the use of those items
- inform their employer of any serious and/or immediate danger in the workplace
- inform their employer of any shortcomings in the protection arrangements that might affect their health and safety.

Thus, in summary, employees must obey all the rules, do as they have been taught and report any hazardous situations or shortcomings they may observe in the workplace, whether or not it affects them personally.

Cooperation with health and safety representatives (Regulation 17)

The duties of the employer to cooperate with health and safety representatives are enshrined in section 2(6) of the HASWA and Regulation 4 of the Safety Representatives and Safety Committees Regulations 1977. The Schedule to the MHSW Regulations 1992, Regulation 17, has further enhanced these duties.

You must consult with any health and safety representatives 'in good time' (that is, well before the event), regarding:

- the introduction of measures in the workplace that substantially affect the health and safety of employees
- the competent persons appointed to oversee health and safety (or act as adviser to the company, if externally appointed) under Regulation 6(1) (see Health and safety assistance, earlier in this chapter)
- the competent person appointed to control emergency evacuation procedures and procedures for danger areas under Regulation 7(1)(b) (see Emergency procedures and procedures for danger areas, earlier in this chapter)
- any health and safety information that affects those employees represented by the health and safety representatives
- details of any training and instruction planned and organized concerning health and safety
- any new technology that will be introduced and will affect those employees represented by the health and safety representatives.

You must also provide such facilities and assistance as health and safety representatives may reasonably require. This may include use of a small office, if there are several representatives, the use of a photocopier, access to secretarial facilities and making available copies of any relevant documents that will help them in their duties.

Multiple-occupancy premises (Regulation 9)

Where there are multiple-occupancy premises — that is, premises in which more than one employer is situated — then there is a requirement for cooperation and coordination between those respective employers. This includes instances where premises are shared with self-employed people, to whom the same rules apply. All of the foregoing information and advice given in this chapter applies equally to multiple-occupancy premises but there can be problems in implementing it.

Health and safety coordinators Where there are several employers who are controlled by one parent company, then that parent company must appoint a health and safety coordinator to coordinate health and safety activities. However, where there are several independent and unrelated employers, including self-employed people, then those employers and self-employed persons must appoint a health and safety coordinator by joint arrangement. This is particularly important and advantageous where the management of health and safety is fragmented due to varying management structures and systems. It will be the duty of the coordinator to ensure that all statutory obligations placed on employers and self-employed people in those multiple-occupancy premises are fulfilled.

Risk assessments In all multiple-occupancy premises, there will be hazards and risks peculiar to individual occupiers of *sections* of the premises as well as those common to *all*. It will be the duty of the coordinator to conduct risk assessments (as outlined earlier) for the whole premises in order for any necessary solutions to be effective. This is important when you consider that the activities of one person or a group of persons can hold implications for others not in their employ but who work near to them. This suggests that a coordinator should have a minimum level of qualification and experience, perhaps similar to those of a 'competent person', as only a person fully competent in health and safety can effectively carry out risk assessments for this kind of premises.

Persons in control In multiple-occupancy premises, the person in control of those premises (the owner or their agents) cannot devolve their responsibility (section 4 of the HASWA), but must cooperate and coordinate with the occupants of their premises to ensure that their obligations as owner and/or controller of the premises are fulfilled.

Emergency evacuation It is important that procedures for evacuation in the event of an emergency and for dealing with danger areas be established and controlled. It is suggested that the persons in control (see above) should control these procedures, though this could feasibly be undertaken by the health and safety coordinator.

Separate workplaces Many multiple-occupancy premises are divided into completely separate workplace units. For example, where each unit in a multiple-occupancy premises is separated by a fire-resistant structure, they are treated as separate buildings for the purposes of the Fire Precautions Act 1971. In such instances, these rules concerning multiple-occupancy premises will not apply. However, notwithstanding the separateness of units, where they share a common reception, canteen or other workplace, then these rules *will* apply and a health and safety coordinator will need to be appointed to cover those areas.

Other Regulations

In the remaining chapters, we shall outline some further subsidiary or 'daughter' Regulations to the MHSW Regulations 1992. All that has been said about the management of health and safety and these Regulations applies to all these other topics. Where, therefore, there is common ground in daughter Regulations, the management aspects are not repeated.

Sources of help

There are numerous sources of help regarding the management of health and safety, of which the following are but a few.

- Your local HSE office (their address and telephone number can be found in your local telephone and/or business directory).
- Your local environmental health officer (their address and telephone number can be found in your local telephone and/or business directory).
- Institution of Occupational Safety and Health, 222 Uppingham Road, Leicester LE5 0QG (tel: 0116 21768424).
- Independent Safety Consultants Association, 21 Eldridge Close, Abingdon, Oxfordshire OX14 1YQ (tel: 01235 526370).
- Abundance Management Services, Abundance House, 17 St Michael's Crescent, Oldbury, West Midlands B69 4RT (tel: 0121 552 2073).

Some useful reading

Management of Health and Safety at Work Regulations 1992 (No. 2051) (available from HMSO)

Management of Health and Safety at Work ACOP (available from HMSO)

Health and Safety Briefing (Croner Publications Limited, Croner House, London Road, Kingston-upon-Thames, Surrey KT2 6SR (tel: 0181 547 3333)), a subscription-only publication

Successful Health and Safety Management (HSE booklet HS(G)65, available from HMSO)

Essentials of Health and Safety at Work (HSE, available from HMSO)

The Management of Health and Safety at Work: A guide to implementing the 1992 Regulations (Electrol, Omega House, 22 Barnmead Road, Beckenham, Kent BR3 1JE)

The Employer's Survival Guide, Brimson, Terence, J. (McGraw-Hill, 1992)

Health and Safety Monitor (Monitor Press, Rectory Road, Great Waldingfield, Sudbury, Suffolk CO10 0TL) (tel: 01787 78607).

19

Visual display screen equipment safety

The proliferation of computers, word processors and related electronic equipment since the early 1980s has brought visual display screen equipment (DSE) such as visual display units (VDUs) and terminals (VDTs) to many workplaces. Such advanced information technology has improved the efficiency of business by increasing the ease and speed with which various operations can be done. However, technological advances have also brought about potential problems.

When electronic equipment is installed, much attention is paid to the type of hardware, workstation equipment, including the VDU itself, programming and costs, but, until recently, comparatively little attention was paid to those who used or operated that workstation or to its effects on them. Increasing concern has been expressed about eye and eyesight problems and the other ill-health effects that VDUs and workstations have caused users. Much scientific research has been conducted into this, particularly in Sweden and the USA.

Working with VDU screens is not the only cause of ill-health covered in this chapter. Many people have suffered from repetitive strain injury (RSI) or from work-related upper limb disorders (WRULD) resulting from the constant, repetitive movements made at many keyboards, as well as during assembly and packaging operations in industry. A number of claims for compensation for ill-health suffered as a result of using VDUs and other repetitive movement operations have been successful in the UK in recent years with awards of up to £100 000 being made against employers.

Some of the subject matter on VDU safety is controversial and still unresolved as there are differing scientific opinions. In this chapter we offer advice on the actions you should take to comply with the Regulations, as well as the best ways to safeguard your employees' health.

The terminology

The following are terms used in the VDU Regulations and/or in this chapter and definitions of what they refer to in these contexts.

- *Computer or word processor* any electronic information processing, storage and retrieval system.
- *Visual display unit (VDU)* a display screen connected directly to a computer or word processor.

- *Visual display terminal (VDT)* a display screen connected to a mainframe computer, which may be sited some distance from that terminal.

  Note that the terms VDU and VDT are often used synonymously as there is really little or no difference in appearance or operation. Throughout this chapter, we shall mainly use the term visual display unit (VDU) as this is probably the most familiar name for this equipment, but the information applies equally *all* display screen and similar equipment.

- *Display screen equipment (DSE)* Any alphanumeric or graphic VDU or VDT, including both cathode ray tube screens and liquid crystal displays.
- *Workstation* The whole working area, including the VDU/VDT and optional accessories, the keyboard, disk drive, document holder, telephone, desk, work chair, lighting and the immediate working environment around the DSE.
- *Radiation* The emission and propagation of waves or particles, such as light, sound, radiant heat or radioactivity.
- *Electromagnetic radiation (EMR)* A form of radiation consisting of electrical and magnetic fields (including ionizing and non-ionizing radiation) emitted by the sun, light from the sun, televisions, VDU/VDT screens and, to varying degrees, other electrical and electronic equipment.
- *Ionizing radiation* Radiation that converts, or partially converts, into ions.
- *Non-ionizing radiation* Radiation that does *not* convert, or partially convert, into ions.
- *Use* In connection with work; thus, the Regulations do not cover DSE used in leisure time.
- *User* Any *employee* who habitually works at a VDU/VDT workstation, including employees who work from home. The term 'worker' is used in the EC Directive, while 'user' is used in the UK Regulations.
- *Operator* Any *self-employed* person who 'habitually' uses any DSE. This is a curious distinction, as the terms 'user' and 'operator' could be taken to be synonymous. We use the term 'user' throughout this chapter.
- *Environment* The whole physical location and atmosphere around the workstation.
- *Lighting* The method of providing light (whether natural, fluorescent, filament bulb, or ceiling, wall or from the floor upwards) in the working environment.
- *Ill-health effects* Sickness or illness that may result from working with VDUs and associated workstations.
- *Upper limb disorders (ULDs)* An illness in the shoulders, shoulder-blades, arms and hands, that is, parts of the body controlled by the upper part of the spinal cord.
- *Work-related ULDs (WRULDs)* Those ULDs caused by a working situation.
- *Repetitive strain injury (RSI)* A disorder occurring in the hands or arms especially, resulting from repeatedly doing the same rapid movements for long periods of time (e.g., using a keyboard or lever or push-pull operations), such as tenosynovitis, which is inflammation of the thin inner sheathing around the tendons of the hands and wrists.
- *Risk assessment or analysis* Detailed survey of all VDU workstations an employer uses in the course of their business and on which users or operators work on their behalf to determine the risks to health and safety.
- *Habitual user/operator* A user or operator who uses VDU/VDT apparatus more or less continuously on most days (see page 155).

The legislation

The Health and Safety (Display Screen Equipment) Regulations 1992 (known as the DSE Regulations) became effective on 1 January 1993. A European Community (EC) Directive and these Regulations were produced in response to evidence of ill-health effects such as eye and eyesight problems, RSI and ULDs. DSE workstations and their equipment, whether purchased new or second-hand, must conform to the new standards. Employers with existing equipment have until 31 December 1996 to comply with the requirements, except where assessments identify specific risks (see below).

The main parts of the DSE Regulations are:

- 2, analysis of workstations
- 3, workstation requirements
- 4, daily work routine
- 5, eye and eyesight
- 6, training
- 7, information.

They require all employers to:

- conduct risk assessments to analyse the risks to users of DSE
- eliminate or reduce those risks
- plan the daily work routine to avoid extended or continuous DSE work
- provide eye and eyesight tests and corrective appliances to users who need them
- provide information and training.

Exclusions

Certain types of DSE are excluded from the requirements of the DSE Regulations, provided they are 'not in prolonged use at a workstation'. They include:

- certain laptop and portable systems not in prolonged use
- small items such as calculators, cash registers or bank cash dispensers with a small data display required for direct use of the equipment
- typewriters with a window display (not connected to a VDU)
- display screens mainly used to show television or film pictures
- vehicle drivers' cabs or machinery control cabs
- DSE on board any means of transport
- DSE for public use, say for entertainment or self-help purposes.

However, do remember that all *these*, and other, types of equipment *are* subject to the Provision and Use of Work Equipment Regulations 1992 and, therefore, the requirements for risk assessments, control measures, ergonomic design and training all apply to them.

The nature of the problem

There are three apparently different yet connected potential problems associated with VDUs:

1. the effects on the eyes and eyesight
2. a range of ill-health effects
3. the controversial subject of emissions of electromagnetic radiation (EMR).

Ill-health effects do not arise from one source alone but often from a combination of factors. Problems related to or caused by VDUs may arise from the:

- VDU screen
- keyboard
- design of the workstation
- user's work chair
- working environment
- way the work is organized
- personal factors
- emissions of EMR,

all of which may combine to produce ill-health effects. As with many situations, it is often not one, single factor that causes problems, but a combination of factors.

Let us look at each of these problem factors in turn and some solutions, as well as the legal requirements. If you purchase a new computer or word processor in the future, it is most probable that its VDU and peripheral equipment will conform to all legal requirements for the equipment itself, but you will need to pay attention to the whole working area, as outlined below. Further, if you still have (or acquire second-hand) any computer or word processor that was manufactured before 1992, you may need to update them also.

The VDU screen

There have been many problems with VDU screens themselves. They include:

- static monitor/screen, with no twist-and-tilt adjustment
- no filter on the screen to protect from the effects of glare
- flickering images on the screen
- 'feathered' lettering/images on the screen, with no sharpness
- lettering/images on the screen that are too small
- absence of adjustment controls for brilliance and contrast, or difficulty in accessing adjustors (usually at the back)
- static imbalance between contrast and brightness
- poor colour contrast (or the absence of it) within texts
- 'buzz' from the disk drive (not common)
- dust, dirt and fingermarks on the VDU screen, causing distortion and lack of clarity of the images.

The keyboard

Keyboards themselves can cause problems where they are:

- fixed or rigid or, sometimes, moulded into the VDU casing
- non-adjustable (this is difficult to resolve if the keyboard is a typewriter with an interface to the VDU screen)
- have shiny surfaces (this is sometimes due to poor design, but often due to wear in long service).

The design of the workstation

There are many potential problems that stem from the design of workstations, that is, the area immediately around the VDU in which the user has to work. The concerns here are for the physical relationship of the user to the VDU screen and the light source, including the following situations:

- too little space for movement, resulting in cramped conditions
- lack of leg space under the desk or table so that the user has to lean forward to reach the keyboard or hold it on their lap
- shiny surfaces on the desk and table, reflecting glare from fluorescent lights and sunlight through windows, all having an effect on the eyes
- absence of a document holder or the document holder placed in a bad position so that the user has to make frequent head and eye adjustments, causing disorientation, eye strain and fatigue
- VDU screen too near to the user or too far away, straining the eyes
- the VDU placed with the screen directly facing or angled towards windows or other sources of direct light, causing glare and reflections on the screen.

The user's work chair

So little attention is paid to the work chair, but it is equally as important as the VDU because the user sits on it for long hours and the consequences of an unsuitable chair are often quite serious. Many problems reported by users and found during health and safety audits are that their chairs:

- have no lumbar support (often even new chairs have high shoulder supports, but these are of no benefit to the VDU user)
- are fixed, with no swivel or adjustable back rest
- have no foot rest — so important for spinal comfort
- have no height adjustment
- have old and worn seats, with pieces missing
- are executive, conference or 'bucket' chairs, which are quite unsuitable for VDU users.

The working environment

Problems in the working environment affect VDU users, and others working in the vicinity, quite considerably. They are often associated with 'sick office syndrome' and are either the cause of ill-health or are at least contributory factors. Some of these factors are as follows.

- *Lighting* The brightness and positioning of artificial light and lighting that is reflected on to VDU screens can cause serious problems to the eyes and eyesight of users, the mildest of these being strained, tired eyes. The most common source of problems is fluorescent lighting, often with flickering, faulty tubes or tubes missing and no diffusers. Also, variations in levels of light around the room in which the VDU workstation is placed can cause problems to users, particularly those of focusing and screen clarity.
- *Noise* Normal background noise is rarely a problem, but monotonous and aggravating noises, such as buzzing from faulty fluorescent tubes, noisy printers or telephone switchgear can cause loss of concentration and problems such as headaches or fatigue.
- *Humidity* Many offices have low humidity, often due to central heating, well-sealed windows and a lack of ventilation. A further problem is that computers and word processors give off dry air and attract dust, absorbing what little humidity there may be. A very dry atmosphere causes dry eyes, making them feel gritty and sore.
- *Ventilation* Poor ventilation and lack of fresh external air can cause ill-health, as we have just seen.

- *Decor* In many offices, little attention is paid to decor. Often, ceilings and walls are painted in brilliant white, which reflects the glare from fluorescent lights and sunlight from windows.
- *Natural light* The source and direction of natural light is critical in relation to VDUs. Windows without coverings to filter out sunlight will cause glare on VDU screens and people working near them could become overly hot.

See also Chapter 26.

The way the work is organized

Very often, users are given one type of work to do continuously. They spend excessive amounts of time working with VDUs doing one type of work, which causes visual and mental fatigue, because of the constant focusing of the eyes on the screen and the lack of variety in terms of mental demands. A further cause of mental fatigue and eye strain is the lack of natural breaks, with users spending many hours at their workstations without being permitted a coffee or tea break (unless the drinks are brought to their desks); this is often associated with high demands for keying output. Another example of poor organization of work is a workstation arrangement that allows the user to be affected by reflections and glare from lights and windows, and to be distracted by passers-by and those on social visits.

Personal factors

Often little or no attention is given to the personal requirements of individual users. We are all different physically and psychologically and affected differently by a whole host of factors, including medical problems. Eyes and eyesight vary and our reactions to environmental factors vary, too. Some examples of problems that occur in this respect are that:

- workstations have been designed or laid out without consideration for the individual users
- purchasing decisions have been made and equipment sited, to which the individual has had to adapt on the assumption that personal adaptation and practicality will be no problem
- new furniture has been purchased, including work chairs, without giving consideration to ergonomic factors
- poor eyesight, which existed before taking up VDU operations and has not been corrected by obtaining prescription glasses, is aggravated by working with the VDU screen
- other personal factors have been overlooked, such as the need for rest breaks, to have refreshments at individual times rather than set times for all, to have changes in activity and the need for personal social contact in the immediate working area.

Why be concerned?

A study that was sponsored by the HSE was undertaken by the Institute of Occupational Medicine in Edinburgh in 1989. Their report was called 'The Edinburgh Report'. The Institute investigated ULDs and RSI treated at three main orthopaedic clinics in the United Kingdom and established a clear correlation between keyboard operations and WRULDs. They found that all were caused by a combination of factors, including poor workstation and hardware design, lack of attention to lighting or the environment. There was also found to be inadequate information, training and instruction (or none given at all), bad working practices and poor organization of work.

The first HSE guidance on VDUs was published in 1983. Following the Edinburgh Report, they issued their Guidance Notes, *Work-Related Upper Limb Disorders: A guide to prevention*, in 1990, the same year in which the EC Directive was issued.

Thus, there are a number of reasons for being concerned to prevent the causes of these ill-health effects. They are:

- legal
- legal-financial
- medical
- costs
- moral and ethical.

Legal First, general and specific legal and moral obligations have been placed on employers by virtue of sections 2(1) and 2(2) of the HASWA. Section 2(1) provides a general catch-all duty to safeguard, so far as is reasonably practicable, the health, safety and welfare of all employees while they are at work. The DSE Regulations lay down very strict minimum standards that were required for all workstations from 1 January 1993. It may appear that the legislation is all *new*, but, in fact, the duty to protect the health, safety and welfare of employees by providing safe systems of work, good working practices and information, training and instruction have been with us for some time by virtue of sections 2(2)(a) and 2(2)(c) of the HASWA. It is only in recent years that, with the proliferation of VDUs and other high-technology operations that clearly laid down standards for VDUs became necessary as a result of the many reports of ill-health effects. (The standards are covered later in this chapter.)

It is worth mentioning some cases from case law on this subject.

In two cases in July 1991 (His Honour Judge Griffiths) and December 1991 (His Honour Judge Byrt), judgments were given that the employers concerned had failed in their duty to inform their users of the risks of RSI and ULD and to minimize those risks. They also failed to warn their employees of the necessity to report any pain in the wrist or arm at once and to seek medical advice. One case involved benchwork in a printing company; the other concerned high-performance keyboard work.

Legal-financial Until recently, there were few successful claims against employers for WRULD as, under common law, claimants had to prove that their condition was work-related, but steadily more and more cases are becoming successful. In each of the above cases, compensation of between £6000 and £10 000 was awarded, plus costs. However, in April 1992, a female machine operator in the motor industry won damages of £59 617, while in January 1994, a typist working for the Inland Revenue was awarded a record £79 000; both awards were for RSI injuries. There have also been a number of out-of-court settlements in the region of £55 000.

This said, it is much more important to get things right *now* to save much time and expense, of all kinds, later.

Medical The problem with the effects of working with VDUs and repetitive movement operations is that they are not visibly apparent to a third-party observer and may even be unnoticed by the sufferer until the condition is well advanced. The effects are cumulative over time until there is a rapid manifestation as RSI, ULD or WRULD, eye defects or eyesight problems. Maintaining a static position and/or carrying out repetitive, rapid, awkward operations for long periods can lead to pain or discomfort. These movements may involve the head, shoulder-blades, shoulders, arms, wrists, hands or fingers. These movements are typical of all keyboard functions and other repetitive work such as machine operating, packaging and assembly operations. Ill-health problems of different kinds can also arise out of the nature of the electronic apparatus in use, as it is a source of EMR, and the problems of glare and poor atmosphere. Some of these ill-health effects are as follows.

- *Pain and discomfort* In the early stages, the pain and discomfort of RSI or WRULD may disappear when the user ceases operations. However, as they continue to work in unsatisfactory conditions and with poor posture, the condition worsens and the pain increases and remains for longer periods, leading to chronic disorders. In addition to pain, there may be swelling of the joints — especially the fingers — restricted movement of the limbs and an inability to function. In most cases, the patient recovers with rest and medical treatment, but there have been cases of permanent disability, leading to large compensation claims. In the USA, it is estimated that RSI and WRULD are among the main causes of lost working days. In the UK, it has been stated that one third of journalists have suffered from RSI symptoms, with many being served notices of dismissal because they were unable to carry out their jobs.

- *Eye and eyesight defects* While there is no conclusive evidence that working with VDUs causes damage to or deterioration of the eyes or eyesight, there is some agreement that such is the case, with many users complaining of visual fatigue, blurred vision, headaches and sore, red eyes — sometimes necessitating stronger prescription glasses. Every person's eyes and eyesight are different; what may be satisfactory for one may not be so for another. The most common features of VDU work and workstations that do cause these problems are:
  —extended periods of concentration on a task from one position
  —poor design and ergonomic position of VDU equipment
  —poor lighting, often with glare from fluorescent tubes and reflections on to screens
  —poor legibility of VDU screen and documents
  —poor character images with flickering, drifting and jittering
  —lack of facilities to adjust the brightness and contrast of VDU screens or of lighting around the workstation.
  Note that eyesight is a matter of health and the provision of health protection is seen as a duty under sections 2(1) and 2(2)(a) of the HASWA as well as the new DSE Regulations.

- *Stress* Many users interviewed in surveys have complained of experiencing stress, including irritability, particularly when spending extended periods of time working with VDUs accompanied by the following conditions:
  —excessive expectations of speed and quality
  —underutilized skills, being confined to single occupations
  —lack of attention to good organization of work
  —social deprivation, working either in isolation or on tasks that demand exclusive attention, precluding social contact
  —lack of control over one's own work
  —poor design of the workstation and surrounds

—fatigue, resulting from extended periods in repetitive-movement operations and/or poor working environments or with poorly designed VDU workstations.

- *Skin problems* Perhaps a corollary with stress, there have been reports of dermatitis, with reddening and itching of the skin of face and/or neck. A further suggested cause is poor atmosphere with static electricity and lack of humidity.
- *Photosensitive epilepsy* It must first be stated that, so far as is known, work on VDUs cannot *cause* epilepsy. However, if a person working on a VDU workstation *already* suffers from epilepsy, it is possible that they could be prone to photosensitive epilepsy. This condition occurs where an epilepsy sufferer is adversely affected by striped patterns or flickering lights — both side-effects of fluorescent lights and poorly designed VDU workstations.
- *Reproductive risks* There is no conclusive evidence at present that working with VDUs causes problems of premature births, miscarriages or foetal abnormalities; there are as many research papers that conclude that there are *no* adverse effects as those that say that there *are*. The National Radiological Protection Board does not consider that radiation from VDU screens puts unborn children at risk. However, there have been reports that abnormal pregnancies may have links with working with VDU workstations. The HSE's advice is that pregnant women should seek professional medical advice if they have any concerns in this regard, particularly in view of the unnecessary stress that such concerns may cause. Such workers should observe all the guidelines of the VDE Regulations.

Moral and ethical Even where there is no statutory responsibility to prevent certain conditions or social consequences, there are clear moral and ethical reasons why employers should take care of the well-being of their employees who work at VDU workstations. Workplaces that have a reputation for causing sicknesses of varying kinds will encourage low morale and motivation and may result in adverse social conditions for users, not to mention the poor reputation that the employer will gain. Examples of these conditions are:

- loss of income due to absence from work
- lost confidence
- ill-feeling towards employers
- unhappiness with the workplace and so on.

Taking care of moral and ethical values can enhance morale, motivation and working relationships; it may also raise the esteem in which an employer is held by its employees and the perception outside the company that it is caring.

Costs There are numerous hidden costs in *not* having the right kinds of conditions in which users can work, arising out of a number of side-effects. Some of these costs result from:

- low or reduced productivity
- increased error rates and correction time
- increased absences due to sickness
- increased labour turnover and recruitment and selection costs
- additional costs of training and retraining
- increased time away from the workstation
- lateness and absenteeism problems
- time spent in apparent 'disciplinary' problems

- time spent investigating ill-health and other effects of VDUs
- legal costs of defending claims for compensation
- increased insurance premiums following payments of compensation.

Being 'hidden', such costs are often difficult to quantify exactly. However, if you have a number of these cost problems in areas where VDUs are widely used, a look at the differences in the balance sheet, profit and loss statements or cost analyses for these departments before taking remedial action and, say, one year afterwards will demonstrate the point quite well.

What are the solutions?

All things are possible, but not all things may be immediately practicable. In this section you will find information about what the law says you *must* do and suggestions for ways in which you can comply with it easily by implementing some beneficial remedies and precautions. If you follow the statutory rules and advice given in this chapter, you will be both complying with the law and, more important, caring for the health and welfare of your users and operators. Remember, too, that these Regulations apply equally to self-employed people and employees who are users of VDUs.

The EC Directive recognizes that to make sweeping changes in all VDU workstations would be an enormously expensive exercise for many organizations and so has given a period of grace for the complete implementation of the following statutory requirements.

- *New installations* All new installations put into operation on or after 1 January 1993 *must* comply fully with all the requirements from the outset. Be warned, if you move an existing workstation from one place to another, you are effectively setting up a 'new' situation and it must comply from the moment it is set up in the new location. Also, if you purchase second-hand equipment and furniture, that creates a new situation and must also comply fully with the Regulations.
- *Existing installations* If an installation existed on or before 31 December 1992, you have until 31 December 1996 to bring it up to standard (except when you relocate or modify it — see above). If you have a large number of existing VDU workstations, it will be more practicable to plan and phase-in each section over a period of affordable time. Begin with the most critical first, e.g. the one on which the largest number of users spend most of their time. (See also Risk assessments, below.)

The message is: don't wait until December 1996 before taking action to update your workstations, start implementing an action plan *now*.

Risk assessments

A regular feature of past UK Regulations has been the requirement to carry out assessments of risks to workplace health and safety. These new Regulations, effective from 1 January 1993, require employers to carry out more detailed and far-reaching assessments into the total health and safety situation, such as under the MHSW Regulations (see Chapter 18). This general requirement is extended in specific terms under the DSE Regulations and includes workstations. Note that paragraph (3) of DSE Regulation 2 equates the term 'analysis' in the DSE Regulations with 'assessment' in other Regulations and states that, by carrying out analyses of VDU workstations, you will satisfy the requirement for assessments in the MHSW Regulations.

Existing equipment You should note that, where your risk assessments identify risks to your users, you must take *immediate* steps to eliminate or minimize those risks.

The purpose of risk assessments The purpose of assessments (or analyses) is to determine:

- who are the 'users' (employees) and 'operators' (self-employed on your premises)
- what VDU equipment and workstations are in use
- what possible hazards those workstations may pose to users (including outworkers) and operators working on them (whether actually exposed to them or not)
- what levels of risk those users (including outworkers) and operators could be exposed to
- what is the extent of those risks to which they may be exposed
- what action is necessary to eliminate or reduce those risks or the exposure of users and operators to those risks
- what organizational aspects could cause problems to users
- what aspects of the workplace (into which the workstation is incorporated) could cause problems to users
- what possible problems are in the interface between user and VDU work-station.

What form should the assessment take? There is no stipulated method for carrying out VDU workstation assessments, but, whatever way you decide to conduct them, they should be systematic and appropriate to your particular situation. In very simple operations, a simple inspection may suffice, but where there are complicated or multiple workstations, you may need a check-list to help you carry out your assessments. We would suggest that if you:

- check whether or not any of those adverse conditions outlined under The nature of the problem, above, exist and
- check that those correct or ideal conditions outlined under The solutions to problems identified in risk assessments, below, exist,

you will adequately satisfy the requirements.

Who qualifies as a user or operator? The guidelines in the VDU ACOP are a little vague on this so it is up to you to determine in your assessments whether a person is a user or operator or is not covered. There is a strong suggestion in the ACOP that a user or operator is someone who works at a screen continuously for one hour or more per day, but the HSE also states that this period could be an aggregate of, say, six ten-minute periods of concentrated focus on the screen. It is an equation of usage plus a complex assessment of the risks and hazards associated with the workstation over varying periods of time. The complexity of the operation and the nature of the workstation will be important factors in your risk assessments. Examples of those who *are* users or operators are:

- word processing pool worker
- secretary or typist
- data-input operator
- news sub-editor or journalist
- sales or customer relations operator.

What records should you keep? Again, there are no rigid rules. If your situation is a simple one, then perhaps no records are needed. However, if you have many, complex situations, then you will need to keep detailed records. An easy method is to compile a check-list, as advised under The purpose of risk assessments, above, and, beside each point, write the date each time an assessment is done, and duplicate sufficient copies for repeated use.

The solutions to problems identified in risk assessments

There are certain *legal requirements* for minimum standards, which you must attain within the *time constraints* outlined above. If you follow the *statutory rules* and the advice in this chapter, you will go a long way to both complying with the law and, more important, caring for the health and welfare of your users or operators. Remember that these Regulations apply equally to self-employed persons as they do to employees as 'users'.

Let us look at each of the problem areas likely to arise that were identified under The nature of the problem earlier in this chapter and what should be done to eliminate or significantly reduce the risk of ill-health resulting from them.

The VDU screen The screen used must conform to the following minimum standards:

- it must be large enough and the characters displayed on it must be clearly formed, well-defined and of adequate size, with adequate spacing between characters and lines — this applies especially to smaller characters
- letters and numbers should be clearly identifiable, so that S and 5, 1 and I, A and H and so on are clearly distinguishable one from the other
- the images must be stable with no flicker, drift, swim, jitter or other fluctuations
- there must be the facility to adjust both the brightness of the characters and the contrast between them to suit both the personal requirements of the user and environmental conditions around the workstation (contrast ratios of 4:1 to 15:1 between the screen background and character brightness are generally quoted as being acceptable)
- there must be a swivel-and-tilt facility on which the VDU sits so that the operator can adjust the screen position to suit their personal requirements
- there should be either a separate base for the screen *or* an adjustable table or ledge so that the height of the screen can be adjusted in relation to the user by raising or lowering it
- there must be *no* reflective glare or reflections on the screen, which can cause discomfort to the user (see also The working environment later in this chapter)
- you should ensure that the VDU is fitted (as a design feature) with a filter screen, but, if not, that a filter screen can be fixed on to it (this should not be confused with brightness and contrast adjustment controls).

A screen filter will significantly reduce the problems of glare, which makes it difficult to focus on the text on the screen and causes eye strain. They are cheap in relation to the costs of absence, lost time due to fatigue and the possibility of having to provide eye care and so are a worthwhile investment.

Prices vary, and the price tag does not always indicate quality — so shop around.

No clear preferences exist for negative over positive polarity of characters or the other way round — negative polarity being light characters on a dark background and positive polarity being dark characters on a light background. Some users may prefer negative polarity, saying that the characters are more legible and that there is less flicker, but positive polarity may be preferred where the lighting levels are required to be above 300 lux.

The keyboard Some older computers and word processors still in use have the keyboard moulded as an integral part of the VDU. These need to be replaced *as soon as possible* as they are very restrictive and likely to cause WRULDs.

The standards to which your keyboards should comply are as follows:

- the keyboard must be separate from the VDU screen, to allow users to adopt a comfortable position and so avoid fatigue of the arms, wrists or hands
- it should be adjustable, tilting up or down
- the keys and casing of the keyboard must be in a matt finish and non-reflective, with clearly distinguished letters (watch for wear as, with long and frequent use, surfaces will become shiny and reflect light, which can cause discomfort to the eyes).

The design of the workstation and ergonomics There is more to VDUs than just the monitor and keyboard. Consideration of the immediate vicinity, including the desk, work chair, equipment and access to it, are most important if fatigue, RSI and WRULD are to be avoided. You must ensure that the following standards are attained:

- the desk or table on to which the VDU screen and associated apparatus are placed must be:
  —of a matt finish, so that there are no reflections of glare and light, either to the users' eyes or on the VDU screen itself (this is especially important where fluorescent tube lighting is used)
  —sufficiently large so that the user can have ample space to both work in and adjust the position of the screen and other apparatus to personal requirements (though, while some movement is desirable, repeated stretching movements are not)
- the desk size should take into consideration such things as positioning the telephone and supplying headsets to avoid the user wedging the hand-set between their ear and shoulder while working on the VDU screen (say, in the case of telesales work); you should also make adequate allowance for the storage of materials
- the VDU screen should be a sufficient distance from the user, that is, a minimum of 50 centimetres, or just over an arm's length, which will both facilitate the proper organization of work and protect the user from emissions (see Radiation under The working environment, later in this chapter)
- the space in front of the keyboard must afford adequate support for the hands and arms of the user
- it is suggested that, where hands and wrists could touch the surface of the desk or table, the front edges of the keyboard should be rounded to avoid possible pressure on blood vessels and joints
- the provision of a document holder is recommended, one that is separate from the VDU and positioned in such a manner as to facilitate:
  —easy reading of documents
  —the avoidance of the need to constantly refocus on document and screen

—prevention of fatigue due to repeated head movements between screen and document — ideally, it should be positioned at the same level and distance as the screen (assessments may determine that this is essential)

- you should permit each user to experiment with the workstation so that they can organize it to suit their individual dispositions (rigid uniformity is undesirable as people's needs vary)
- the VDU screen should be positioned so that it faces away from windows, or at least at 45 degrees to them, so that reflections of direct light on screens is avoided.

The workstation and the user A further consideration regarding the workstation is the nature of the interaction between it and the user. The Regulations require that:

- the software must be suitable for the work undertaken, so the selection of VDUs and equipment are important
- the software must be easy to use and suited to the level of knowledge and experience of the users
- there must be adequate vertical and horizontal space to allow for postural changes, with sufficient clearance for the thighs, knees, lower legs and feet
- no monitoring facility, quantitative or qualitative, may be used without the knowledge of the users
- systems must provide feedback to users on the performance of those systems
- the information displayed on the screen must be in a format and at a pace that is suited to the users
- the design of VDUs and workstation equipment must incorporate principles of ergonomics, so that they are compatible with the users and with human data processing (as opposed to electronic data processing).

The Regulations do not require you to comply with the standards of ergonomic design and use of VDUs as contained in BS 7179. However, the Regulations do *commend* these standards and suggest that, if you comply with them, you would meet, and in most cases go beyond, the minimum requirements of the Schedule to the Regulations. The European Standards Organisation (CEN) is preparing an international multipart standard (EN 29241) that will eventually incorporate and supersede BS 7179. This CEN standard will, in turn, be based on the International Standards Organisation (ISO) Standard ISO 9241, covering ergonomic design and the use of VDU workstations, including screens, keyboards, peripheral and environmental requirements. Thus, complying with the standards of BS 7179 *now* will stand you in very good stead for the future. Another set of standards that is commended and which, in similar fashion, will become statutory through CEN, is BS 3044 for office furniture.

The user's work chair The type of work chair employed and the way in which it is used is crucial to the avoidance of RSI and WRULD. The work chair must:

- be stable (not rock backwards, forwards or sideways); to ensure this, a 'five-star' wheel support is legally required
- permit the user freedom of movement, that is, to be on wheels and turn on a spiral stem
- enable the user to adopt a comfortable position
- have a seat that is adjustable in height
- have an adjustable back that:
  —provides adequate lumbar support

—tilts forwards or backwards, according to need

—is adjustable in height

• have a footrest available for any user who wishes to use it (it is suggested that the chair have an integral footrest, but the Schedule to the Regulations does not specify such and, thus, a separate footrest is acceptable).

It can be very tiring, and restrict the blood circulation, for the backs of the thighs to be constantly pressing down on the edge of the chair seat. A footrest will ease this problem.

Advice on work chairs can be found in the HSE's booklet HS(C)57 *Seating at Work.*

The working environment Closely associated with the 'sick office syndrome', the working environment can have positive or negative effects on the comfort and health of users. The requirement to provide a working environment that is safe and without risks to health is already encapsulated in section 2(2)(e) of the HASWA, but the following will help you comply with both the HASWA and the DSE Regulations.

• *Lighting* The lighting should be adequate, of high frequency (to eliminate flicker), but not so bright that it produces glare on the VDU screen or eye strain. Many users prefer working with filament bulbs to fluorescent lights as these do not produce glare or flicker and, providing there are enough of them and they are of sufficient (but not too high) brightness, there should be no problem.

• *Fluorescent lights* should be:

—capable of being switched on and off by individual controls, so that users can control their individual light levels, not with one 'all or nothing' switch

—fitted with diffusers (covers over the tubes themselves) so that glare is sufficiently reduced and diffused (many new buildings have fluorescent lighting inset into ceilings with diffuser panels, which help to greatly reduce this problem)

—regularly maintained so that buzzing and flicker from the tubes are avoided, as these problems can cause visual fatigue, headaches or eye strain.

• *Floor-up lighting* An excellent alternative to ceiling fluorescent lighting is the installation of floor-up lighting, that is, where the lights are installed on the floor against the walls, projecting light upwards. This has the benefit of providing good levels of light without causing glare and reflection on screens (note that ceilings should then be decorated with pastel shades to avoid the light being reflected back down, causing glare). A suitable alternative is *wall*-up lighting, where the lights are fitted to the walls and directed upwards instead of downwards. If floor- or wall-up lighting are used, care must be taken to ensure a sufficient level of light as semi-darkness can be just as injurious to the eyes as glare.

• *Noise* Background noise, such as that from printers, photocopiers, telephone switchgear, facsimile machines or shredders, can cause mental fatigue, stress or headaches and can impair concentration. All peripheral equipment should be checked for noise and either serviced, soundproofed (say, by means of a screen) or relocated.

• *Humidity* VDUs produce heat and static, which attracts dust, and having large numbers of VDUs can affect the level of humidity in the surrounding atmosphere. This will be made worse where there is no direct means of ventilation to external air or where static electricity is also produced by nylon pile carpets and so on. Dry atmospheres can cause visual fatigue and dry out mucous membranes (causing headaches or migraine attacks) and thus provision of sufficient humidity is important. Relative humidity should be at about 40 per cent. This can be accomplished quite simply by supplying suitable vessels of water to place near or on radiators, (but not electrical ones), or humidifiers or water fountains and providing means of ventilation. Most air-conditioning systems afford good humidity, but should be adjusted upwards to provide increased humidity where large numbers of VDUs are in use.

- *Temperature* Under section 3 of the Factories Act 1961 and section 6 of the Offices, Shops and Railway Premises Act 1963, a minimum temperature of 16°C (60.8°F) must be provided within one hour of commencing work. However, this may be a little low for sedentary VDU users and, thus, a comfortable temperature of, say, 17 or 18°C (62.6 or 64°F) would be preferable.

  However, beware temperatures that are too high, which further reduces humidity and increases discomfort. Additionally, the Regulations require that the heat emitted by VDUs be controlled. Thus, adequate ventilation is important.

  Also, it is not always remembered that, under the Fuel and Electricity (Heating) (Control) (Amendment) Order 1980, it is an offence to use *energy* to generate a temperature above 19°C (66.2°F).

- *Decor* The way in which the workplace is decorated can have a therapeutic or adverse effect on VDU users, depending on its nature. Brilliant white, whether gloss or matt finish paint or wallpaper, reflects light and glare on to VDU screens, causing problems, so avoid this colour. It is suggested that pastel shades of grey, blue, green or pink in matt finish are excellent colours because they create a pleasing atmosphere to work in and are non-reflective. Alternatives are wall-papers or wallboards in non-white colours or wood-effect finishes (but, again, ones that have non-reflective surfaces).

- *Windows* A frequent source of problems for VDU users is light and glare from windows. You should fit either blinds (of any suitable type), curtains or filter film to screen out the sun's rays and protect workers from sun-generated heat in summer, and reduce downdraughts from single-glazed windows in winter. Venetian blinds and walk-through strips are not suitable for this purpose.

- *Radiation* All computers and word processors emit EMR to varying degrees. The Regulations require that these emissions from VDUs, 'with the exception of the visible part of the electromagnetic spectrum', be reduced to negligible levels to protect users. This means that emissions from the sides and back are greater and must be adequately controlled. It is, thus, good practice to site VDU screens with their backs facing walls or at an angle to windows rather than other workers (backs should not be sited against windows as this may place users in direct sunlight). Users and others who may work in the immediate vicinity of the workstation should not be situated or spend prolonged periods of time close to the backs or sides of VDUs. (The level of emissions of EMR from the front of VDU screens is minimal.)

The way the work is organized It is most important that the work and working patterns are organized in such a manner as to preclude or relieve physical, mental and visual fatigue and monotony. Such arrangements include:

- providing a variety of different tasks to be done using VDUs
- affording physical breaks for users
- providing breaks by undertaking tasks of a different nature
- maintaining a balance between the need for social contact to relieve pressures and stress and the need for concentration with the avoidance of unnecessary distractions

- discussing with the user the job design and organization, the workstation, its apparatus and furniture.

Regular work patterns should be established that include regular rest breaks from the screen — you should not wait until the onset of fatigue and then allow breaks in order for users to recuperate. The timing and frequency of breaks is more important and of greater benefit than their length. Also, breaks should be incorporated into the working day and not be unpaid.

There are no rigid rules, but rest breaks should be for approximately five to ten minutes in every hour of working at the VDU screen and/or keyboard (not in periods during which *no* VDU or keyboard work is undertaken). Breaks can be 15 minutes in every 2 hours, but it is unlikely that this will be so beneficial. Frequent short breaks are more beneficial and enable greater productivity than infrequent longer breaks.

It is not essential that users actually take a physical break, that is, rest completely. Their break can take the form of work of a different nature, but it must be away from the screen. Indeed, research shows that a system of regular changes in task is more beneficial than frequent actual rest periods. This is where careful planning and organization is invaluable.

Personal factors There are a number of ways in which you can avoid some of the hazards associated with RSI, WRULD, eye and eyesight problems and other ill-health effects. You can do this by building personal and ergonomic factors into the workstation and the way work is organized. For example:

- allow your users some discretion in how they carry out their tasks, with individual control over the nature and pace of work, so that they can distribute their workload and effort to advantage over the working day
- allow some user discretion in when they take breaks and the frequency of liquid refreshments — remembering that every person has differing needs (this does not, of course, mean losing management control over rest periods)
- consider the user's views and needs when purchasing workstation furniture, especially the table and work chair (this is not about personal tastes, which will vary, so much as physical attributes because, for example, smaller or shorter users will adapt to workstation designs in a different way to larger or taller users)
- consider the medical factors that may affect your users, including eye conditions, eyesight and the individual dispositions of disabled users
- the provision of good training, information and instruction, advice on possible hazards associated with VDUs and how to avoid them.

Information, training and instruction
As with all health and safety matters, good information, training and instruction in VDU safety are central to both compliance with the law and avoidance of any possible adverse consequences. To further reinforce the duty laid down in section 2(2)(c) of the HASWA, Regulation 6 of the DSE Regulations lays down certain minimum requirements regarding this duty.

In a judgment given in July 1991, His Honour Judge Griffiths created case law in advance of these Regulations when he ruled that an employer should have issued proper warnings to employees concerning the risks of RSI- and WRULD-type injuries arising from repetitive-movement operations and that their failure in this regard was a breach of their statutory duty to employees. Compensation awards in the group of claims to which this judgment related totalled £100 000. Thus, EC and UK statutes and UK case law now place heavy responsibilities on employers both to train users in the correct and safe operation of VDU screens and to inform them of the risks of working on them.

So, what is information, training and instruction all about where VDUs are concerned? Sometimes there is confusion about these three terms and 'training' and 'instruction' are often used synonymously. In summary, 'information' means telling and/or giving written data about a subject, such as health and safety; 'training' is telling a person about and showing them a subject or skill, such as how a whole workstation is constructed; 'instruction' is imparting specific, practical proficiency skills by telling, showing and demonstrating, such as keyboard skills. To relate these to the subject of this chapter, you need to do the following for *each* of these terms:

- *information* Tell employees and issue written information about the nature and functions of the workstation and its apparatus; tell them about the possible hazards associated with work on VDUs, including suitable warnings about the risks of being exposed to those hazards
- *training* Tell them about the correct and safe use of the workstation, keyboard and VDU
- *instruction* Give them practical hands-on instruction in the physical operation of the workstation, including keyboard techniques and VDU operation, and the best techniques of operation to use to avoid causing ill-health effects.

To whom should you provide information and on what? With so many people employed as users working on their own company's premises, outworker users who work in their homes, other employers' users who work on your premises and self-employed persons who work on your premises, the dilemma facing you may be 'who am I required to give information to and what information should I give?' Table 19.1 may help (see also Regulation 7).

Training objectives The training given to users should have stated objectives, that is, reducing, minimizing or eliminating the three main risk areas associated with VDUs:

Table 19.1   How to comply with the requirement to provide information on VDU safety

			Information required on:			
type of employee	risks from VDUs and workstations	risk assessments	breaks and acitivity changes	eye and sight tests	initial training	training on modified equipment
Your own users	Yes	Yes	Yes	Yes	Yes	Yes
Other employers' users	Yes	Yes	Yes	No	Yes	Yes
Self-employed (operators) on your premises	Yes	Yes	No*	No*	No	No

*This is because the law requires and permits self-employed persons to determine their own arrangement of working hours and work patterns and because they are responsible for their own costs (though the employer to whom they are contracted may stipulate the number of hours worked).

1. musculoskeletal problems, such as upper limb pains and discomforts like RSI and WRULD
2. visual fatigue, possibly leading to eye and eyesight problems
3. mental stress, including fatigue.

Keyboard technique Many employees are becoming users without the benefit of previous training in keyboard operation — in other words, knowing how to type reasonably fast and accurately. Trained typists and secretaries have no problem in adapting to word processors and computers, but for others the lack of familiarity with keyboards and the consequent two-finger struggle to find letters is not only slow and unproductive, but adds to the strain of trying to work with speed and accuracy. It is suggested, therefore, that training in basic keyboard skills for those with no experience of typing would prove to be most beneficial. This is not something that software suppliers can undertake for you, as training in keyboard skills takes quite a long time, but your local college or training organization will be able to help.

VDU workstation training Initial training will, of course, concern the keyboard and peripheral function keys, their layout and operation and the relationship with other apparatus (such as linking a terminal with the mainframe computer). This training is normally included in the initial package by your software suppliers. You must also provide suitable training where a workstation and its associated apparatus have been significantly modified. Once these have been covered, you will need to compile a training programme that will familiarize users with the workstation and the health and safety aspects of working with VDUs. This must include:

- adapting users' skills to particular hardware, software, workstations, work environments and the requirements of the job
- retraining users after long periods of absence, such as after maternity leave or long-term sickness, or when women return to work after bringing up children. This will be particularly important where sickness absence has been due to RSI or WRULD
- the user's role in recognizing hazards associated with VDUs and workstations, including:
  —the necessity for *desirable* features, such as correct and comfortable desk and work chair, correct lighting and its adjustment
  —the necessity for the absence of *undesirable* features, such as glare and reflection on screens
- the particular risks involved with being exposed to those hazards arising from work using workstations and how to avoid them (RSI and WRULD, for example)
- the risks associated with prolonged use of VDUs without breaks
- simple explanations of the physical causes of RSI, WRULD, visual, physical and mental fatigue, and eye and eyesight defects over which the user may have personal control
- how the user can avoid those ill-health effects, by correct ergonomic arrangement of their workstation and maintaining a comfortable position in relation to the apparatus, to suit personal requirements (see Figure 19.1):
  —by maintaining a comfortable posture and making regular postural changes
  —holding the head in a balanced position with the chin up, with the eyes looking downwards at an angle of up to 15°
  —relaxing the shoulders
  —maintaining the upper arms in a vertical position while the forearms are held in an approximately horizontal position

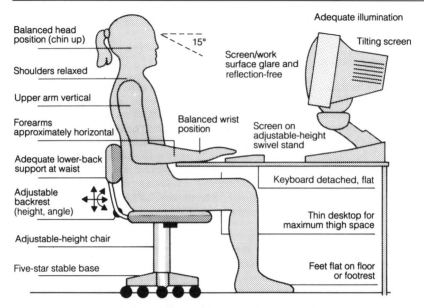

Fig. 19.1 The ideal ergonomic arrangement for personal comfort at a workstation (following these guidelines will considerably reduce back and neck strain, minimize the risks of RSI and WRULD and eliminate or minimize the risks of eye and eyesight problems)

> —ensuring adequate lower-back support by adjusting their work chair at waist level and adjusting the height and angle of the back rest
> —checking that the work chair has a five-star wheel base
> —keeping feet either flat on the floor with one foot behind the other or on a footrest, which may be an integral part of the work chair or separate, as convenient

- maintaining the VDU screen and document holder at eye level, so that the neck and shoulders are straight (this is accomplished by adjusting the VDU table height and lever arm of the document holder)
- by correctly and regularly adjusting VDU screens (by means of the swivel-and-tilt mechanism) and furniture in keeping with task and environmental changes, such as for different document types and variations in natural and artificial light
- the correct and safe use and arrangement of workstation furniture and components, including keyboard, document holder and VDU screen, to facilitate good posture, prevent visual strain, prevent overreaching and avoid glare and reflections on VDU screens
- controlling their own work environment, by, say, making adjustments to lighting, ventilation, humidity (where possible), noise and social distractions
- regular cleaning (or arranging inspection) of screens and associated apparatus
- how to make use of adjustable window coverings (blinds, curtains and so on) to avoid glare, heat of the sun and so on
- taking regular breaks and/or changes in task away from their screen and workstation (and others' workstations), which, as we have seen, need not always mean physical rest breaks but can be brief periods on work of a different nature, as convenient or desired

- the measures that you have taken to comply with the Regulations
- the arrangements you have made for users to report to their manager:
  —any symptoms or problems that they may experience in the course of their work
  —any defects in the VDU screen and associated equipment, the workstation or surrounding work environment (users must be actively encouraged to bring any problems to the attention of management and not to delay doing so until problems become too serious to be quickly and easily remedied)
- their rights to eye and eyesight tests at the employer's expense and arrangements you have made for them to be carried out
- the assessments you have carried out, the reassessments that will be carried out and the user's role in these
- the arrangements you have made for users to take rest breaks from the VDU screen.

Figure 19.1 shows the ideal layout for a VDU workstation. Following these guidelines will considerably reduce back and neck strain, minimize the risk of RSI and WRULD and eliminate or minimize the risks of eye and eyesight problems.

Reviews of training One-off training or information sessions are never adequate. There will need to be regular reviews of the workstation, its equipment and environment, new or modified equipment and further training that will be required. Refresher training should also be a regular feature of your education programme.

Some particular points to consider

Eyes and eyesight
The duty to protect the health of employees has been established by virtue of sections 2(1) and 2(2) of the HASWA since 1974. However, it has not been appreciated by many employers that eyesight and the state of one's eyes are matters of health just as are other more obvious health problems. One may recover from an industrial disease and from RSI or WRULD, but most eye defects are permanent with long-lasting consequences for sufferers, so the need to protect the eyes is as important as anything else. The Guidance Notes on the Regulations (reference L26) state that 'there is no "reliable" (scientific) evidence that work with DSE causes any permanent damage to eyes or eyesight'. However, there is much anecdotal evidence that it does. For this reason, the duty to protect employees' eyes and eyesight is now made specific by the EC Directive and Regulation 5 of the DSE Regulations.

There are a number of important points to consider with regard to protecting your users' eyes and eyesight. Regulation 5 does not specifically address the question of precautionary measures with new or prospective employees and it is suggested that there are important considerations to be taken into account here, if only to protect the interests of you, the employer. To this end the following three actions are strongly advised.

1. Include in the application form of any candidate for a position that includes working with VDUs a question that will satisfy you as to the health of their eyes, for example, 'Do you have any known eye or eyesight defects?' or 'Do you wear prescription appliances?'
   Additionally, you may also consider asking prospective employees 'Do you suffer from epilepsy?' and 'Do you currently suffer from or are you susceptible to eye diseases such as glaucoma, stigmatism, eye-muscle strain, eye-strain headaches

and so on?' There is no evidence that working with VDUs causes epilepsy, but a person *already* suffering from the condition may, in rare instances, find that their photosensitivity can trigger an epileptic attack.

These types of questions would both highlight any existing eye problems that the new employee may be unaware of which are relevant to the job and protect you in the case of any claim for compensation which you cannot be held responsible for (eye problems that existed pre-employment with you).

2. Offer (or reserve the right to ask for) ophthalmic eye tests for all selected new employees before they take up work with VDUs. The report from the ophthalmic optician (not a dispensing optician) would inform you of any problems so you can then act accordingly. If, for example, the prospective or new employee does not wear spectacles but the report says they should, you can then take the appropriate measures not only to protect yourself, but to safeguard the employee's eyes and show that you are a caring and conscientious employer. Similarly, for new and existing employees, you should do the following.

3. Consider the effects of any new or existing workstation, its apparatus, including the VDU, and the work environment on the eyes and eyesight of users (not forgetting also the effects on other physical health matters, such as RSI and WRULD).

Eye and eyesight tests Regulation 5 of the DSE Regulations places specific requirements on employers with important innovations in respect of eye and eyesight tests. Where an employee:

- *is* an existing, habitual user, as at 1 January 1993
- is *not* a habitual user, but is to *become* a user in the undertaking in which they are already employed

you *must* provide, at your expense, an eye and eyesight test by a 'competent person' at the request of that user and as soon as possible after that request is made.

Ophthalmic tests A 'competent person' for eye and eyesight tests in terms of Regulation 5 is either an ophthalmic optician (optometrist) or a registered medical practitioner (doctor) with suitable qualifications (see also Vision screening, below).

The requirement for the employer to bear the costs of eye and eyesight tests is a similar concept to that in section 9 of the HASWA, that employers provide all protective equipment and wear free of charge to employees.

In the case of non-habitual users who are to become users, the Regulation requires that the test be carried out *before* the employee takes on those new VDU duties. While, as stated above, the Regulation does not apply to *prospective* employees, once they *become* employees then the rules do apply to them, although there is no requirement to preclude new employees from actually working with VDUs *until* they have undergone suitable tests.

Additionally, you *must*, at your expense:

- provide further eye and eyesight tests to users on request, at regular intervals after the initial test, also carried out by a competent person as defined above
- provide an additional eye and eyesight test to any user who experiences visual difficulties that may reasonably be considered to be caused by work on VDUs
- ensure that the user is provided with corrective appliances which are suitable for the work being undertaken (these may be spectacles specially dedicated to VDU work, but see also point 2, below).

Five important points should be noted.

1. No user can be compelled to undergo eye and eyesight tests
2. Your liability is only to pay for corrective appliances that are 'appropriate for the work being done by the user', so you pay only for *basic* appliances for VDU work and, should the employee wish for anything beyond that (such as tinting, safety glass, contact lenses, expensive frames or whatever), then they must pay the excess that is over and above your liability
3. If the ophthalmic optician's report suggests that a user is suffering from an eye injury or disease, they may refer that user to a doctor for further examination, which is free of charge under the National Health Service
4. These rules apply to your employees who may actually work on another employer's premises and/or workstations. You are still responsible for them
5. Regulation 5 does not apply to self-employed persons (operators).

Vision screening Though not a legal requirement, larger employers are strongly recommended to consider vision screening as a precursor to eye and eyesight tests, to determine who will and will not need tests. Vision screening will identify those who have existing or potential eye and eyesight problems and eliminate those who do not require any attention (for sources of provision for in-company vision screening, see Sources of help at the end of this chapter).

You may decide to acquire vision-screening equipment and undertake your own visual testing in-house. The DSE Regulations permit vision screening to be undertaken by any 'competent person' who has basic knowledge of the eye and, of course, is familiar with the workings of the vision-screening equipment. In addition to a basic qualification, your competent person needs to be trained in this function and they will be assisted by the comprehensive instructions that accompany most screening equipment.

How many of those screened will need tests? There are varying estimates of how many of those VDU users whose vision is checked will require eye and eyesight tests, ranging from 22 to 40 per cent. Elaborating on the first of these figures, it is estimated that 78 per cent of those screened will *not* require eye and eyesight tests, while of the 22 per cent who do, only about a third (7 per cent of the total screened) will be prescribed glasses to wear for VDU work. Screening thus provides you with a cost-effective solution, avoiding the unnecessary costs of providing time off work for every VDU user to attend ophthalmic tests. A study of vision screening undertaken at Moorfields Eye Hospital by J. H. Silver and R. D. Daniel in conjunction with the Mitsubishi Corporation (UK) found that few people under the age of 50 years should require corrective appliances to enable them to view correctly from a distance of 50 to 90 centimetres the 'normal' intermediate distance) from the screen (*Occupational Medicine*, 1992).

Electromagnetic radiation and ill-health

Other VDU-related problems are said to be caused not by what is *seen* but what is *not* seen. We all know that the sun produces forms of EMR. Certain types of EMR can be seen (light, glare, reflection and images, for example) while others are invisible. We can see the light of the sun and the effects of excessive exposure to it, such as sunburn, melanomas (cancers of the skin), temporary blindness. Problems that can be seen in this way can be accepted and understood, but the unseen part of EMR also concerns some scientists.

A very diverse range of electrical and electronic apparatus, from electricity pylons to X-ray machines to computer and word processor VDUs and ordinary television sets, give off electromagnetic radiation. Many varying forms of EMR are emitted and are invisible; therein lies the potential problem. VDUs give off EMR, though more is emitted from the back and sides of the screen than is emitted from the screen itself, which is regarded by some researchers as negligible.

This radiation is emitted in frequencies or cycles per second, expressed as hertz. There are various frequencies: ultra high frequency (UHF), very high frequency (VHF), ultraviolet (UV), infra-red (IR), microwaves, radio frequency (RF), very low frequency (VLF) and extra-low frequency (ELF).

There are two forms of electricity: alternating current (AC) and direct current (DC), at whatever appropriate voltage and amperage. All computers, word processors, printers, electronic equipment and VDUs in industry (unless truly portable and battery-operated) use AC electricity. All AC power generation (not DC), as well as other sources of energy such as the sun, produce EMR. As the name suggests, EMR is a combination of electricity and magnetism. EMR is also emitted from all AC electric cabling, even when an appliance is switched off but still plugged in, because power is still present in the cable (unless completely disconnected), just as water remains in a water pipe after you have turned the tap off — hence the sound advice to unplug televisions before going to bed at night. But EMR emitted by VDUs is much stronger from the screen and back of VDUs than from the cable, and the concern of scientists is that it is EMR that may cause ill-health.

It has been suggested that EMR has properties that may cause serious ill-health effects if no protection is afforded, and much research has been conducted to find out if this is so, but it is by no means conclusive. Some scientists believe EMR to have adverse effects on human and animal cells as it emits positive ions, for example, *from* VDU screens, and attracts negative ions *to* the screen. This may create an imbalance in the positive and negative ions in the atmosphere, bombarding humans and animals with too many positive ions.

Some scientists suggest that this excess of positive ions to the body can ultimately cause bio-hazards by creating imbalances in the body's biological systems, for example, in blood cells which themselves have a fine balance of positive and negative charges. They tell us that, by upsetting the fine balance of positive and negative charges in body cells, such as in the bloodstream, this can result in ill-health effects. Studies into possible types of bio-hazards associated with frequent and extended use of VDUs continue, the following being examples of existing research (with many findings 'for' *and* 'against'):

- general ill-health (1981 to 1990):
  —for, 8 reports; against, 3 reports, including the HSE's
- carpal tunnel syndrome (1991):
  —for, 1 report
- depression and anxiety (1981 to 1990):
  —for, 5 reports
- RSI (1990), much proven and with court cases resulting in large settlements or awards:
  —for, 1 report
- spontaneous abortion (1983 to 1990):
  —for, 7 reports; against, 5 reports

- congenital birth defects (1984 to 1990):
  —for, 6 reports; against, 1 report
- blurred or impaired vision (1980 and 1991):
  —for, 6 reports
- short-term memory loss:
  —no data available
- chronic lower-back pain
  —no data available
- facial blemishes and rashes (1981 to 1990):
  —for, 4 reports
- lymphocytic leukemias (1991):
  —for, 1 report
- solid tumours (1988 and 1990):
  —for, 2 reports
- cardiovascular abnormalities (1984 and 1985):
  —for, 2 reports
- photosensitive epilepsy (aggravated epilepsy):
  —no data available
- chronic myalgic encephalomyelitis:
  —no data available.

I have summarized the findings analysed in *Desktopchernobyl?: An evaluation of bio-hazards for computer screens, et al.*, by Coghill Research Laboratories (1991).

Some opinion is that, although it would seem from this that there are more reports 'for' than 'against' ill-health effects, some of the 'fors' are unreliable. Either way, it is stressed that research into the ill-health effects of EMR is as yet inconclusive and not all scientists or health and safety authorities agree. While there may be no *conclusive* evidence that EMR from VDUs *is* harmful, there is, equally, no conclusive evidence that it is *not*. There would, however, appear to be sufficient evidence to suggest that taking a precautionary approach in your health and safety policy, though not with panic measures, would be wise. Thus, to be prudent, until positive, conclusive evidence is produced one way or the other, some measures to protect employees from the possible ill-health effects of VDUs have been suggested and are listed here. Some of these are established and accepted while others may be new to you.

- Fitting filters on to VDU screens (for eyesight care) will not eliminate EMR.
- It has been suggested by scientists that, although standard filters will reduce the 'electro-' part of EMR, they will not protect from the 'magnetism' in EMR. So, an additional filter may be needed, to protect parts of the body other than the eyes. A new filter is being developed, called a 'mu metal' filter. It consists of a triple layer of mu metal and is a very effective shield to the body to reduce the magnetism. Note that the HSE, in its Guidance Notes on the DSE Regulations, states that 'There is no need for users to be given protective devices such as anti-radiation screens'.
- Reduce the electric fields emitting EMR around VDUs to a maximum of 50 hertz for both electric and magnetic vertical fields (most modern VDU screens already comply with this and have '50 hertz', instead of the amperage, printed on the back). The maximum in Sweden (since January 1991) is 25 volts per metre at a distance of 50 cm from the screen for electricity, or 2.5 milli-Gows (2.5 mG) or 250 nano-Teslers (250 nT) for magnetism. An EC Directive implemented from 1 January 1993 is in line with this Swedish standard. Note that the maximum

recommended by the National Radiological Protection Board is currently 12 128 volts per metre for electricity and 1000 mG for magnetism.

- Seat users a minimum of 50 cm (or just over an arm's length) from the VDU screen.
- Reduce the actual exposure to VDU screens (including non-hands-on operating time), if possible, to 20 hours per week, which might be difficult. Also, as required by the EC Directive, provide breaks as advised earlier.
- Provide high-output ionizers near to VDUs, to emit negative ions into the work environment to counteract the positive ions emitted from the screens. Experience has shown that where used, problems of sinus headaches, other headaches and colds are reduced.

Sources of help

There are four areas where you may need help and advice when addressing your VDU safety requirements: on risk assessments and control measures, ergonomics, eye and eyesight tests and EMR. Various sources of help are available to you regarding these areas.

For risk assessments and control measures

Unless you have your own in-house services, you will need to call on specialist advisory services for practical help and advice in undertaking risk assessments and implementing control measures. They must be competent persons to carry out assessments on your behalf and able to produce detailed risk assessment reports for you (see Chapter 18). Among the specialist services available are the following.

- Abundance Management Services, Abundance House, 17 St Michael's Crescent, Oldbury, West Midlands B69 4RT (tel: 0121 552 2073).
- Your local environmental health officer — for offices, shops, catering and retail premises (their address and telephone number can be found in your local telephone and/or business directory).
- Your local HSE office's enforcement officer — for industrial establishments (their address and telephone number can be found in your local telephone and/or business directory).

For ergonomics

Ergonomics consultants can advise on the ergonomics of workstations and posture for VDU users and operators. For advice on reputable ergonomics consultants contact:

- The Association of Professional Ergonomics Consultancies (tel: 0171 636 5912).

For eye and eyesight tests and advice

Several organizations provide on-site specialist eye-care services, including ophthalmic tests to identify genuine potential eye and eyesight problems and prescribe VDU-dedicated spectacles. They also provide vision-screening equipment of basic design for use by your 'competent person'. These services will protect you and your employees in very cost-effective ways. They will not only reduce costs considerably, but also save you much lost time involved when off-site visits to opticians have to be made (though they may only be cost-effective for large numbers of relevant employees). The following addresses are for organizations offering on-site services.

- Bolle (UK) Limited, Brunel Close, Ebblake Industrial Estate, Verwood, Wimbourne, Dorset BH31 6BA (tel: 01202 824535/6). They are suppliers of vision-screening equipment and spectacles.

- Healthcall Corporate Optical Services, Healthcall Group PLC, Central Milton Keynes, Buckinghamshire MK9 2PH (tel: 01908 691919).

For electromagnetic radiation

The earlier comments on the possible ill-health effects of EMR are not intended as definitive statements or to create anxiety, but, rather, to draw attention to possible problems, summarize current scientific views and thinking on them, and to stimulate discussion on a subject that cannot be ignored. The controversy may yet continue for some time.

Employers and other interested people may obtain help and advice on EMR and lighting problems from the following.

- Your local HSE office (their address and telephone number can be found in your local telephone and/or business directory).
- Coghill Research Laboratories, Ker Menez, Lower Race, near Pontypool, Gwent NP4 5UF (tel: 01495 763389). For scientific research information and advice on electromagnetic radiation.
- Electric light manufacturing companies, such as Thorn-EMI, some of which have regional light engineering departments.
- The Lighting Industry Federation, Swan House, 207 Balham High Road, London SW17 7BQ (tel: 0181 675 5432). The Federation will provide you with a list of approved lighting experts.

Some useful reading

EC Directive (90/270/EEC) (DSE Directive) (available from HMSO).
The Health and Safety (Display Screen Equipment) Regulations 1992 (IBSN: 0-11-025919-X) (available from HMSO).
Guidance Notes on the 1992 DSE Regulations (available from HMSO).
Health and Safety (Croner Publications Limited, Croner House, London Road, Kingston-upon-Thames, Surrey KT2 6SR (tel: 0181 547 3333)) a subscription-only publication.
HSE leaflets, available free from your local HSE Information Centre:

- *Working with VDUs* (IND(G)36L)
- *Ergonomics at work* (IND(G)90L)
- the HSE also published supplementary practical advice during 1993.

Electropollution, Coghill, Roger (Coghill Research Laboratories) (Thorsons Collins, 1990).
The Dark Side of the Brain, Coghill, Roger, and Oldfield, (Element Books, 1990).
'A Practical Guide to Office Lighting and Healthy Use of VDUs', Bell, Bob, BSc, MCIBSE, MIES (*Safety and Health Practitioner,* April 1991).

20

Safety in the workplace

Because we are so familiar with the physical places where employees work (whether factory, workshop, office, shop or school/lecture room), and which visitors, customers and contractors come to, we often become unaware of health and safety problems that may arise in them.

We pay much attention to such things as plant and machinery, raw materials and hazardous substances, because they are *movable* items or have *moving* parts and are mostly governed by specific Acts of Parliament and their Regulations, but, somehow, floors, walls, ceilings, windows, doors and so on — all fixed items we pass by or through frequently in our daily routines — are often overlooked. Their condition can progressively deteriorate to the point where they present hazards with risks of injury to our workforce and damage to, or spoilage/contamination of, our product.

Many injuries have arisen from simple, unsatisfactory situations, such as people falling because floors are uneven or broken, surfaces are slippery, housekeeping is poor or access and egress are unsafe. Thus, the EC considered it necessary to take action to improve safety standards and reduce accidents.

The legislation

Physical workplaces have been governed by legislation for some time, including the Factories Act 1961, Offices, Shops and Railway Premises Act 1963, the Fire Precautions Act 1971, the Fire Precautions (Places of Work) Regulations 1995, section 2(2)(d) of the HASWA and their respective supporting Regulations, including the COSHH Regulations.

The European Community (EC) issued the Workplace Directive (89/654/EEC) on minimum workplace standards, which has been implemented by the Workplace (Health, Safety and Welfare) Regulations 1992 (known as the Workplace Regulations) that came into force on 1 January 1993. There are also correlations with the Environmental Protection Act 1990 and the Food Safety Act 1990.

The scope of the Workplace Regulations

The Workplace Regulations cover the following areas:

- all buildings used as workplaces, including means of access and egress
- the initial structure of those buildings (design features and so on)
- the building–worker interactions (such as temperature, ventilation, heating)

- the welfare provision for employees and others (such as sanitary conveniences, washing facilities and so on)
- traffic routes, both inside and outside buildings within employers' premises.

The Regulations apply to all factories, shops, offices, schools, hospitals, hotels and places of entertainment. Included also are common parts of shared buildings, such as private roads and paths on industrial estates, business parks and temporary work sites.

There are a few new ideas in the Regulations also, including protecting non-smokers from tobacco smoke and provision of rest facilities for workers who are pregnant and for nursing mothers.

Exemptions
Any of the home forces or visiting forces and their headquarters may be exempt from complying with these Regulations for reasons of national security, on issue of an exemption certificate by the Secretary of State (Regulation 26).

Exclusions
By definition, extractive industries (mines, quarries and mineral extraction), external transport work and other non-fixed workplaces are excluded from the Regulations. Ships, boats, hovercraft, aircraft, trains and road vehicles are also excluded, except that Regulation 13 does apply to any aircraft, train or road vehicle that is stationary in a workplace and being worked on by employees.

Construction: Construction sites are also excluded, being governed by separate Regulations. Similarly, if construction is underway inside an employer's premises (a workplace), then that part of the workplace under construction is excluded, *providing* it is fenced off, preventing access by non-construction employees.

Farming and forestry: Farming and forestry workplaces that are outdoors are also excluded, except for the provisions of Regulations 20–22.

Implementation of the Workplace Regulations

All *new* workplaces — those taken into use for the *first time* on or after 1 January 1993 — *must* comply with *all* aspects of the Workplace Regulations right from the start. All other *existing* workplaces — those that were in use on or before 31 December 1992 — have until 31 December 1996 to fully comply.

But, if any modification, extension or conversion of an existing workplace, commenced on or after 1 January 1993, that workplace must comply with the Regulations from its inception. If only a *part* of an employer's premises is modified, extended or converted, then only *that* part of the premises need comply immediately and the remainder comply by 31 December 1996. However, the message is, do not wait until the last month of this period of grace to take action, plan and cost out any necessary action now.

Summary of the requirements of the Workplace Regulations

Many of the requirements of the Workplace Regulations are already provided for under existing legislation and, thus, their role is to reinforce it. For example, the working environment is already governed by the Factories Act, the Offices, Shops and Railway Premises Act and section 2(2)(e) of the HASWA. There are, however, some new provisions not previously addressed, such as the safe cleaning of windows, protection of non-smokers from tobacco smoke in rest areas and rest facilities for pregnant or nursing mother workers.

There are also correlations with other Regulations, such as those regarding workstations in the DSE Regulations. Before commencing a brief analysis of the Workplace Regulations, it is helpful to have a list of the working parts of the Regulations. You can see that they are quite extensive, but, in view of the considerable overlap with other legislation, in this chapter the requirements are only summarized, and I expand only on those provisions that are new. The Regulations are:

5, maintenance
6, ventilation
7, temperature in indoor workplaces
8, lighting
9, cleanliness and waste disposal
10, room dimensions and space
11, workstations and seating
12, conditions of floors and internal traffic routes
13, falls and falling objects
14, windows, transparent or translucent doors, gates and walls
15, windows, skylights and ventilators
16, safe cleaning of windows
17, external traffic routes
18, doors and gates
19, escalators and moving walkways
20, WCs
21, washing facilities
22, wholesome drinking water
23, accommodation for clothing
24, changing facilities
25, facilities for rests and meals.

Maintenance

This is the subject of Regulation 5, which has correlations with the Factories Act, the Offices, Shops and Railway Premises Act and section 2(2)(a) of the HASWA.

There is a requirement to maintain the workplace, its equipment, devices and systems (Regulation 1). This includes equipment and mechanical ventilation systems that affect health, safety and welfare in the workplace itself, including the cleaning of the workplace. These items must be kept in an efficient state, in efficient working order and in good repair. Note that this does not include worker-operated equipment and machinery, which are covered by the Provision and Use of Work Equipment Regulations 1992.

Refer also to Chapter 18, concerning the requirement to appoint 'competent persons' in matters affecting health and safety and to report serious dangerous shortcomings in health and safety precautions.

Ventilation

This is the subject of Regulation 6, which has correlations with the Factories Act, the Offices, Shops and Railway Premises Act and section 2(2)(e) of the HASWA.

The requirement to provide adequate ventilation with sufficient quantities of fresh and purified air is reinforced in Regulation 6.

Any ventilation plant and equipment (installed to comply with the Acts) in a workplace must have audible warning devices incorporated to warn of malfunction where health or safety is affected.

Any enclosed workplaces already covered by existing legislation do not come under the remit of these requirements as they are already adequately covered. They are those matters dealt with by:

- section 30 of the Factories Act
- Regulations 49–52 of the Shipbuilding and Ship-repairing Regulations 1960
- Regulation 21 of the Construction (General Provisions) Regulations 1961
- Regulation 18 of the Docks Regulations 1988.

Temperature
This is the subject of Regulation 7, which has correlations with the Factories Act, the Offices, Shops and Railway Premises Act and section 2(2)(e) of the HASWA.

The requirements for ventilation (along with heating and lighting) are already laid down in existing legislation. The minimum temperature required in any workplace is 16°C (60.8°F), except where 'severe physical activity' takes place, in which case the minimum temperature is 13°C (55.4°F). Food manufacturing and processing premises, such as those where meat or dairy foods are produced, are exempt as, logically, high temperatures would be detrimental to the product. However, then, adequate protection against the effects of cold should be provided to workers.

Fumes No heating equipment should be used if it results in the emission of fumes, gases or vapours into the workplace (Regulation 7(2)) and a sufficient number of thermometers must be provided to enable workers to determine room temperatures (Regulation 7(3)).

High temperatures There is no maximum temperature, *per se*, for workplaces, except where power is used to produce such temperatures, in which case the maximum is 19°C (66.2°F). However, under the ACOP, steps should be taken to achieve 'reasonably comfortable' temperatures. This may be achieved by installing cooling equipment, insulating hot plant or pipes, fitting shading on windows or siting workstations away from sources of excess heat.

Low temperatures Where low temperatures are unavoidable or the workplace is exempt from the minimum requirements (as above), steps should be taken to raise the temperature as near as practicable to the minimum and to isolate cold areas from other areas and keep them as small as practicable.

Lighting
This is the subject of Regulation 8, which has correlations with the Factories Act, the Offices, Shops and Railway Premises Act, the Fire Precautions Act and section 2(2)(e) of the HASWA.

However, whereas existing legislation speaks of 'lighting', this Regulation states that, so far as is reasonably practicable, the workplace should be lit by natural light. There must also be suitable and sufficient emergency lighting where a failure in artificial lighting would expose employees to danger, say, where there is no natural light or where night work is undertaken.

Cleaning All windows and skylights providing natural light to work areas must be cleaned regularly (ACOP).

Cleanliness and waste disposal

These are the subjects of Regulation 9, which has correlations with section 1 of the Factories Act, the Environmental Protection Act, the Food Safety Act and section 2(2)(d) of the HASWA.

The requirement to keep premises clean — for example, by painting once every 7 years, washing down of floors once every 14 months, regularly clearing refuse and so on — is already enshrined in the above legislation. This is now extended, however, to include furniture, fixtures and fittings (Regulation 9(1)) and to making floors, walls and windows '*capable*' of being kept sufficiently clean (Regulation 9(2)).

Room dimensions and space

These are the subjects of Regulation 10, which has correlations with the Factories Act, the Fire Precautions Act and the Fire Precautions (Places of Work) Regulations.

Personal space in a workplace, as outlined in previous legislation, was given in cubic metres of air space but with an assumed maximum height of 4.2 metres. Personal air and floor space has now been further defined by this Regulation and the Fire Precautions (Places of Work) Regulations 1995.

There are three very important basic points concerning minimum room dimensions and space:

- personal floor space specifically *excludes* desks, equipment, machinery and so on and refers only to *unoccupied* space
- every employee must be given a *minimum* personal air space of 11 cubic metres (14⅓ cubic yards)
- the law assumes a maximum ceiling height of 3 metres.

Assuming a maximum ceiling height of 3 metres, this means that there must be a minimum area of 3.7 square metres given as personal floor space. However, where the ceiling height is *less* than 3 metres, then the floor space must be enlarged accordingly. For example, if the ceiling is 2.4 metres high, the minimum floor space given must be 4.6 square metres.

Older premises Where a building already existed before 1 January 1993, was subject to the provisions of the Factories Act 1961 and was/is not a new workplace, extension or conversion, then it will be sufficient to assume a maximum ceiling height of 4.2 metres providing the personal air space is no less than 11 cubic metres based on 4.2 metres height and providing that there is no overcrowding (Schedule 1 to the Workplace Regulations).

Workstations and seating

These are the subjects of Regulation 11, which has correlations with section 2(2)(d) of the HASWA, the DSE Regulations and the Fire Precautions (Places of Work) Regulations.

Workstations must take account of ergonomic considerations, that is, the relationship between workers and their environment, and be suitable for them to work in, so that, for example, they can do their work without undue bending or stretching. They should be suitable for the nature of the work undertaken, allowing for work to be carried out safely and comfortably.

Outdoor work Where workers need to work outdoors, there must be:

- protection from adverse weather conditions
- provision for assistance in an emergency
- the ability to escape quickly and easily in an emergency
- measures taken to ensure that no one will be likely to slip or fall.

Seating Where the whole or a substantial part of a job involves being seated, then the seating provided must be:

- suited to the individual using it
- suitable for the operation being undertaken
- provided with a suitable footrest where necessary
- in good condition
- maintained.

There is a correlation here with the DSE Regulations (see Chapter 19).

Conditions of floors and internal traffic routes

This is the subject of Regulation 12, which has correlations with the Factories Act and the Food Safety Act. Many workplace accidents are caused by floors that are uneven, holed, slippery, sloping or have deteriorated. The importance of the condition of floors is emphasized by this Regulation. They must:

- be constructed with the physical safety of workers and of vehicle movements in mind
- be regularly repaired and maintained in such a way as to ensure that no hazards are presented to employees and others
- have adequate drainage where appropriate, such as those in food factories or where there are toxic, corrosive or highly flammable substances
- allow for adequate arrangements to be made to clear up any spillages in the workplace.

Housekeeping Every floor space and traffic route must be kept free of all obstructions and anything that may cause a person to slip, trip or fall. The Factories Act 1961 also lays down requirements for clearly painting lines to denote walkways and traffic routes in factories.

Slopes Slopes should be no steeper than is necessary and handrails must be fitted where slopes present hazards, particularly to the disabled (Regulation 12(4)(b) and 12(5)).

Stairways Where stairways present any risks of falling or spillage, or have narrow treads, they must be fitted with a handrail on at least one side. Where there is a risk of falling to two sides of a stairway, or where they are heavily used, they must be fitted with suitable handrails on both sides. Where a permanent handrail would impede access, such as in a loading area, then removable handrails are permitted, provided they are replaced at all times when access is *not* required (see also Removable fences under Falls and falling objects, below).

Falls and falling objects

These are the subjects of Regulation 13, which has correlations with the Factories Act, sections 2(2)(b) and (d) of the HASWA, the Construction Regulations and the COSHH Regulations.

Fencing The duty to provide secure fencing and guarding to machinery is already enshrined in section 14 of the Factories Act. Similarly, the requirement to fence off openings in floors is in section 28, teagle openings and doorways in section 24 and any place from which a person is liable to fall more than 2 metres in section 29 of the Factories Act.

All these points have been reinforced and extended by this Regulation. For example, fencing is required where a fall is likely to be *less* than 2 metres but where factors exist that would make the likelihood of injury greater, such as the person might fall on to machinery, into tanks or into the path of vehicles. All fences must be of adequate strength and should be fitted with toeboards to prevent objects or fluids being spilt over edges, say, during cleaning operations.

Covers Where covers are fitted to holes in the ground, they must be capable of withstanding the weight and effect of vehicles passing over them or of heavy loads being placed on them.

Removable fences Where regular access is required (for example, for loading with a fork-lift or reach truck), then fences erected at any height must be so constructed as to be capable of being removed without the employee venturing too close to the edge, risking falling over it.

Fixed ladders Staircases are always preferred to provide access from one level to another, but where a staircase is impracticable, a fixed ladder access is permissible, providing it conforms to the minimum standards laid down. Fixed ladders must also be provided in pits, tanks and similar structures into which employees will need to descend. The specifications for fixed ladders are as follows:

- where the fixed ladder has a vertical height of more than 6 metres, it must have a landing at least every 6 metres
- where a fixed ladder passes through a floor, the hole for that ladder must be as small as is practicable, still allowing access
- any fixed ladder set at an angle of less than 15° to the vertical and more than 2.5 metres in height, must be fitted with suitable safety hoops not more than 90 centimetres apart, each commencing at 2.5 metres above the base of the ladder, with the top hoop being in line with the fencing on any platform (an alternative to safety hoops is a permanently fixed fall-arrest system)
- any fixed ladder that rises *less* than 2.5 metres but the base of which is elevated so that a fall of more than 2 metres is possible, then a single hoop must be fitted in line with the top of the fencing.

Note that the term 'fixed ladder' includes a steep stairway on which a person has to face the rungs/treads in order to ascend and descend safely.

The British Standards for fixed ladders are contained in booklets fixed ladders are contained in booklets about the Standards BS5395: 1987, BS4211: 1987 and BS 6399: Part 3 1988.

Roofing The same rules apply to the roofing, except that where roofing is undertaken on a temporary basis, then the same precautions and provisions for safety of workers must be provided. In addition, prevention of falls through fragile roofing materials must be taken into account. Also, regular access to roofing is to be treated as for permanent access. Advice on safe roof work is contained in the HSE's booklet (HS(G)33; HMSO, ISBN: 0 11 8883922 5).

Hazardous substances Where there are risks of falls into hazardous substances, then adequate fencing must also be provided. This includes vessels, tanks, silos and kiers (vessels for boiling textile materials and waste) into which people could fall.

Changes in level Where there are marked changes in level of floors and/or ceilings, these must be suitably marked. This is normally indicated by black and amber or yellow diagonal stripes.

Stacking and racking Section 2(2)(b) of the HASWA already lays down requirements for handling, storage and transportation to ensure that these operations are safe and without risks to health (see Chapter 6). This is further reinforced by this Regulation as follows:

- palletization must be safe and without risk of items falling
- banding or wrapping should be used to prevent individual articles falling out
- safe limits should be set on heights of stacks
- stacks should be inspected regularly to detect and remedy any unsafe conditions
- special arrangements should be made for irregularly shaped objects and workers should be specially trained in safety aspects concerning them.

Guidance on safe stacking and racking is contained in the HSE's booklets (HS(G)76; HMSO, ISBN: 0 11 885731 2) and in IND(G)125L; HMSO, 1992 for agriculture.

Loading and unloading vehicles Wherever possible, climbing on top of vehicles should be avoided, but where it is *unavoidable*, suitable measures must be taken to avoid people falling from them, for example, by the use of fencing on fixed gantries, in maintenance bays or, where regular access is required to the tops of vehicles, portable access steps and fencing may be appropriate.

Scaffolding The requirements for scaffolding are contained in the Construction Regulations. However, the provisions of the Workplace Regulations' ACOP may be followed.

Windows, transparent or translucent doors, gates and walls
These are the subject of Regulation 14.

There are many occasions when transparent material is used in buildings, such as in partitions or in doors. The problem with this is that people often do not realize that there is a physical barrier there and there have been many instances of injury resulting from people simply walking into them.

Where transparent or translucent materials are used, they must:

- be made of safety material or be protected against breakage
- be appropriately marked or have features that make them apparent to anyone who may unwittingly seek to 'walk through' them.

Table 20.1 The thickness and size criteria for ordinary annealed glass

Thickness	Maximum size
8 mm	1.1 × 1.1 m
10 mm	2.25 × 2.25 m
12 mm	3.0 × 4.5 m
15 mm	Any size

Safety materials The ACOP to the Regulations describes 'safety materials' as being the following:

● inherently robust materials, such as polycarbonates or glass blocks
● safety glass that, if broken, will break safely
● ordinary annealed glass that meets thickness and size criteria.

Glass thicknesses and sizes The minimum thickness and size criteria for ordinary annealed glass are as shown in Table 20.1, with the *minimum* thickness being 8 millimetres.

The alternative to the provision of safety materials is, of course, the provision of adequate protection against breakage, such as erecting a screen or barrier to prevent contact.

Windows, skylights and ventilators
These are the subject of Regulation 15.

Anyone who opens a window, skylight or ventilator should be able to do so in a safe manner, without placing themselves or anyone else at risk of accident and injury.

Safe cleaning of windows
This is the subject of Regulation 16.

How often have you seen window cleaners perched on a narrow ledge outside a window and five storeys up from a pavement without the protection of fall-arrest apparatus? This practice is *definitely* outlawed. Any window-cleaning operation must be undertaken in a safe manner, with safe access and egress. In the case of tall buildings, either the windows should be capable of being cleaned from the inside by swinging them inwards or there must be cradles of safe design or fall-arrest apparatus provided (Regulation 16(1)).

For new workplaces, the safe cleaning of windows and so on must be designed into the construction of the premises (Regulation 16(2)).

Organization of traffic routes
This is the subject of Regulation 17.

There are high incidences of major injuries and deaths arising, for example, as a result of people being struck by reversing lorries where no lorry marshalling system has been in force and where no system for the separation of people and vehicles exists and where people stray from pedestrian walkways into the path of vehicles. It is most important that all traffic routes inside employers' premises be safe and without risk of injury to those who may move about within them, taking into account the volume of traffic and numbers of pedestrians likely to use the routes.

Clear systems for routing vehicles should be designed, preferably with vehicular access being segregated from that for pedestrians. Clear walkways should be marked, protected by barriers painted with black and amber/yellow stripes, and pedestrian crossings across vehicle routes should be clearly marked and workers instructed to use them.

No lorries, particularly articulated lorries, should be permitted to reverse in any area where pedestrians are likely to move about, *unless* they are marshalled by a trained person. *Only* trained and authorized persons should be permitted to undertake such lorry marshalling operations. They must only give recognized signals and must ensure that the drivers of vehicles under their guidance can clearly see both their signals and themselves at all times during any marshalling operation. To this end, marshals should be suitably dressed in identifiable and high-visibility clothing and carry such aids as may assist them, such as reflective bats or gloves.

Although acting under the direction of lorry marshallers, the driver of any vehicle moving under such guidance must understand that they retain responsibility for their vehicle and the safety of others and must satisfy themselves that they understand all instructions given by lorry marshallers.

Guidance on the design of safe vehicle movement systems and safe lorry reversing can be obtained from the HSE's booklet (GS.9(Rev): 1992); available from the HSE. MOTEC (formerly the Road Transport Industry Training Board (RTITB)) also produce an excellent booklet on lorry reversing. See also Appendix 16 for a suggested safe reversing schedule and training document for lorries.

Loading bays Loading bays must be provided with at least one exit point, but, in the case of wide loading bays, two exits. If no exit points from loading bays are provided, there must be safe refuges built into the walls into which a person may go to avoid being struck or crushed by a vehicle.

Warning signs All traffic routes must be clearly identified by warning signs. All hazards on traffic routes, such as sharp bends, junctions, crossings, blind corners, steep gradients or roadworks, must also be clearly marked by warning signs.

Doors and gates
These are the subject of Regulation 18.

All doors and gates must comply with the following requirements, as appropriate:

- sliding doors must be incapable of coming off their tracks
- upward-opening doors or gates must have devices fitted that prevent them from falling back
- powered doors and gates should have suitable devices fitted, such as detectors and associated trip devices, which prevent people from becoming trapped; they must also be capable of being opened manually in the event of failure of the mechanical device and have a device to limit the closing force so that it is not sufficient as to cause injury
- doors or gates that are capable of swinging open both ways must be fitted with a transparent window to provide a clear view from either side.

Escalators and moving walkways
These are the subject of Regulation 19.

The requirements for escalators and moving walkways are already provided in the HSE's booklets (PM.34. HMSO, 1983) HMSO, ISBN: 0 11 883572 6, (PM.45. HMSO,

1984) HMSO, ISBN: 0 11 883595 and (CRR.12/1989) HMSO, ISBN: 0 11 885938 2 (all available from HMSO). There is also a British Standard for escalators and passenger conveyors — BS.5656: 1983.

Sanitary conveniences

These are the subject of Regulation 20, which has correlations with the Factory Act and the Offices, Shops and Railway Premises Act. The requirements for the provision of sanitary conveniences were already enshrined in section 7 of the Factories Act 1961 (FA 61) and section 9 of the Offices, Shops and Railway Premises Act 1963 (OSRP 63) and, before then, were detailed in the:

- Sanitary Accommodation Regulations 1938 (for factories)
- Construction (Health and Welfare) Regulations 1966, for building and engineering construction
- Sanitary Conveniences Regulations 1964, for premises under the Offices, Shops and Railway Premises Act
- Food Hygiene (General) Regulations 1970, for food premises

but see the details in Facilities requirements under Washing facilities, which follows.

The Workplace Regulations also reinforce the requirements for adequate ventilation, lighting, cleanliness and tidiness in WCs.

Washing facilities

These are the subject of Regulation 21, which has correlations with the Factories Act and the Offices, Shops and Railway Premises Act and its Regulations.

The Workplace Regulations require that 'suitable and sufficient' washing facilities, including showers if required by the nature of the work or for health reasons, be provided and readily available. The requirement to be 'suitable and sufficient' is also laid down in FA 61 and OSRP 63 but is made specific for premises within the scope of OSRP 63 and, where more than five persons are employed, by the Washing Facilities Regulations 1964.

Facilities requirements The Workplace Regulations' ACOP, sections 201 and 202, specifies how many such facilities need to be provided for the number of people employed, as shown in Tables 20.2 and 20.3.

Table 20.2 Numbers of facilities required for groups of workers*

Number at work	Number of WCs	Number of washstations
1 to 5	1	1
6 to 25	2	2
26 to 50	3	3
51 to 75	4	4
76 to 100	5	5

*Groups of workers may be men, women, office workers or manual workers, with a separate calculation made for each group.

Table 20.3 Sanitary conveniences required for use only by men

Number of men at work	Number of WCs	Number of urinals
1 to 15	1	1
16 to 30	2	1
31 to 45	2	2
46 to 60	3	2
61 to 75	3	3
76 to 90	4	3
91 to 100	4	4

Note that communal, unisex WCs are not permitted where there are more than five employees or where none of the employees works for more than two hours per day; separate male and female facilities must be provided.

Note, too, that where there are more than 5 employees and the number of employees includes females, there must be a minimum of 1 WC for every 25 female employees, irrespective of Table 20.2.

Where certain sanitary accommodation is provided for use only by men, the standards in Table 20.3 may be followed, if desired, as an alternative to the first column of Table 20.2.

Note that the figures quoted in Tables 20.2 and 20.3 vary from those specified in section 7 of the Factories Act, section 9 of the Offices, Shops and Railway Premises Act and quoted Regulations, although they follow the same basic pattern.

Remote workers When employees are located in remote places where there are no supplies of running water, sufficient containers of water for washing or other means of personal hygiene must be provided.

Wholesome drinking water
This is the subject of Regulation 22, which has correlations with section 57 of the Factories Act and section 11 of the Offices, Shops and Railway Premises Act. The requirement to provide wholesome drinking water has existed for some time under these other two Acts.

The Workplace Regulations state that this supply must be:

- readily accessible to employees
- in suitable places
- conspicuously marked by an appropriate sign where necessary for reasons of health and safety
- sufficient supply of suitable drinking cups or other vessels, if necessary
- a supply from a water jet.

Accommodation for clothing
This is the subject of Regulation 23, which has correlations with section 59 of the Factories Act, section 12 of the Offices, Shops and Railway Premises Act and the Food Safety Act, plus their Regulations — no less than at least 17, in fact. They require employers to provide accommodation in a suitable location for employees'

clothing, with separate accommodation for personal clothing not worn during the normal working routine and for work clothing that is removed at the end of the shift and not taken home. There should also be facilities for drying clothing, where appropriate. This was further enhanced by the requirements of the Food Safety Act and is reinforced by this Regulation.

Changing facilities
This is the subject of Regulation 24, which has the same correlations with other legislation as Regulation 23 above.

Where employees have to remove normal clothing in order to wear clothing required for working, such as in food premises, foundries and furnaces, or where workers' own clothing could become contaminated by harmful substances (such as lead), there must be adequate and suitable changing rooms provided. There must be separate male and female facilities with adequate facilities for privacy and they should contain seating.

Facilities for rests and meals
This is the subject of Regulation 25, which has correlations with the Factories Act, the Food Safety Act and Control of Lead at Work Regulations.

In workplaces such as factories, engineering workshops and leadworking operations, employees are not permitted to consume food in the workplace as this would endanger their health. Also, neither food nor drink is permitted to be consumed in the workplace in food premises for reasons of food safety and hygiene, that is, food could become contaminated. Separate rest and meals accommodation *must* be provided. These points have been established for some time, but the following are new requirements of the Workplace Regulations.

Workplace eating Where consumption of food in the workplace *is* permitted, suitable and sufficient facilities must be provided for this. It is not sufficient that a worker consumes their food at their workbench.

Non-smokers Separate and suitable rooms must be provided to protect non-smokers from the effects of tobacco smoke (Regulation 25(3)). The HSE has produced a booklet entitled *Passive smoking at work* (IND(G)63L(Rev) 1992, available from the HSE). The Institute of Personnel Management has also produced a booklet, *Non-smoking policies in the workplace*.

Pregnant women and nursing mothers Separate, suitable facilities must be provided for pregnant women and nursing mothers to be able to rest (Regulation 25(4)). These facilities should be close to WCs and should include the facility to lie down when necessary.

The HSE has produced the booklet *Occupational aspects of pregnancy* (MA6 1989, free from your local HSE office).

21

Personal protective equipment

The need for personal protection for workers is an established feature of health and safety, yet many injuries still occur because workers who may be exposed to risks of injury or ill-health are not issued with any protective equipment, the equipment issued is not adequate for its intended purpose or else workers fail to wear that which is issued.

A careful review of any accident book (DSS Form BI510) will invariably indicate needs for an appraisal of the issue of personal protective equipment (PPE) or more close supervision of the wearing of it where there is laxness in obeying the rules. This chapter is, therefore, most important in terms of preventing injuries to employees.

The legislation

The rules governing PPE are spread around many pieces of industry-specific legislation. The European Community (EC) Directive on PPE (89/686/EEC) came into force on 1 January 1993 and was implemented in the UK by the Personal Protective Equipment at Work Regulations 1992 (known as the PPE Regulations), which deal with the issuing of PPE to workers. These Regulations are supported by an ACOP issued by the Health and Safety Commission (HSC). There is no period of grace, as with certain other aspects of sister Regulations, compliance being required, in full, from 1 January 1993.

The PPE Regulations were supplemented by the Personal Protective Equipment (EC Directive) Regulations 1992 (PPE CE Regulations), which deal, principally, with the manufacture and marketing of PPE. The PPE CE Regulations require most types of PPE to achieve minimum levels of safety as certified by an independent inspection body, which will then issue a 'certificate of conformity' (called a 'CE' mark — hence the 'PPE CE' Regulations). The PPE CE Regulations require manufacturers of PPE to supply information (in similar fashion to product data sheets required under the COSHH Regulations) on the following:

- storage, use, cleaning, maintenance and disinfection
- performance standards, as recorded during technical tests
- accessories and characteristics of appropriate spare parts
- classes of protection appropriate to levels of risks
- types of packaging suitable for the transportation of PPE.

What is covered?

PPE includes:

- clothing worn for personal protection, such as aprons, gloves, safety footwear, safety helmets, high-visibility waistcoats and protective clothing for adverse conditions
- equipment such as eye protectors, life-jackets and safety harnesses
- any item of PPE not necessarily worn on the body but carried with or on a worker for use as personal protection, such as respirators or breathing apparatus
- other items that protect workers from bodily injury, extremes of heat or cold, the effects of noise or from breathing in or ingesting hazardous substances, gases or fumes.

Exclusions These Regulations do not include sea-going ships or on-board activities under the direction of the ship's master. Members of the home forces, visiting forces and their headquarters may also be exempt on orders of the Secretary of State. Further, the Regulations do not cover the following items:

- ordinary working clothes and uniforms that do not specifically protect the health and safety of the wearer or the product
- offensive weapons used as self-defence or deterrent equipment (such as police and security guards' batons)
- portable devices for detecting and signalling risks and nuisances
- PPE used for protection while travelling on public highways
- equipment used when playing competitive sports.

Also, Regulations 4 and 6 to 12 inclusive do *not* apply to PPE where there are existing comprehensive Regulations that require PPE, as they are adequately covered in those Regulations. These include the:

- Control of Lead at Work Regulations 1980 (see Chapter 16)
- Ionizing Radiations Regulations 1985
- Control of Asbestos at Work Regulations 1987 (see Chapter 17)
- Control of Substances Hazardous to Health Regulations 1988 (see Chapter 10)
- Noise at Work Regulations (see Chapter 12)
- Construction (Head Protection) Regulations 1989.

Provision of PPE as a last resort

The law requires an employer to seek, *first*, to completely eliminate the risk of a hazard arising or eliminate the risk of exposure to a hazard by enclosure of that hazard if elimination of it is not practicable. Where elimination or enclosure are *not* practicable, then, as a *last resort*, workers must be protected from injury or ill-health effects that could result from exposure to that hazard and PPE must be issued.

The provision of PPE

Every employer must ensure that all employees are provided with PPE (Regulation 4(1)) and every self-employed person must ensure that they and their employees wear PPE (Regulation 4(2)), whether on their own or on other employers' premises.

The Regulations require employers and the self-employed to:

- provide PPE where risks to health and safety cannot be controlled adequately by other means (that is, as a last resort, as described)
- select PPE that is suitable for the risks to be protected against (as determined by the risk assessments carried out under the Management of Health and Safety at Work Regulations 1992 — see Chapter 18)
- ensure that all PPE is readily available to those who will need it and not merely on the premises
- ensure that no charge is made for any PPE issued in compliance with any statute or in accordance with company health and safety policy (section 9 of the HASWA)
- ensure that ergonomic factors are taken into account when supplying PPE to workers, both in the general sense of its relation to the work undertaken and in the sense of its particular relationship to the individuals who will use it
- ensure that all PPE is of the minimum standard required
- ensure that all PPE has been certified as such and carries (where practicable) the CE mark referred to above (most PPE carries at least a British Standards Kitemark).

The compatibility of PPE

All PPE worn in conjunction with other items of PPE must be compatible when worn together, for example, a protective helmet worn with protective goggles or visor (Regulation 5). Also, when two or more items are worn together, they must be comfortable and one must not negate the purpose of the other.

Assessments

Before any PPE is determined as needed or suitable, assessments must be carried out to determine what the requirements are (Regulation 6).

First, identify the risks to which people may be exposed, that is:

- items to which the PPE Regulations apply in full (except where the Construction (Head Protection) Regulations 1989 apply):
  —*mechanical*:
    falls from heights
    blows, cuts, impact, crushing
    stabs, cuts, grazes
    vibration
    slipping, falling over
  —*thermal*:
    scalds, heat, fire
    cold
  —*other*:
    immersion
- items to which the PPE Regulations apply in part only, that is, except for Regulations 4, and 6 to 12 (being already covered by existing Regulations, as listed above):
  —noise
  —hazardous dust fibres
  —gases, vapours
  —fungi
  —ionizing radiation
  —hazardous fumes
  —harmful viruses
  —non-microbiological antigens

—hazardous vapours
—splashes, spurts and emissions of harmful substances.

Then, assess the parts of the body that may be exposed to those hazards:

- *head*:
  —cranium (top of head)   —ears
  —eyes   —respiratory tract
  —face   —whole head

- *upper limbs*:
  —hands
  —forearms
  —upper arms

- *lower limbs*:
  —feet
  —lower legs
  —upper legs

- *various*:
  —skin   —trunk
  —abdomen   —whole body.

A suggested PPE assessment proforma, incorporating these factors, is given in Appendix 12. See also Risk assessments in Chapter 18 for detailed advice on how to conduct assessments.

Maintenance

All PPE must be adequately maintained in an efficient state, in efficient working order and in good repair (Regulation 7). PPE should be replaced when it is no longer efficient or in good repair.

In this respect, an effective, planned system of maintenance must be implemented to ensure that the PPE is properly maintained and that it does its job efficiently and effectively. This will include such matters as examination, testing, cleaning, disinfection, repairing and replacement.

Accommodation

Suitable accommodation should be provided for all PPE, appropriate to its type (Regulation 8). This should ensure that the PPE can be protected from accidental damage, abuse, theft, and contamination by dirt or harmful substances. Goggles hanging on the side of a grinding wheel in an engineers' workshop does *not* count as suitable accommodation.

Information, instruction and training

Employees and other users should be given suitable and adequate information, instruction and training. This requirement reinforces that laid down in section 2(2)(c) of the HASWA (see Chapter 6, which covers this aspect).

The use of PPE

The employer must ensure (Regulation 10) that:

- PPE is issued as required by statute or company health and safety policy
- all employees and contractors or self-employed people working on their premises use and/or wear that PPE
- PPE is used correctly and in accordance with the instructions given orally or in writing
- all PPE is returned to its proper accommodation when not in use.

It should be noted that it is not enough to say 'Well, I have issued them with PPE', or 'Well, I did tell them' — get them to sign for it, then enforce its correct use and/or wear by ensuring that there is adequate supervision and control (section 2(2)(c) of the HASWA). Employees, contractors and self-employed people to whom PPE is issued should be informed that they have a personal responsibility in this respect.

Under the Management of Health and Safety at Work Regulations 1992, a contractor or self-employed person working on your premises has a duty to ensure that they comply with all your relevant safety rules, including the wearing/use of PPE by themselves and their employees, but it is your responsibility to ensure that they do this (see also Chapter 18).

Defect or loss

There is now a legal duty (Regulation 11) on every employee and contractor or self-employed person who has been issued with PPE that becomes defective or lost to report that defect or loss to the employer.

Guidance

Part 2 (Guidance) of the ACOP to the Regulations gives very detailed and excellent advice on the selection, use and maintenance of PPE, including details and illustrative examples of head protection, eye protection, foot protection, hand and arm protection and body protection (Guidance booklet L25, HMSO).

22

The safety of work equipment

There has been a long-standing obligation on employers to securely fence off all dangerous machinery and to fit guards to them where appropriate (as laid down, for example, by the Factories Act 1961, sections 12, 13, 14 and 16). Despite this, 12 per cent of all deaths and reportable injuries suffered in industry are caused while operating machinery — not to mention the many injuries that are not 'reportable', in terms of the RIDDOR, nor those numerous accidents that are never reported at all.

The legislation

The EC issued a Directive on the use of work equipment (89/655/EEC) that was implemented in the United Kingdom by the Provision and Use of Work Equipment Regulations 1992. These became effective on 1 January 1993 and are being implemented in stages up to 1 January 1997.

There should be little difficulty in complying with most of the requirements of these new Regulations as they do not go significantly beyond current good practice as laid down by the Factories Act. Thus, although the Provision and Use of Work Equipment Regulations 1992 (Wk. Eqpt. Regs) are themselves lengthy and quite detailed, they are summarized briefly here, with only those aspects that are new additions to existing requirements being discussed.

Following is a summary of the overall requirements of the Wk. Eqpt. Regs:

- in selecting work equipment, the working conditions and hazards in the workplace must be taken into account
- additional hazards that may be created by the installation and use of work equipment must also be taken into account
- all work equipment must be suitable for the purpose for which it is intended
- all work equipment must be properly maintained and must be designed to facilitate safe maintenance operations
- where specific risks exist in relation to the use of work equipment, the use of that equipment must be restricted to those who have been appointed and properly trained to use it
- adequate information, instruction and training must be given to all employees in the use of work equipment.

The scope of the Work Equipment Regulations
The Regulations apply to all work equipment provided for use by any employee in non-domestic premises and factories, including those operations carried out in

190

offshore installations under the scope of the Offshore Safety Act 1992. They also apply fully to self-employed persons.

By 'work equipment' is meant all kinds of plant, machinery and equipment in use in the workplace. This includes power presses, assembly machines, product-filling machines, guillotines, circular saw benches, overhead projectors, portable drills, handtools, drill bits, butcher's knives, car ramps, ladders, lawnmowers and laboratory apparatus, such as bunsen burners and test equipment. Also covered are multiple assemblies that are arranged and controlled to function as a whole, such as bottling plants and process plant. This list is not exhaustive; basically, if it is an item of equipment that is used in the work situation, it is included.

The Regulations also cover the stopping and starting of work equipment and the repair, modification, maintenance and servicing, cleaning and transport of work equipment. In this context, 'transport' means, for example, when a fork-lift truck carries work equipment around a factory or warehouse.

Road transport vehicles (tankers, cranes, tractors and so on), when operated inside firms' premises, also come within the scope of the Regulations. They would not, however, be covered when on the public highway as they are then governed by road traffic legislation.

Construction The Regulations also cover all work equipment used on construction sites. Where there is a multiplicity of contractors on construction sites, it is for each individual contractor to ensure that all the work equipment for which they are responsible fully complies with the Regulations, as given below. However, in multiple-occupancy sites, your attention is drawn to the necessity to appoint a health and safety coordinator, whose role should include ensuring the safety and use of work equipment (see Chapter 18).

Exclusions

Plant and equipment that are part of the structure and fixed to the premises, not being used to manufacture products, such as ventilation or air-conditioning systems, are covered by the Workplace (Health, Safety and Welfare) Regulations 1992 rather than the Work Equipment Regulations (see Chapter 20).

Home forces, visiting forces and their headquarters may be exempted by the Secretary of State by issuing an exemption certificate.

Compliance

All new installations of work equipment effected for the first time on or after 1 January 1993 must conform, by design, with all the requirements of these Regulations from day one of installation. Similarly, any equipment adapted or modified on or after 1 January 1993 must conform in all respects (Regulation 10).

Where work equipment was *already* in place on or before 31 December 1992, then employers have until 31 December 1996 to comply with Regulations 11 to 24, but Regulations 4 to 10 apply immediately.

The requirements of the Work Equipment Regulations

It is helpful to have a list of the relevant elements in these Regulations, which are:

5, suitability of work equipment

6, maintenance
7, specific risks
8–9, information, instruction and training
10, conformity with EC requirements
11, dangerous parts of machinery
12, protection against specific hazards
13, high or very low temperatures
14–18, controls and control systems
19, isolation from sources of energy
20, stability of work equipment
21, lighting
22, maintenance safety
23, health and safety markings
24, health and safety warnings.

Suitability of work equipment

All work equipment must be suitable for the use for which it is intended (Regulation 5). This will take account of three aspects:

- its initial integrity
- the place where it will be used
- the purpose for which it is to be used.

Work equipment must be suitable by design and construction for particular intended uses, with risks to health and safety designed *out* and health and safety protection designed *in*, rather than merely adapted for uses, unless such adaptation can be accomplished with all health and safety factors catered for (Regulation 5(1)). Note that the word 'use' in the context of Regulation 5(1) includes any routine work or planned preventative maintenance undertaken on work equipment.

Maintenance

The requirement to maintain plant and equipment is already laid down in section 2(2)(a) of the HASWA. This is enhanced by the Wk. Eqpt. Regs with their requirements that:

- work equipment must be maintained in:
  —an efficient state
  —efficient working order
  —good repair
  so that the performance of the machine does not deteriorate with the result that it puts people at risk of injury or ill-health
- maintenance logs must be kept up-to-date
- work equipment must be regularly checked to ensure that safety-related features of the equipment are properly maintained, such as guards, fail-safe devices, moving parts, prevention of overheating.

These requirements clearly extend that laid down by section 2(2)(a) to mean that a planned preventative maintenance system must be instituted to cover all aspects of work equipment maintenance and servicing.

In addition to such a system, there must also be routine maintenance to ensure safe day-to-day running, such as with lubrication, inspection and testing of work equipment. This should be based on the manufacturer's recommendations. Also, other existing legislation lays down specific requirements for maintenance that must also be adhered to, for example, that relating to power presses. And there are further requirements for maintenance in the Work Equipment Regulations, Regulation 10, for new equipment, and Regulation 22, for existing equipment. See also Maintenance safety later in this chapter.

Specific risks
Regulation 7 simply reinforces previous legal requirements. Where there are specific risks relating to the operation and/or maintenance of work equipment, then that operation and maintenance must be restricted to those who have received adequate information, instruction and trainimg. It should also be noted that, under existing legislation, certain items of work equipment are prohibited to those under the age of 18, such as power presses, industrial guillotines, meat slicers, dough mixers and so on.

Information, instruction and training (Regulations 8 and 9)
Regulations 8 and 9, similarly, reinforce previous legal requirements to provide information, instruction and training, respectively, as laid down by section 2(2)(c) of the HASWA. This information, instruction and training must include all relevant safety factors involved in the operation of work equipment, precautions to take, PPE to wear, and action to take in an emergency. These data should also be in the form of written instructions to back up verbal instruction and training given (see Chapter 29).

Supervision The requirement for information, instruction and training is accompanied by the duty to provide adequate supervision (also section 2(2)(c) of the HASWA), and this is further reinforced by Regulation 12 of the Management of Health and Safety at Work Regulations 1992 (see Chapter 18).

Dangerous parts of machinery
The legal obligation to protect people from dangerous parts of machinery is well established in health and safety law, such as in sections 12, 13, 14 and 16 of the Factories Act. These are reinforced here in Regulation 11.

The duty is to:

- fit fixed guards or other protective devices to prevent access to any dangerous part of machinery or to any rotating stock-bar
- fit fail-safe devices to stop the movement of dangerous parts of machinery or rotating stock-bars when guards/cages are moved
- provide jigs, holders, push-sticks or other protective devices where fixed guards or devices are not practicable
- information, instruction and training must be provided to all users of work equipment in the safe operation of all equipment they use, and, attached to this, is the duty to provide effective supervision (this correlates with section 2(2)(c) of the HASWA).

Quality Minimum quality standards of suitability, construction, sound material, adequate strength, maintenance and repair are also required. No guard or other device should be capable of being bypassed or disabled, and guards should be positioned at a sufficient distance to any physical danger so that no one can get their fingers through the guards and into or onto moving parts.

Maintenance Guards and other protective devices should be designed so as to facilitate ease of maintenance and access by those authorized to the part(s) of the machine on which work is required to be undertaken without having to dismantle the guard or device.

Protection against specific hazards

There is a continuing duty on employers to protect their employees and others who may be affected by their operations against specific risks arising from use of work equipment (Regulation 12). This includes the following:

- materials falling from equipment, such as loose metal or boards
- materials held in equipment being unexpectedly thrown out, such as metal pieces in chucks or swarf
- parts of equipment being broken off and flying out, such as an abrasive wheel that shatters
- equipment, such as scaffolding, collapsing
- effects of fire or overheating, such as from hot bearings, burned-out electric motors, welding torch burns, failed thermostats or cooling systems failing
- explosion due to a build-up of pressure
- explosion of substances due, for example, to chemical reactions or unplanned ignition of gases and vapours, dust explosions (even flour will explode) or flammable residues in welding situations.

Assessments These risks should be identified by your risk assessments, carried out under Regulation 3 of the Management of Health and Safety at Work Regulations, with plans drawn up to eliminate, completely enclose or protect workers against them (see Chapter 18).

Equipment design The first obligation of employers, as we have seen, is to eliminate or enclose risks where new equipment is installed. If this is not possible, then adequate protection must be afforded (Regulation 12(3); see also Risk reduction, below).

Where there are intentional and necessary discharges of hazardous substances during normal processes, these are permissible under Regulation 12(1), but you must provide adequate protection for workers against the hazards these discharges create by means of enclosure and/or the issuing of suitable PPE. (See also Suitability of work equipment, earlier in this chapter.)

Risk reduction It is acknowledged that even when all reasonably practicable steps have been taken to prevent a dangerous occurrence from arising, such an incident can, nevertheless, occur. Regulation 12(2)(b) thus requires employers to mitigate the effects of any dangerous occurrence should it arise by, for example, installing pressure relief valves and panels or blast walls to minimize the effects of any mishap. These contingency measures should all be built-in by design, as above (Regulation 12(2)(a)).

Abrasive wheels The provisions of Regulation 12 are applied also to existing requirements under the Abrasive Wheels Regulations 1970. For example, wheels must be run at the correct rotation speeds specified, as required by Regulation 23 of the Abrasive Wheels Regulations. These speeds are marked on larger wheels, but, for smaller wheels, notices should be fixed in workrooms where they are used giving the maximum permissible rotation speeds of each wheel type. Guards must be fitted to contain fragments of wheel that may fly off and so preventing them injuring anyone in the vicinity. Remember, also, the requirement under the Abrasive Wheels Regulations to provide training in the correct mounting of abrasive wheels, with only trained and authorized people allowed to mount and change abrasive wheels.

Exclusions Regulation 12 does *not* apply to working situations where the following Regulations apply, as they already contain adequate provision for the protection of workers:

- Control of Lead at Work Regulations 1980
- Ionizing Radiations Regulations 1985
- Control of Asbestos at Work Regulations 1987, as amended in 1988
- Control of Substances Hazardous to Health Regulations 1988, as amended in 1990 and 1991
- Noise at Work Regulations 1989
- Construction (Head Protection) Regulations 1989.

High or very low temperatures
Where any item of work equipment emits high temperatures or has a very low temperature, workers must be protected against the risks of direct contact with these extremes of heat or cold. This can be by engineering methods in design, such as reduction of surface temperatures, limiting maximum temperatures, installing inter-locking fail-safe devices that will not permit contact with hot surfaces or substances and so on. If these are not reasonably practicable, then protection must be by insulation, enclosure or the issuing of protective clothing.

Controls and control systems
Where machinery is powered and operated other than by human effort, that is, by electrical, steam-driven, pneumatic, hydraulic or other non-human means, or where the work equipment does not necessarily stop when human effort ceases, then Regulations 14 to 18 require that controls and control systems must be fitted to that equipment, such controls to be designed so that they are incapable of being inadvertently operated. The respective Regulations specify particular types of con-trols, as follows.

Starting or changing operations Starting, stopping and changing speed or operation of work equipment must be possible only by operation of controls (Regulation 14). One or more controls must be provided to start powered work equipment and to change the speed, pressure or other operating conditions of that equipment. The same requirement applies to restarting equipment after stopping it. Controls for changes in operation must be so designed that users or others are not caught unawares by those changes, but, rather, that the *operator* takes the conscious action to initiate those changes, for example, in the operation of multipurpose machining centres (Regulations 14(1)(b) and 14(2)).

Automatic machinery Where automatic equipment is controlled by program-mable computer systems, such as computer-aided design and computer-aided manu-facture, then separate controls for changing operations are not appropriate. However, such machines must be protected as required by Regulations 11 and 12, above (Regulation 14(3)).

Stop controls The primary requirement of Regulation 15 is that a stop control must bring machinery to a safe condition and in a safe manner. By this is meant that:

- all moving parts become stationary, except, for example, cooling fans, which are safely encased (Regulation 15(2))
- the sources of all energy must be isolated after operating the stop control (Regulation 15(3))
- internal sources of energy, such as hydraulic power, should also be cut off by activating the stop control (Regulation 15(3))
- stop controls must operate independently of any other controls that start or change operations.

A 'safe manner' (Regulation 15(1)) takes account of the fact that, in some situations, an immediate stop would be detrimental to either the product, the machinery or the people operating it and, thus, a shut-down sequence to the end of a cycle will be appropriate.

Emergency stop controls Regulation 15 would, of course, not apply in a situation of absolute emergency where there is a choice between product or machine safety and worker safety, in which case an immediate stop is essential, except where such immediate stopping would lead to further serious hazards, such as stopping the mixing mechanisms in reactors or certain chemical reactions, which could lead to exothermic reactions. Emergency stop controls must operate independently of any other controls for starting, stopping and changing operation and shall operate in priority to those other controls (Regulation 16(2)).

Controls Regulation 17 deals with controls other than stop, start, change operation or emergency controls and is concerned with the normal operation of machinery. Controls must:

- be easily identified (by wording or symbols, colours, shape and position) for specific purposes and on which equipment the controls have effect (established markings for controls are set out in British Standard BS3641, prEN 50099), though you may require additional designs tailored to your situation (Regulation 17(1))
- normally be positioned so that they are safe and present no risk to people using them, the exception to this being controls used for setting-up or fault-finding procedures, in which cases safety features must be built into the controls, such as hold-to-run controls, limitations or reduced capability of machines while those controls are in operation (Regulation 17(2))
- be so positioned that the operator of those controls is satisfied that no other person can be put at risk by their operation, which would apply, for example, where it is not possible to completely deny access to dangerous working parts of machinery as required by Regulations 11(2)(a) and (b) (where access to machinery is required, for example, by maintenance engineers, interlocks should be fitted to prevent it starting up while workers are at risk; Regulation 17(3)(a))
- be accompanied by audible and visible warnings when work is about to start (Regulation 17(3)(c)) (where workers are in noisy environments and/or not in a position to see visual warnings, suitable alternative systems of work and warnings must be employed (Regulation 17(3)(b)) and these must be totally unambiguous, easily perceived and understood; Regulation 17(3)(c))
- be supplemented by a system of work that will ensure that no other person is placed at risk when the person who operates the controls cannot see others who may be at risk when the machinery is started by the control systems (examples of this may be signallers to assist crane or tractor drivers or newspaper printing machines; Regulation 17(3)(b))

- be given sufficiently in advance of machinery actually starting, in the case of any person who may be placed at risk by that machinery starting (this may also, where appropriate, include an override or warning to the operator, by which means the person at risk can prevent start-up or warn the operator of their presence; Regulation 17(4)).

Note that Regulation 17 does not preclude a person being in a position of risk, but its aim is to prevent an operator *unintentionally* placing *others* at risk. This would, for example, allow engineers who may necessarily *have* to approach dangerous parts of machinery for the purpose of maintenance to do so. However, such access to dangerous parts of machinery must *only* be under strictly controlled conditions and in accordance with Regulation 11 as outlined earlier in this chapter.

Control systems A control system is 'a system or device which responds to input signals and generates an output signal which causes the equipment under control to operate in a particular manner' (Work Equipment Regulations ACOP and Guidance).

Under Regulation 18, all control systems must be:

- safe (Regulation 18(1))
- free from risks to health and safety in normal operation (Regulation 18(2)(a))
- free from further risks to health and safety in the event of any fault, damage of any part or loss of supply of energy (Regulation 18(2)(b))
- unable to impede the operation of any stop control or emergency stop controls required by Regulations 15 or 16 respectively (Regulation 18(2)(c)).

Isolation
Isolation means 'establishing a break in the energy supply in a secure manner, ie, by ensuring that inadvertent reconnection is not possible' (Work Equipment Regulations ACOP Guidance).

The purpose of isolation, then, is to enable machinery to be made safe under particular circumstances, such as when engineering maintenance is underway, when an unsafe condition develops or where temporary adverse conditions cause the machinery to be unsafe.

Any work equipment that has dangerous working parts must:

- be capable of being isolated from all sources of energy used by that equipment (electrical, hydraulic or pneumatic; Regulation 19(1))
- have isolation devices clearly identifiable and readily accessible to operators (Regulation 19(2))
- be capable of reconnection to sources of energy without exposing any person to any risk to their health and safety.

It is important that no person, except an authorized person with a work permit to do so, should be able in any way to interfere with or override any isolation device. This may, in certain prescribed circumstances, mean having a multiple-locking device where more than one person has access to the device with their own authorized key to unlock it.

Stability of work equipment
Many types of plant and machinery are capable of falling over, collapsing or overturning unless suitable measures are taken to stabilize them. They can be secured

to the ground or tied, fastened or clamped, as appropriate to their design (Regulation 20).

Fixed work equipment Most machines that are used in a fixed position and do not require moving should be bolted or otherwise clamped to the ground. Machinery can slowly, even imperceptibly, move during operation, especially where there are vibrations; clamping or bolting will ensure that it does not rock or otherwise move. If severe conditions may aggravate the stability of work equipment or stability is not built-in by design, then additional measures may be required. In this respect, scaffolding is vulnerable to strong winds and additional ties to buildings on to which it is assembled will be necessary.

Movable work equipment Certain industries, such as food processing, have equipment that is necessarily capable of being relocated to different positions in factories to service different requirements. The Regulations would appear to require that these should be clamped or bolted when positioned and in use.

Mobile work equipment Equipment such as mobile cranes and tractors needs to have counterbalance weights fitted to increase their stability. Every item of equipment has its limits, and cranes, tractors and fork-lift trucks should not be used beyond their stated load or over terrain for which they are unsuitable. While mobile equipment cannot be clamped or fixed to the ground, it should be fitted with outriggers to increase stability.

Lighting

There is already a requirement to provide lighting under section 2(2)(e) of the HASWA and this is enhanced by Regulation 21. Where work equipment is in use, adequate lighting must be provided, both in the workplace and locally at the equipment itself, to ensure that those operating it can do so safely and efficiently. Lighting should be suitable for the operations being carried out.

Maintenance safety

In addition to the requirement for regular and planned maintenance to be carried out on work equipment (Regulation 6), such maintenance operations should be capable of being conducted in a safe manner and without risks to the health and safety of any person (Regulation 22).

Machinery construction All machinery must be designed, constructed or adapted so that any routine or planned preventative maintenance that is carried out while that machinery is shut down will be safe (Regulation 22).

Worker safety If the machinery is *not* shut down, maintenance operations must be capable of being conducted without exposing the person carrying out that maintenance to risks to their health or safety (Regulation 22(a)). Also, measures must be taken to protect anyone who is carrying out maintenance that involves a risk to their health or safety (Regulation 22(b)).

Operational servicing There are some aspects of routine servicing that can be carried out while machines are running, such as oiling, greasing or adjustments. These aspects should be designed-in in such a way that no maintenance person or operator is placed at risk and, ideally, should not have to open any safety guards, gates or doors.

Maintenance with machinery running Where it is necessary for maintenance to be carried out on machinery while it is running, suitable measures should be taken to enable that maintenance to be conducted with the minimum of risk by the addition of extra safeguards such as:

- the provision of temporary guards
- limiting the power available to the machine
- providing limited-movement controls
- fitting hold-to-run speed controls
- using a second, low-powered, visible laser beam to align a powerful invisible laser beam
- issuing PPE where it is not possible to eliminate or significantly reduce the risks involved.

The provision of adequate information, instruction, training and supervision is indispensable in ensuring safe and efficient maintenance operations.

Health and safety markings
All work equipment must carry suitable and sufficient health and safety markings. These markings must be clearly visible and appropriate to the particular hazard they are warning about, for example:

- stop and start controls
- maximum rotation speeds for abrasive wheels
- maximum safe working loads (marked on lifting beams)
- gas cylinder contents
- hazardous substances vessels and containers, together with the associated hazards of those substances.

These markings may incorporate words, letters, numbers, symbols and the use of colour codes.

The specific situations in which markings are required are already laid down in the:

- Ionizing Radiation Regulations 1985
- Highly Flammable Liquids Regulations 1972 (Regulations 6 and 7)
- various pressure vessel Regulations, which include requirements for marking those vessels with specific information.

There are various other markings employers can devise themselves that would be suitable to their own purposes and helpful in identifying work equipment and associated hazards, including:

- the numbering of machines to assist in their identification
- labelling controls or isolators that are not directly attached to machines so that confusion is avoided.

Note that all markings should conform to the standards of BS5378 or the Safety Signs Regulations 1980.

Health and safety warnings
As with markings, all work equipment must carry sufficient warnings and warning devices about actual or likely risks to health and safety that may remain after all other steps to eliminate or minimize risks have been taken (Regulation 24). These warnings

must be clear, unambiguous, easily perceived and understood by anyone reading them.

Warning signs may be permanent and printed, temporary and portable, attached to or printed on work equipment, incorporated into equipment or positioned closely to it. Examples of warnings are:

- those included in systems of work
- those included in permits to work
- handouts to reinforce information, instruction and training
- warning notices giving safety instructions, such as 'hard hats must be worn' or 'ear defenders must be worn'
- warning notices of prohibitions, such as 'not to be operated by persons under 18 years of age'.

Warning devices may be audible, such as alarms or sirens, or visible, such as flashing red or amber lights. There may also be lights on control panels.

Combined markings and warnings On many occasions, it will be beneficial to *combine* marking *and* warning signs together in one, which is quite acceptable. Care should be taken, however, to ensure that the differences in the information conveyed are clear.

Guidance Notes

All guards and fences should conform to British Standards. To assist you, the British Standards Institution has produced an excellent book, *British Standard Code of Practice for Safety of Machinery* (BS5304, 1988), which is commended by the HSE to employers who have duties under the HASWA. It is available from the British Standards Institution, 2 Park Street, London W1A 2BS (tel: 0171 629 9000). This Standard supersedes BS5304 (1975), which has been withdrawn.

Sources of help

Your local HSE office will be pleased to advise on any aspect of work equipment safety and guarding (their address and telephone number can be found in your local telephone and/or business directory and callers can remain anonymous if they wish).

23

Manual handling

During the 1980s and 1990s manufacturing industry in Britain has been very much on the decrease, while service and retail industries have grown considerably. With the opening of warehouses, assembly plants and many very large supermarkets, the number of people employed in occupations likely to involve significant amounts of manual handling now exceeds 10 million. Employees across all industries move heavy objects often with little or no mechanical assistance, but service industries present steadily increasing manual handling risks as employees move and store products, set up display areas and load shelves.

In 1972–74, manual handling accounted for 27 per cent of all reportable (that is, over three days' absence) work-related injuries; by 1984 this figure had risen to 29 per cent. By 1991/92 manual handling injuries had further risen to a staggering 34 per cent of all injuries (an HSC statistic), or over 55 000 injuries. A conservative estimate of the total cost to industry of manual handling injuries, in terms of lost output and medical treatment, is put at £90 million per year; while the cost to the nation of musculoskeletal disease exceeds £25 billion per year.

By far the most common cause of back pain is the mechanical failure of some part of the structure of the spine. This usually results from overexertion, such as lifting weights that are too heavy for the individual, overreaching, pulling, pushing and carrying, and from awkward movements that put additional stress on the vertebrae and nerves. Most injuries are sprains and strains, particularly of the back; others include amputations, fractures, lacerations and bruises. There are also largely unquantifiable problems of cumulative back injuries resulting in temporary or permanent physical impairment or permanent disability.

Not all back problems result from work-related activities. However, increasing instances of absence from work due to back pain/injury (heightened by statistics such as the foregoing) and the growth of associated civil claims for damages have highlighted the need for improved safety standards in manual handling.

Although existing general provisions prohibited the employment of anyone to lift, carry or move a load that was so heavy as to be likely to cause injury, legislation that related specifically to manual handling was inadequate, largely ineffective, applied only to certain industries and had proven difficult to interpret and enforce. Also, whereas certain existing provisions concentrated on the weights of loads to be handled, the new Regulations adopt a modern, ergonomic approach with weight being only one of the considerations.

The terminology

It will be helpful to define certain terms that are used in relation to manual handling.

- *Injury* The Manual Handling Regulations apply to injuries to the spine, upper and lower limbs and the neck caused by manually handling loads and includes those injuries arising from the weight, shape, size, external condition, rigidity or lack of rigidity of the load or the movement of the load's contents.
  Injuries resulting from contact with toxic or corrosive properties of loads because of spillages or leakages or from external contamination are covered by other Regulations, such as the COSHH Regulations 1988. If, of course, a substance such as oil is spilt and causes a person to fall and injure themselves while handling loads, then that *would* be covered by these Regulations, but the risk of skin disease from the oil would be covered elsewhere.
- *Load* A load is a discrete movable object moved by manual handling and not by wholly mechanical means, such as a fork-lift truck. A 'load' in this context would include a human patient during medical attention, an animal during veterinary treatment and material conveyed on a shovel or fork. A lever or handle attached to a machine is not included.
- *Manual handling operation* Manual handling is the movement or supporting of a load by human effort and not by wholly mechanical means, such as a fork-lift truck. This includes lifting, putting down, pushing, pulling, carrying, supporting a load while stationary and moving a load by hand or by bodily force. The utilization of handling aids would be included in these Regulations if some manual effort is involved, such as when pulling a load on a manually operated hydraulic pallet truck. The test applied is the question 'Is the force applied human or mechanical?' If it is human, then it is included.
- *Risk assessment* The process of identifying if hazards exist, what those hazards are (whether manual handling hazards or arising from other factors, such as repetitive activities) and assessing the risk factors in relation to manual handling hazards. The objective of risk assessments is to determine those risk factors, eliminate or minimize their impact and otherwise control those risks (this aspect of the Regulations is covered in some depth in Chapter 18).
- *Ergonomics* The study of the application of physical and biological factors to the relationship between individual workers and their tasks and working environment. Ergonomics includes the following subjects:
  —an individual's ability to carry out a manual handling activity
  —the nature, shape, weight and size of the load being handled
  —the working environment in which the handling takes place
  —what control measures are necessary to comply with ergonomic factors.
- *Risk factors* Risk factors arise from two main sources:

1. posture and activities that can cause lower-back injuries
2. incorrect lifting techniques, which increase the risk of worker error and injuries.

These can be further subdivided into two factors:

1. *biomechanical risk factors* the further away from the body a load is held, the heavier becomes the effective weight and the greater the stress on the spine and thus the risk of injury, and, when the spine is twisted and/or bent forwards while the force of a load is applied to it, the risk is still further heightened

2. *exposure risk factors* the greater the number of times a load is handled during a shift, the greater the chances are that the cumulative effects of fatigue and the biomechanical risk factors mentioned above will cause injury.

• *Repetitive strain injury (RSI)* An injury, usually to the upper limbs, caused by constant, repetitive movements and resulting in a disorder, such as tenosynovitis, which is inflammation of the myelin sheathing around the tendons in the fingers, wrist or elbow.

• *Upper limb disorder (ULD) and work-related upper limb disorder (WRULD)* Another result of constant repetitive movements can be ULD, which is a problem of pain and soreness in the arms and shoulders. When this occurs in the workplace, it is called *work-related ULD* (WRULD).

The legislation

In 1990, the EC produced a Directive (90/269/EEC) on the manual handling of loads. This Directive was implemented in the UK by the Manual Handling Operations Regulations 1992 (Man. Hdlg. Regs), which became effective on 1 January 1993. These Regulations are accompanied by an ACOP and cross-refer to that part of section 2(2)(b) of the HASWA that deals with handling. The Man. Hdlg. Regs further refine other manual handling requirements laid down by mines and quarries, agriculture, factories, offices, shops and railway premises legislation.

The scope of the Manual Handling Regulations

The Manual Handling Regulations apply to all manual handling of loads, that is, where loads are handled by human effort as compared to mechanical handling by crane, fork-lift or hoist. They apply to all industries where manual handling is carried on, including mines, quarries and offshore oil and gas industries. Self-employed people also have a duty under these Regulations towards themselves and anyone they employ.

The Man. Hdlg. Regs do not apply to sea-going ships in normal activities undertaken on board under the direction of the master, but would apply when the vessel is in dock or port or when shore-based contractors carry out work on the ship when within territorial waters.

The requirements of the Manual Handling Regulations

It will be helpful to first list the Regulations and then to summarize the most important overall requirements. The Regulations are:

4, duties of employers
4(1)(a), to avoid manual handling
4(1)(b)(i), risk assessments
4(1)(b)(ii), to reduce the risk of injury
4(1)(b)(iii), the load; additional information
4(2), to review the assessment
5, duties of employees
6, exemption certificates
7, extension outside Great Britain
8, repeals and revocations.

Further important elements are:

Schedule 1, factors to be considered when making assessments
Appendix 1, numerical guidelines for assessment
Appendix 2, example of assessment check-list.

The duties of employers

The Manual Handling Regulations place three main duties on employers, with the qualification for each one 'so far as is reasonably practicable'. They are to:

1. avoid manual handling activities wherever possible
2. carry out risk assessments of all manual handling activities that take place in the workplace and cannot be avoided; this (in summary) has four basic steps:
   - first, determine the likelihood of injury, taking account of individual workers' capabilities
   - second, determine whether the injury is likely to be a handling injury or one arising from repetitive movements, such as RSI or WRULD (do not ignore RSI or WRULD but deal with them separately to those arising from manual handling)
   - third, assess the risk of injury in each manual handling activity, highlighting factors that most contribute to that risk of injury
   - fourth, decide on the extent to which the risk of injury should be reduced
3. eliminate or otherwise minimize any risks of injury arising from manual handling operations that have been identified in those assessments
4. do not forget to assess the risks in the one-off jobs that maintenance and other workers undertake.

Accompanying these three duties is the requirement to consider ergonomic factors in relation to handling, not simply the actual weight-value of the load being lifted. A method of determining approximate numerical values for maximum weights lifted, depending on how the load is handled in relation to the body, is given in Appendix 2 of the ACOP.

Avoidance of manual handling

Can you avoid manual handling by moving the load in some other way? The first requirement of the Regulations is for employers, so far as is reasonably practicable, to avoid the need for employees to undertake *any* manual handling operations that involve the risk of injury.

This is not always easy and depends very much on the nature of the load, the individual(s) who will lift it and the working environment. You may prefer to move a load by fork-lift truck, but it may not be possible to bring a fork-lift truck in, due to the design and construction of the workplace. Some other means should, therefore, be sought, such as a manually operated hoist or hydraulic truck.

If it is *not* possible to move the load by other means, then you move to the next step in the procedure, assessments.

Assessments and reducing the risks

Assess the risks The first requirement is to carry out a risk assessment. There are five main steps specified in the assessments procedure (steps A to E), and it is important that each is carried out in sequence to assure completeness.

Reduce the risks Having assessed the risks in manual handling, the second requirement is to *reduce* the risks. There are four main steps in the procedure for reducing risks (which follow exactly steps B to E of the risk assessment).

Precursors to risk reduction Before looking at each of the four points (B to E) individually, there are a number of important considerations that will need to be taken account of, some of which are included in your assessments:

- ergonomics
- mechanical assistance
- involvement of the workforce
- industry-specific guidance
- appropriate steps
- check-list.

It will be important, in seeking to reduce the risks of injury, to take an *ergonomic* approach to the task, the load, working environment and individual capability. Examine the relationship between each of these and the ergonomics of the workforce, fitting the manual handling operations to the individuals instead of the other way around (which so often happens). If the task, the load and the working environment are designed with the worker in mind, this will go a long way to reducing or even eliminating risks of injury.

Wherever possible, *mechanical assistance* of some kind should be brought in to reduce the risk of injury by taking some or all of the load off the handler. If, of course, you can completely eliminate manual handling by utilizing, for example, fork-lift trucks, this will also eliminate manual handling risks (but do not forget to also assess and deal with risks associated with fork-lift trucks themselves). If it is not possible to completely eliminate manual handling, then mechanical assistance, such as the following, should be used, instead of the handler carrying the load:

- a hydraulic pallet truck on which to put a load (but remember to assess the likely risks in pulling it in the working environment — see D: assess the working environment, later in this chapter
- a hydraulic hoist on which the load is conveyed
- roller conveyors or moving conveyors
- trolleys of various types, from glass-carrying to bins for bolts
- rotating lift-tables (to avoid manually manoeuvring)
- hydraulic cranes to lift goods on to lorries
- sack trolleys
- patient lifts and chairs in medical contexts
- electric lifts and mobile gantries
- overhead crane and boom, with slings
- powered vacuum lifters (for glass or heavy, smooth objects).

Sections 2(4), 2(5) and 2(6) of the HASWA require employers to cooperate with employees and this is extended in the Management of Health and Safety at Work Regulations 1992 to *involvement of the workforce* (see Chapter 19). This is further enhanced in Regulation 4(1)(b)(ii). You should consult with all your employees where manual handling is undertaken, to ensure that they understand the requirements and can contribute to the design and implementation of safe working practices, as a worker who is involved in this way is more likely to be motivated into compliance than one who has had a method imposed on them. Where there are safety representatives or safety committees, these should be consulted with and involved on behalf of the employees.

You should seek *industry-specific guidance* from recognized sources pertaining to risks peculiar to your particular industry and/or group of occupations. These might be employers' associations by industry or professional bodies. Your local HSE office or your local EHO will always be pleased to put you in touch with specialists in your industry and occupation grouping.

Throughout the various Regulations, little specific advice or direction is given, but the words 'adequate' and 'appropriate' occur frequently. You must take *appropriate steps* to reduce the risks of injury, but it is for you to determine what those appropriate steps are. It is also for you to satisfy an inspector that your steps are, in fact, appropriate as well as 'reasonable and practicable' in terms of section 40 of the HASWA.

It is an almost impossible task to undertake inspections or audits without the aid of a *check-list*. This is even more true with complicated risk assessments, the objectives of which are to reduce the risks of injury from manual handling. An example of a check-list, based on Appendix 2 of the Regulations, is given in Appendix 13.

Having laid the foundation, we can now begin to assess and determine how to reduce the risks of injury in manual handling. It will be advantageous to follow the same structured approach in both your risk assessment and risk-reduction plan, that is, take each aspect in turn in steps A to E, which are:

- A, determine whether manual handling is involved in the job and, where it is,
- B, assess the task
- C, assess the load
- D, assess the working environment
- E, assess individual capability,

taking 'appropriate' steps to reduce the risks presented by each aspect as you progress.

Precisely how much emphasis is placed on reducing the risks presented by *each* of the four factors B to E will depend on the findings of your assessments and the handling jobs being done. It will be a matter of striking a balance between the different aspects.

Step A: determine the manual handling element Before carrying out your assessments and devising a risk-reduction plan, *determine* whether actual manual handling is involved in your operations. If loads are moved by, for example, fork-lift truck, conveyor belt or hoist with no human effort involved, then employees are not handling anything manually. However, if a combination of human and non-human power is used, as with a manually operated pallet truck or hydraulic hoist, which have to be pulled or pushed by a worker, then this *is* manual handling, comes under the Regulations and should be assessed.

If the task is not manual handling *per se*, but, rather, moving products in repetitive movements, such as pulling products from an assembly line or filling machines and packing them, then this is not a manual handling risk and should be assessed separately.

Accident records An excellent way of identifying actual or potential manual handling injuries is to review your accident book (DSS Form BI510). Where problems of strains and sprains have occurred, these will possibly be due to manual handling, so assess the departments and jobs where those injuries occurred. Note, however, that some injuries may be *described* as handling injuries, but you will need to carefully examine them to confirm whether or not they actually are. Could they possibly be RSI or WRULD injuries caused by repetitive movements when moving products around, such as described above? In this case, these are *not* manual handling injuries and should, again, be assessed separately. You do not want to waste time in this context on non-applicable items.

Having determined that manual handling is involved in your operations, you can now assess those jobs and begin to reduce the risks your assessments identify. The Regulations treat 'assessments' and 'reducing the risks' separately (Regulations 4(1)(b)(ii) and (ii) respectively), going through the total process of assessments before dealing with risk reduction. However, to avoid confusion and the need to continually refer back in the text, we shall deal with both assessment *and* risk reduction under each heading in steps B to E.

Steps B to E: *Assess* the likelihood of injury arising from those manual handling activities, then take steps to *reduce the risks*; taking account of the following four main aspects of the job:

B1. Assess the TASK;	**B2**. Reduce the risk in the TASK.
C1. Assess the LOAD;	**C2**. Reduce the risk in the LOAD.
D1. Assess the WORKING ENVIRONMENT;	**D2**. Reduce the risk in the WORKING ENVIRONMENT.
E1. Assess INDIVIDUAL CAPABILITY;	**E2**. Reduce the risk in INDIVIDUAL CAPABILITY.

Step B1: assess the task and reduce any risks The task involves a number of factors and these all need to be *assessed*:

- distance of the load from the trunk
- weight forces
- activity loads on the spine
- general posture
- trunk posture, whether or not the task involves:
  —twisting the trunk
  —stooping
  —reaching upwards
  —combined twisting, stooping and/or reaching
  —excessive lifting upwards or lowering distances
- work pattern, whether or not the task involves:
  —excessive pushing and/or pulling of the load
  —rigidity of the load
  —sudden movement of the load
  —frequent or prolonged physical effort
  —a rate of work imposed by a system or process
- carrying distances, whether or not they are excessive
- breaks, whether or not there are sufficient rest or recovery periods
- whether or not handling is carried on while seated
- whether or not the load is lifted from a low level while seated
- whether or not there is team handling.

Having summarized the important factors of the task, let's look at each of these factors in a little more detail.

Regarding the *distance of the load from the trunk*, the further a load is held away from the body, the lower is the individual capability of lifting it. This is shown in Table 23.1 and Fig. 23.1.

Table 23.1 Reduced individual handling capability as hands/load moves away from the body

Distance from spine	Individual capability
−20 cm (elbows back)	100%
35 cm	80%
50 cm	50%
70 cm	30%
over 70 cm*	20%

*At this distance from the body, the back begins to bend forwards, as shown in Fig. 23.1.

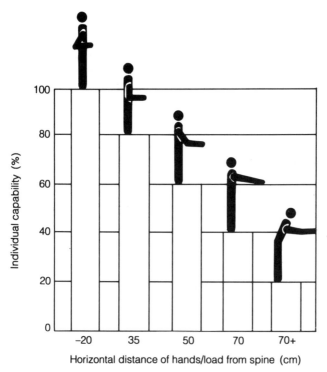

Horizontal distance of hands/load from spine (cm)

Fig. 23.1 Reduced individual handling capability as hands/load moves away from the body

Regarding *weight forces*, the further a load is held away from the body and the higher it is held, the heavier the effective weight and the lower is the individual's capability of lifting it. There are ideal maximums of weights that you should permit men and women to handle, dependent on personal factors, and these are outlined in Tables 23.2 and 23.3.

The weights given in Tables 23.2 and 23.3 are those laid down in the Regulations as a guide and may, in carefully assessed situations, be exceeded by a factor of two (for example, a male could possibly lift a 50-kg weight at elbow height, or a female

Table 23.2   Maximum weights of loads for men

Height held at	Close to body	At arm's length from body
Head height	10 kg	5 kg
Shoulder height	20 kg	10 kg
Elbow height	**25 kg**	15 kg
Thigh height	20 kg	10 kg
Mid-lower leg height	10 kg	5 kg

Table 23.3   Maximum weights of loads for 95 per cent of women

Height held at	Close to body	At arm's length from body
Head height	6.7 kg	3.3 kg
Shoulder height	13.3 kg	6.7 kg
Elbow height	**16.7 kg**	10 kg
Thigh height	13.3 kg	6.7 kg
Mid-lower leg height	6.7 kg	3.3 kg

Table 23.4   Weight forces on the spine

Distances from the body	Force ratio
25 cm	5:1
75 cm	15:1

could possibly lift a 33.4-kg weight at elbow height). However, you must be careful, if these guidelines are exceeded, to ensure that no employee is asked to handle a weight that is beyond their personal capability (Regulation 4(1)(b)(ii)) as to do so could increase the risk of injury and have consequences for the employer in the event of injury.

In addition to the increase in effective weights as a load is held further away from the body, as shown in Tables 23.2 and 23.3, there is also an increase in the ratio of weight forces on the spine as the load is held away from the body. How a load is handled, the size of the load and its weight are all related directly to stresses that are applied to the spine and back muscles, as shown in Table 23.4.

Thus, the increase in the force on the spine as the load is held further away from the body is far greater than the increase in the 'effective' weight of a load — ample reason for exercising great care when designing systems of work for manual handling.

This leads on to *activity loads on the spine* Each activity a person undertakes places a load on the spine. This load varies according to the activity and the weight of the

Table 23.5 Approximate effective loads on the L3 disc in a 70-kg individual during various activities or postures (*Source*: Nachemson — Lumbar intradiscal pressure)

Activity or posture	Load
Supine	30 kg
Supine (lying on back) in traction	10 kg
Standing	70 kg
Walking	85 kg
Twisting	90 kg
Bending sideways	95 kg
Sitting upright, unsupported	100 kg
Coughing	110 kg
Isometric abdominal exercises	110 kg
Straining (overreaching, lifting)	120 kg
Bending 20° forwards	120 kg
Active back extension beyond normal limit	150 kg
Doing sit-up exercises, knees straight	175 kg
Doing sit-up exercises, knees bent	180 kg
Bending 20° forwards with a 10-kg weight in each hand	185 kg
Lifting a 20-kg weight in each hand, knees bent, back straight	210 kg
Lifting a 20-kg weight in each hand, knees straight, back bent	340 kg

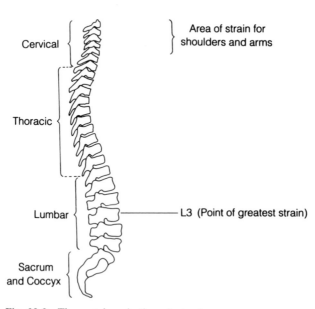

Fig. 23.2 The vertebrae in the spinal column

individual. In Table 23.5 is detailed the approximate load on the third lumbar disc (disc L3). See Fig. 23.2 to find out where it is located in the spine. Note the curve of the spine, especially of the lumbar region and how the spaces between the vertebrae in this region are larger at the front than the rear.

Regarding *general posture*, poor posture can bring increased risks of loss of control of the load and, with it, sudden unpredictable increases in stress on the spine. The stability of an object during manual handling can affect posture, and if the hands and feet are not well placed to transmit forces efficiently between the floor and the load, the risk of injury is further increased.

The following questions should be asked while observing handlers to assess the likelihood of injury being caused by poor general posture.

- Is the handler in a stable body position, whether standing or crouching, and with a straight and substantially upright back?
- Are both hands used to grasp the load?
- Are the hands no more than shoulder-width apart?
- Is the load:
  —positioned centrally to the handler
  —symmetrical (that is, not uneven and peculiarly shaped)
  —stable
  —able to be readily grasped?
- Does the working area restrict the handler's posture and inhibit adjustment?
- Does the working environment interfere with the handler's ability to perform tasks without risk of injury? (Environmental factors include heat, cold, wet, floor conditions and PPE.)

Related to this is the subject of *trunk posture*. Ask whether or not the task involves the following:

- *Twisting the trunk* Stress in the lower back area is increased considerably if the trunk is twisted, particularly if there is a repeated twisting to and fro and if a static twisted-trunk posture is maintained.
- *Stooping* Stooping can also increase stress on the lower back, both bending forwards or leaning forwards with the trunk straight. By bending or leaning, the effective weight of the load is increased and this is added to by the weight of the trunk itself.
- *Reaching upwards* This movement both causes the spine to lean backwards (causing stress on the lower back) and places additional stress on the arms and back. Controlling the load being handled becomes more difficult and the arms are more prone to injury, being extended and supporting a load.
- *Combined twisting, stooping and/or reaching* The ability of the individual to manually handle loads can be considerably reduced where there is a *combination* of any of these factors. The combined effects on individual ability can be more serious than might be suggested by the simple addition of the effects of individual factors. Thus, these combinations should be avoided wherever possible.

As to *work pattern*, you need to find out whether or not the task involves any of the following:

- *Excessive pushing and/or pulling of the load* The risk of injury to the arms, shoulders and back is increased if the load is pushed with the hands below thigh level (also called knuckle level) or above shoulder height. It should also be remembered that the risk of slipping and resultant injury is greater when pushing or pulling a load; slippery or sloping surfaces increase this risk, of course.
- *The rigidity of the load* The problem of inertia can subject the spine to an unexpected force when the handler pulls on the load and experiences unexpected resistance due to the rigidity of the load. Rigidity can be caused by a number of

things, such as being lodged in place by an obstacle or structure, friction resistance of the surface across which it is being moved or the sheer weight of the load.

- *Sudden movement of the load* Here, the problem of inertia is experienced in a different way, that is, the person does not *expect* the load to move easily or freely and, having applied *extra* human force to the lifting, is not able to retain complete control of the load once it moves. This can arise when freeing a rigid load, for example.

- *Frequent or prolonged physical effort* Even quite modest loads can create large risks of injury if they are handled frequently. This risk is increased if there are jerky or hurried movements. Another risk here is of fatigue, which will further increase the risk of injury as the handler becomes tired and less capable.

- *A rate of work imposed by a system or process* Where the rate of work cannot be controlled by the handler, but is determined by the job, particular care has to be taken to avoid the risk of injury and fatigue. Brief rest breaks or periods undertaking work of a different nature are very beneficial in reducing risks of injury and particularly fatigue (see Breaks, below).

Regarding *carrying distances*, assess whether or not they are excessive. The greater the distance over which a load has to be carried, the greater the effective weight and potential for injury of that weight. We all know from experience how a suitcase seems to get heavier as we carry it for longer. The result is prolonged physical stress, greater fatigue and increased risk of injury. As a rough guide, if a load is carried for more than 10 metres, the physical demands of carrying that load will predominate the demands of lifting and lowering it, the individual's ability to carry it will be reduced and, when it comes to lowering the load after carrying it a long way, the tendency may be to drop the load, thus causing injury not only to the lower back, but to the feet also.

Regarding the subject of *breaks*, ask whether or not there are sufficient rest or recovery periods. The injurious effects of lengthy, uninterrupted periods of physically demanding work have been proven by research and experience. Thought should be given to the provision of adequate rest breaks (total breaks from the work) and giving workers recovery periods (a change of task in which different sets of muscles and movements are used).

Regarding *handling carried on while seated* If workers have to *handle loads while seated*, this can cause considerable strain, especially on the spine and arms, as they do not have the benefit of the use of the more powerful leg muscles and there is no counterbalancing of the handler's body. All the energy is exerted by the arms, shoulders and back, which have comparatively weaker muscles. Similarly, all the weight is concentrated on those upper portions of the body. Handling while seated does not normally allow the load to be held against the body (which could reduce its effective weight) and the handler will have to reach and/or lean forwards with the result that a heavier effective load and strain on the arms, shoulders and back is created.

Similarly, *low-level lifting while seated* If a *load is lifted from the floor or a lower level when handling while seated*, this will inevitably result in a combined twisting and stooping movement with the attendant risks discussed in relation to trunk posture above.

Team handling Is the load too heavy for one person to handle alone? If so, arrangements should be made for *team handling*, in which two or more handlers will lift the load in concert. By this means, the weight of the load is shared equally between the handlers and there is a combined, rhythmic movement. However, if the lift is made out of sequence, with one lifting prematurely or at a different rate to the other(s), there is risk of injury to one or both/all of the handlers. Team members could also impede each others' vision or movement or there could be insufficient handholds for all team members — each of these situations presenting risks of injury. Training should be given in correct methods of team handling.

Step B2: Reduce the risk in the task Having assessed the risks of the task, any risks discovered have to be *reduced*. There are a number of ways in which you can reduce the risk of injury in the task itself, including:

- improving the task layout
- using the body more efficiently
- improving posture
- improving the work routine
- handling while seated
- team handling
- PPE
- maintenance and accessibility of equipment
- safety of machinery.

Let us look at each of these options in turn.

Improving the task layout The first question to ask is 'Does the workplace facilitate good *task layout*?' If the design of the workplace is such that the layout is poor, then first consideration needs to be given to whether or not it would be sensible to relocate the handling operation. If the workplace is OK by design, then changes in layout can bring about improvements in the flow of materials or product, often with the added benefits of increased efficiency and productivity. One less movement or a few less steps distance in just one handling operation can add up to considerable savings in energy and efficiency over a full day. In this respect, the most efficient position for the storage of loads is at about waist height; storage significantly above or below waist height can cause fatigue in handling and should be reserved for lighter loads.

Using the body more efficiently The body has energy that, if utilized effectively, can make the task easier. It is always advantageous to hold or carry a load as close to the body as possible as, in this way, the effective weight of the object is reduced and its descent can be slowed when lowering, as friction with the body acts like a brake. In training, always tell delegates to 'lift with the legs', as when this principle is combined with good kinetic handling techniques, a lot of energy and pain is saved. You should try to organize the task so that the stronger parts of the body (the legs and shoulders) are used effectively, while the weaker parts of the body (the back and arms) are not submitted to strain, for example, so that handlers do not lift heavy objects with the hands/arms while seated (putting a strain on the arms and back) or carry out twisting, stooping or stretching movements (putting a strain on the back).

Improving posture is very important as good posture is crucial to safe lifting. The basic rules are to keep the back straight, as near to vertical as practicable, head raised and (when lifting or lowering) one foot flat on the floor with the heel of the other raised. When designing the task layout, avoidance of stooping, twisting and stretching will aid good posture, as will ensuring that the handler gets as close to the object as possible.

Improving the work routine Careful attention to organizing the work routine can also reduce the risk of injury. 'A change is as good as a rest' is a well-used and proven adage. Apart from the methods of handling, you should also examine the frequency of use of particular methods of handling. If particular postures or methods are repeated continuously or maintained for considerable lengths of time, then this will increase risks of injury. So, you should vary the work routine to ensure that there is a variety of tasks and relief from a set routine. The frequency of use of particular methods can also influence injury risks. Job rotation is a very useful way of relieving stress on the body caused by prolonged exposure to particular types of movement.

Handling while seated Having assessed that the *handling task is carried out when seated*, and considered the weight and dimensions of the load, whether it would produce strain on the back and arms or whether there are twisting, stooping or reaching movements that could cause back injury, you now need to eliminate or reduce the risks of injury by modifying those movements or making the load compatible with them.

Team handling Having assessed that lifting a load would be difficult or unsafe for one handler, you should then use *team handling*, with two or more persons. You should, however, also ensure that the risks of team handling outlined earlier in this section are dealt with. It will also be important to ensure that there is sufficient space for the team to handle loads safely and to manoeuvre as a team. Also, in team handling, one person should be nominated as 'caller' and should control the lift with, for example, the words 'one, two, three, lift', so that both or all handlers move together. If the load is *particularly* awkward, even for a group, see whether the use of lifting aids, such as stretchers or slings, would help to reduce the risk of injury.

Personal protective equipment (PPE) There can, as discussed earlier, be hazards associated with the load due to its design or its contents. If there are risks of injury due to sharp edges, hot surfaces or corrosive substances, then PPE must be issued. This may include gloves, aprons, overalls, gaiters or safety footwear. Better still, particularly with hazardous substances, is there a way of avoiding manually handling this load or alternative methods of handling it so that the risks from the product or load do not present themselves? If PPE does need to be used, it should be comfortable, ergonomically efficient and not inhibit freedom of movement.

Regarding *maintenance and accessibility of equipment*, the requirement here is very similar to that of the PPE Regulations (see Chapter 22). The correct maintenance of all PPE, having it readily available in a convenient place where it is protected and having a system of reporting all defects and losses will do much to further reduce risks of injury where PPE would be of help. PPE that is poorly maintained or not readily available is not likely to be used and, if used, not likely to protect employees.

Safety of machinery The final consideration in reducing risks of injury in the task is the *safety of machinery* itself in relation to the people who are required to handle it. We take for granted, sometimes, that guards are fitted in the manufacture of machinery, but what of safe handling of that machinery? Can handlers manoeuvre machinery safely without risks of injury to themselves? Some provisions may be necessary. This is a requirement of the EC Directive (as amended) on product safety (89/392/EEC), which requires that the design of machinery facilitates its safe handling.

Step C1: assess the load The load needs to be as carefully *assessed* as the task. You need to find out the load's:

- size
- shape
- weight
- stability
- design characteristics.

Let us look at each of these in turn.

Regarding *the size of the load*, if it is very large, even if it is lightweight, it can be very difficult for the handler to control the load during handling and their vision may be obstructed by the load itself. Size can also result in poor posture problems, also.

Regarding *the shape of the load* The way in which a load can be held will be affected by its *shape* and the risk of injury will be increased in the following ways:

- if a load is larger than 75 cm in any one dimension, it is likely to present a handling problem for the average person, especially if this size is exceeded in more than one dimension
- if the load is uneven or wide at one side, but narrow at the other, then this can create problems (for example, a typewriter is normally larger at the rear and the weight is unevenly distributed, so, to avoid risk of injury, it should be carried with the back of the machine against the body, which stabilizes the load)
- if the load is bulky or unwieldy (say, if it is too large for the hands to reach the corners farthest from the body or if the bottom front corners are not within reach when carried waist high), then getting a good grip on the load will not be possible
- if the load does not have convenient handholds, this will present problems for the handler, especially if the surfaces are very smooth and likely to slip from perspiring hands.

Regarding *the weight of the load*, legislation has concentrated on the *weights* of loads for many years, but this is only one factor. While you should follow the principles set out in Tables 23.1, 23.2 and 23.3 above, there are other important considerations. Ergonomics (defined earlier) is a very important consideration — what of that weight and its distribution in relation to the build, age, sex and health of the handler? What if the load is resistant to movement because of its weight or rigidity? These things must also be considered. The way in which a heavy load will be lifted is also important, especially as not all such handling is effected by means of the ideal method — two-handed lift, in front of and close to the body; often lifting involves sideways moves, with twisting of the trunk or it is done in some other asymmetrical way.

Regarding *stability of the load* What of the *stability* of the load? Examples of *unstable* loads would be large vessels partially filled with fluid, stacks of items of non-uniform type, medical patients or livestock. Stress factors on the body are more unpredictable with such loads and this instability may present unforeseen, sudden and unexpected stresses — especially if the handler is unfamiliar with the types of load being handled. Where patients or livestock are handled, this can present problems of a 'load' being unwilling or unable to cooperate with the handler and, thus, presenting further risks. The careful assessment of safe systems of handling will be especially important here.

Regarding *design characteristics of the load* Various *design characteristics* can affect the handler's ability to move the load safely, so find out the following:

- Does the load have a very high centre of gravity? This can present problems of stability and uneven weight distribution.

- Does the load have external features that will make it difficult to hold?
- Does the load have sharp edges or rough surfaces?
- Is the load difficult to grasp, possibly with slippery surfaces?
- Are the contents likely to shift?
- Is the load hot?
- Does the load contain substances that could be hazardous to the handler or others if spilt?

Step C2: reduce the risk in the load Now you have assessed the risks of the load, any you have found now have to be reduced. There are a number of ways in which the risk can be reduced in relation to the load itself. They include making the load:

- lighter
- smaller and/or easier to handle
- easier to grip
- more stable
- safer to carry.

Let us look at each of these in turn.

Regarding making the load *lighter*, many loads are too heavy for one person to handle safely, that is, they could endanger themselves or the load itself. You can, of course, employ team handling, outlined earlier in Step B, but if this is not possible, then the load should be made lighter. Large loads should be broken down into smaller, more manageable weights. Items such as liquids and powders can be separated into smaller containers and large containers that hold a number of small packets/boxes can be broken down into smaller packages. However, do bear in mind the increased handling involved with increased numbers of smaller items — the fatigue of frequent movements may outweigh the gains of easier lifting.

Regarding making the load *smaller and/or easier to handle* is closely related to making the load lighter, but should be considered on its own also, for example, where a load is lightweight but is quite large and unwieldy. If loads are extra large, they can be difficult to grasp, unsteady and easily blown in a gust of wind. A large, unsteady, light load can be just as hazardous as a small, heavy one. If your very large loads are from your production or packaging lines, perhaps a look at the design, production and packaging process might pay dividends.

Regarding making the load *easier to grip* is vital where they have a very smooth surface. Can the material from which the containers are made be changed to give some 'friction' grip or can you provide some supplementary gripping equipment? If there are no handholds, can they be fitted? Handholds should:

- be sufficiently wide to allow a full grip across the palm, not squeezing the hand, allowing for gloves where worn
- positioned so as to avoid stooping when lifting the object from a low level, that is, placed nearer to the bottom
- allow for the arms to be bent while carrying, as holding the arms straight can quickly cause fatigue and strains.

Sharp corners and jagged edges, protrusions or awkward shapes, can also be a problem (see below). If these present difficulties to handlers, can you find some safe and easy way of grasping the load?

Regarding making the load *more stable*, the contents of packages should not be able to shift unexpectedly when being carried. If a load is generally unstable, then some way of safely controlling the load while it is carried should be sought, such as using slings, nets, cradles or (if safe) pallets. If powders or liquids are being carried, the containers should be filled with the minimum of free space so that the contents will not move about. If the contents are not sufficient to completely fill the containers, then use smaller ones.

Look at making the load *safer to carry*. In addition to sharp corners and jagged edges affecting grip (above), care should be taken to ensure that the outside of the load is free from oil, grease, dust, hazardous substances (overspills, say) and anything else that might adversely affect the handler. If containers are either very hot or cold, then they should be adequately insulated or, if this is not practicable, protective gloves/aprons and so on should be given to handlers to use. Do remember the advice on PPE given in Step B earlier and in Chapter 22.

Step D1: assess the working environment The environment in which handling operations take place is very important, as factors outside of the task or the load itself can have a detrimental effect on handlers. Working environment factors to *assess* include:

- limited space
- uneven, slippery or unstable floors
- variations in floor levels and work surfaces
- extreme variations in heights or storage shelving
- extremes of temperature
- extremes of humidity
- poor ventilation
- gusts of air
- poor lighting.

Each of these is briefly dealt with in turn.

Regarding *limited space*, if that available in the working environment inhibits free movement and the adoption of good posture when handling goods, then the risk of fatigue and injury will be increased. Also, restricted headroom will cause stooping, with attendant stresses on the spine. Furniture, fixtures and other obstructions that are placed too closely together will increase the need for twisting or leaning with further stresses on the spine. Finally, working areas that are very compact and narrow walkways will hinder the safe and comfortable movement of bulky loads.

Regarding *uneven, slippery or unstable floors* There are more injuries resulting from slips, trips and falls on *uneven, slippery or unstable floors* than any other cause of accidents. These also make up the greatest number of 'reportable' injuries that arise while engaged in manual handling on unsafe floors. Such floors also hinder smooth and confident movement and create unpredictable hazards. Floors that are subject to movement or instability (such as mobile work platforms, moving trains or boats or detached trailers) can present sudden movements, which can bring unpredictable stresses on the body and further risk of injury.

Regarding *variations in floor levels and work surfaces*, such as steep slopes, steps and changes from one level to another (as with joined buildings), can present real hazards. The risk is greater from variations of this kind if the floor is also wet or slippery or if the handler is pushing or pulling a load up or down a slope, say, on a pallet truck. A 'variation' in levels often not considered is carrying a load up or down a ladder, where a handler has to maintain a safe grip on the ladder *and* the load at the same time — a very difficult and hazardous task indeed.

Regarding *extreme variations* If there are *extreme variations in heights or storage shelving*, this will increase the range of movement upwards and downwards for the handler and, consequently, the risk of injury. For example, repeated lifting from a near floor-level shelf to one at head height will impose considerable stresses on the spine and shoulders.

Regarding *extremes of temperature* Fluctuations in temperature can be withstood by most people, but *extremes of temperature*, either hot or cold, produce problems for handlers. At extremes of heat, the hands perspire and can cause loss of grip. Also, fatigue and dehydration can quite quickly be experienced, resulting in a greater risk of injury. Alternatively, extreme cold will cause a handler's hands and limbs to be stiff and lack dexterity. The issuing of gloves may not resolve the problem as they may hinder movement, impair dexterity and reduce grip. Also, the effect of air movement (hot or cold) on working temperatures should be carefully watched.

Extremes of humidity are also a problem. Poor or low humidity can lead to dehydration in the handler, while very high humidity can lead to perspiration and fatigue. An optimum humidity level should therefore be aimed for.

Poor ventilation People need good ventilation to work comfortably and avoid sick building/office syndrome, whatever their occupation. This is no less important· in manual handling operations. A workplace with *poor ventilation* can cause lethargy, but when there is physical exertion, the available oxygen in the body's system is used up faster, so lack of ventilation will hasten fatigue and increase the risk of injury and ill-health effects.

Gusts of air If there are sudden *gusts of air*, perhaps from doors opening or corridors that are like wind tunnels, this can cause a large load to become unsteady and difficult to handle safely. Care should be taken to screen-off handling areas from such air flows.

Poor lighting If there is *poor lighting*, handlers will not be able to properly assess the nature of the load, nor will they be able to fully see where they are walking when carrying one. If a person has to stoop to see where they are going, this can cause poor posture with its attendant risks of straining the back. Variations in lighting can cause other problems as the shadowed areas cannot be seen into properly (just as an actor cannot see from the glare of the stage lights into the darkened audience), causing the handler to feel unsafe and possibly collide with unseen obstacles. When altering storage areas, remember to reposition light fittings so that they shine between gangways and not over stock areas/shelving themselves.

Step D2: reduce the risk in the working environment Factors in the environment can have adverse effects such as fatigue and lack of well-being, which, sometimes, are more serious than the risks presented by unsafe tasks and loads. Having, therefore, *assessed* the risks in the working environment, you should now seek to *reduce* those risks (eliminating them wherever possible). There are a number of ways of achieving your goal, following the pattern set in your assessments:

- making more space available
- dealing with unsafe floors

- avoiding handling between different levels
- providing optimum heights of storage shelving
- providing optimum temperatures
- providing optimum humidity
- providing ventilation
- controlling gusts of air
- providing good lighting.

Let us look at each of these points in more detail.

Making more space available The amount of *space available* to handlers should be sufficient to facilitate good posture and freedom in handling. Gangways should be sufficiently wide for the size of load being handled, including allowing for a team of handlers to work together safely. Floor space in handling areas should be sufficient both for those working at floor level and those manoeuvring loads within and through the area. But how *can* you provide more space in limited areas? Here are the key ways of achieving this:

- by maintaining good housekeeping standards and ensuring a place for everything and everything in its place so space is not wasted
- by rearranging the furniture and fixtures in the working area to give more available space
- by making the best use of available space; remember that space costs money.

Refer to Chapter 21 for further advice on this aspect.

Dealing with unsafe floors is a priority where manual handling is carried on on a permanent basis. Care should be taken to ensure that the floors are level, even, easily gripped by the feet and free of oil, grease, powders and water, with any spillages cleared up quickly as they occur. On floors liable to become slippery or unstable, slip-resistant surfaces can be laid. Where handling takes place on temporary surfaces, these should be prepared *before* handling commences so that any of these problems are eliminated, with the ground made firm and even. Any platform for temporary working should also be firm and stable.

Avoid handling between different levels as risks of injury will be presented if handlers have to manoeuvre their loads from one floor level to another. Where possible, arrange for all handling to be undertaken at one, even level, but if this is not possible (say, where loads are conveyed between two joined buildings), then you should provide gently sloping ramps with handrails and slip-resistant surfaces. Steep slopes must be avoided. Also, steps should be avoided where regular handling takes place, but, if unavoidable, they should be sufficiently large and evenly spaced (very small steps and uneven spaces between steps create real risks, especially if the handler cannot see the steps properly).

Providing optimum heights of storage shelving will avoid workers reaching excessive distances between very high and very low levels. Storage shelves should be arranged, as far as possible, at a level, ideally, near to waist height (not at or below knee or shoulder height as these will cause stress on the spine as a result of either stooping or overreaching).

Providing optimum temperatures The minimum temperature required in the workplace is 16°C (60.2°F) within one hour of commencement of work, or 13°C (55.4°F) where 'severe physical activity' takes place. These are minimums so work out the *optimum temperatures* suitable for your employees and provide them, for example, remembering that sedentary occupations require higher temperatures for comfort than active ones. Care should be taken that temperatures are not so cold as to inhibit dexterity or movement but not so hot as to cause fatigue or loss of grip through perspiration. (Remember, the *maximum* temperature permitted *with the use of power* is 19°C (66.2°F).)

Providing optimum humidity It is important to provide optimum humidity, that is, enough humidity so that handlers do not dehydrate, but not so high as to cause fatigue. Good ventilation is a great help in getting this right.

Providing optimum ventilation is important to creating a comfortable working environment. Good ventilation is a requirement of section 2(2)(e) of the HASWA. It helps to avoid fatigue, drowsiness, lack of well-being and (as above) high humidity.

Controlling gusts of air helps keep workers safe as loads become unstable and difficult to control if they are affected by gusts of wind. This is particularly so if the load is large and unwieldy yet light — think of what happens with large sheets of wood or plasterboard caught in a gust of wind. Also, handling roofing sheets is very hazardous in these circumstances. Windbreaks or shields should be installed, but, if this is not practicable, team-handling methods should be employed or, if that is not possible either, then you should relocate the handling to a draught- and gust-free area or, in adverse weather conditions, simply reschedule the task.

Providing good lighting, that which is sufficient and well-directed, is essential for safety in areas where handling is undertaken. Shaded passages and walkways along which handlers have to manoeuvre loads must be provided with adequate lighting.

Step E1: assess individual capability Every person *is* different, but this is often overlooked by employers, who will expect person A to carry out a task simply because person B is able to do so. It is very important, however, to appreciate individual differences in capability, which can be influenced by a variety of personal factors. There are two requirements in this area: the first is to *assess* the risk to the individual (Regulation 4(1)(b)(i)); the second, dealt with under E2, is to *reduce* the risks to the individual (Regulation 4(1)(b)(i)).

To *assess* the risk to the individual, the following personal factors should be taken into account:

- sex
- build
- health
- age
- strength
- well-being

The load a person is required to handle should therefore be carefully assessed in the light of these personal factors. There are a few questions to ask concerning individual capability under standardized conditions.

- Does the task require unusual strength or height?
- Does the task present risks to those female employees who are pregnant?
- Does the task present risks to those who might reasonably be considered to be suffering from a health problem?
- Does the task require any special information or training to enable the task to be carried out safely?
- Does the task require PPE?

Each of these are now examined briefly.

Does the handling task require unusual strength or height? If a person is asked to lift and/or carry a load that is too heavy for that individual or if it requires them to reach to a height beyond their stature, then it is *not* within their individual capability. You will need to assess the weight, size, shape and features of the load (as in Step C1 earlier in this chapter) in relation to the six personal factors listed above. For example:

- *women* in general, the lifting strength of women is less than that of men, though the range of abilities for men and women vary widely and often overlap
- *age* normally, lifting ability peaks in the twenties, declines gradually during the forties and reduces more substantially thereafter, so there are greater risks of injury to people in their teens and in their fifties and sixties than in any other age group
- *build* there are marked differences in build in both men and women, with obvious differences in resultant lifting ability
- *health and well-being* it must be recognized that people have health problems that can inhibit their manual handling capabilities and that they have fluctuating states of well-being, with 'up days' and 'down days' (sometimes with known causes, but often inexplicable) that may affect individual capability.

Does the handling task present risks to those female employees who are pregnant? This is a most important consideration and should be taken seriously if either pregnancy is visibly apparent or the employee has informed you that she is pregnant. If a pregnant employee is asked to lift heavy or unwieldy objects, this can result in miscarriage or premature birth. Having assessed the load that a pregnant woman can safely handle, you should also assess what facilities she may need for adequate rest pauses in the working schedule (see also Chapter 21 where the subject of rest areas for pregnant women is discussed).

Does the task present risks to those who might reasonably be considered to be suffering from a health problem? If there are employees with health problems or injuries (not necessarily caused by handling operations), you must assess the effects of handling loads on them. Can you reasonably expect a person with a back problem to lift heavy loads or to carry bulky or unwieldy objects for long distances? Can you reasonably expect a person with a leg injury from a road accident to carry loads? Consider consulting your employment medical adviser or the employee's doctor for advice.

Does the task require any special information or training to enable the task to be carried out safely? If no information or training is given or if the information and training given is inadequate, this can increase the risk of injury, as employees may lift incorrectly, not be aware of the nature, size, weight and features and distribution of the load or be unaware of any hazardous substances the load contains. There may be special systems of work required to lift particular types of loads safely and employees must be trained in those systems. You should also refer to the requirements for information, instruction and training under section 2(2)(c) of the HASWA and the MHSW Regulations (see Chapter 17).

Does the task require PPE? PPE is only to be issued as a last resort, that is, if it is not possible to avoid risks altogether (see Chapter 22). Where the complete avoidance of risks of injury is not possible and the wearing of PPE is unavoidable, you should assess *what* PPE is most suitable, the effects of that PPE on both the employees who wear it and its effect on their ability to carry out the manual handling task without inhibition to efficiency and safety.

Step E2: reduce the risks in individual capability Having assessed the risks in individual capability, you now need to *reduce* the risks arising from those factors.

The first consideration is to the personal factors, of sex, age, build, strength, health and well-being. If you have assessed that the load presents risks to the handler because of any of these personal factors, then you should adapt the load accordingly or ensure that only those with personal factors that give an individual the capability to handle that load are given the task. You will need to reduce risks where the handling task:

- requires unusual strength or height
- presents risks to those female employees who are pregnant
- presents risks to those who might reasonably be considered to be suffering from a health problem
- requires special information or training to enable them to carry out the handling task safely
- requires PPE.

Let us look at most of these briefly, just to reinforce the points made in the assessments (above) and expand on the training requirements.

If the task requires unusual strength or height, ensure that only those who *have* that height or strength are employed in such tasks. Alternatively, and far better, redesign the task so that *no* unusual qualities are required and the average person can do the job.

If the task presents risks to those female employees who are pregnant, ensure that no woman who shows visual evidence that she is pregnant or who has informed you she is pregnant is asked to carry out that task, which might cause injury to herself or the unborn child.

If the task presents risks to those who might reasonably be considered to be suffering from a health problem, remember the general duty on employers under section 2(1) of the HASWA, which is to safeguard the health, safety and welfare of employees. If a person is believed or known to suffer from ill-health, you should not ask them to undertake tasks that could aggravate their condition. If, of course, you believe the person to be malingering and not genuinely suffering from ill-health, you have the prerogative to request an independent medical examination.

If the task requires special information and training, remember that the provision of information, instruction and training are obligations placed on all employers under section 2(2)(c) of the HASWA, Regulations 8 and 11 of the MHSW Regulations (see Chapter 19) and Regulation 4(1)(b)(ii) of the Manual Handling Regulations. The *first* requirement, though, is to design the load being handled and the handling task so that they are safe; you should not rely *solely* on information, instruction and training as a means of achieving safety. Having achieved a safe load and system of work, you will need to devise a training schedule that will ensure competence and complete understanding of manual handling techniques, including:

- potentially hazardous manual handling operations and how they can be recognized
- dealing with unfamiliar handling situations
- using manual handling aids correctly and safely
- identifying and using appropriate PPE

- the working environment, its features and how they are used to effect safety in handling operations
- good housekeeping
- factors that affect individual capability
- good manual handling techniques.

For potentially hazardous manual handling operations, handlers should be given information that enables them to recognize hazards in loads, including the size, weight, shape, contents, design features, the conditions in which they are handled, and the possible risks involved in handling them. Advice should include:

- how to estimate the weight of an object
- how to assess the safe handling of difficult or unusual objects
- how to approach unfamiliar loads, assess their contents and determine methods of handling them safely
- how to take the strain of a load gently and not apply force
- good handling techniques.

Good manual handling techniques are grouped under the heading 'Kinetic handling', which can be described as the use of the energy of the body in association with motion. The body's energy is applied to the load in a rhythmic movement that does not place undue strain on any parts of the body. Here are some basic rules of kinetic handling:

- *stop and think* before lifting a load, assess what its weight, size, features and so on are (see Fig. 23.3)
- *body balance* place the feet apart to give a good balance (see Fig. 23.4)
- *posture* adopt good posture so that no one part of the body is put under strain, observing the following rules (see Fig. 23.5):
  —keep the back straight (not necessarily vertical)
  —keep the head up (helps to keep the back straight)
  —keep the knees bent

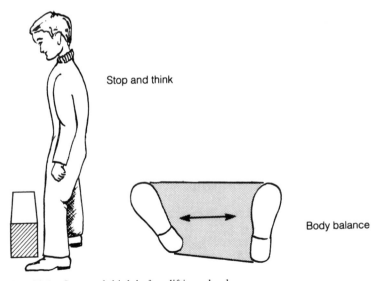

Stop and think

Body balance

Fig. 23.3   Stop and think before lifting a load

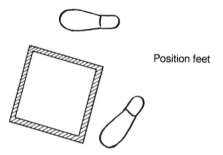

Position feet

Fig. 23.4   Place the feet apart to achieve good balance

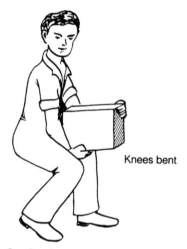

Knees bent

One foot flat, the other raised

Fig. 23.5   Adopt a good, balanced posture

—when crouching down to pick a load up, keep one foot flat on the floor and the heel of the other foot raised
- *grip* ensure that a firm grip is obtained and maintained
- *arms bent* do not carry an object with the arms fully straightened (see Fig. 23.6)
- *lifting* lift gently, taking the strain gradually — do not jerk
- *moving* when moving the load:
  —avoid twisting the body, move the feet first and let the body follow
  —keep close to the load, thus reducing the effective weight and its effect on gravity
- *setting down* when setting a load down, ensure the following things:
  —that no obstacles are in the way
  —you do not reach over obstacles (see Fig. 23.7)
  —you place the load down, with the knees bent and the back kept straight
  —check that the area where the load is to be placed is free and suitable
  —push into the desired position, still with knees bent

Hold load close to body, head up, back straight

Fig. 23.6   Keep the arms slightly bent

Fig. 23.7   When setting down a load, do not overreach

    —stand upright (see Fig. 23.8)
- *team handling* when the load is too heavy or bulky for one person to handle, two or more people should lift it together:
  —both/all should obey the above rules (keep the back straight, head up, left foot flat, right heel raised (see Fig. 23.9))
  —one person should be the 'caller' and speak aloud the words: 'One, two, three, lift'; on the word 'lift', both/all should lift the load in unison.

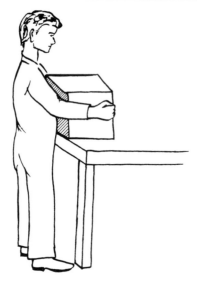

Fig. 23.8 Stand upright when setting down a load

Fig. 23.9 Following the same rules for team handling

There are now vocational qualifications that can be awarded for competence in safe kinetic handling techniques.

Just as a reminder of how important the application of these techniques is, 34 per cent of all reportable (major and serious) injuries in 1991/92 were caused by manual handling accidents. Application of these principles in correct handling methods will help to reduce or even eliminate injuries caused by using poor techniques.

A suggested manual handling assessment check-list is given in Appendix 13. This is based on Appendix 2 of the Manual Handling Regulations. The HSE has waived its copyright on this document so that it can be copied freely.

Additional information

To further reinforce the requirements of the Regulations and the advice of the accompanying Guidance Notes on the load given in Assessing the load, and Reducing the risk of injury of the load, above, the Regulations also require you to give employees additional information with 'general indications' on the load where manual handling cannot be avoided (Regulation 4(1)(b)(iii)), that is:

- the weight of each load
- the nature of the load
- the *heaviest* side of a load, where it is of uneven shape or weight distribution or where the centre of gravity is not central.

This information should be as precise as possible — an important point, bearing in mind the sensitivity of people's spines and lower backs.

Much of this requirement can be satisfied during training sessions as outlined above.

Duties to non-employees Sections 3 and 6 place duties on manufacturers and suppliers of goods to safeguard the health, safety and welfare of those not in their employ, such as the public, customers and employees of customers. Manufacturers may give this 'additional information' by marking it on the loads themselves before they leave their premises.

To review the assessment

Nothing ever stands still and assessments will rapidly become out of date, so you should make arrangements (as per your health and safety policy) to review your assessments periodically (Regulation 4(2)). This should happen:

- as often as is necessary, but it is suggested that this be not less than once every six months (a year is really too long)
- whenever there has been a change to your manual handling operations
- when you have reason to suspect that the assessments are no longer valid
- where changes are required because of such review.

Duties of employees

In Regulation 5, as required by the HASWA, employees must:

- take reasonable care of themselves and others who may be affected by their acts and omissions (section 7(a) of the HASWA)
- cooperate with their employer, including obeying all the manual handling rules and instructions given during training (mentioned above) and using PPE issued as given in Chapter 21 (section 7(b) of the HASWA and Regulation 12 of the MHSW Regulations; see also Chapter 18)
- generally not misuse or abuse any equipment or PPE provided for manual handling and in the interests of health and safety (section 8 of the HASWA).

The HSE Guidance Notes do not preclude an employee deviating from the rules of safe handling (what they call 'well-intentioned improvization') in a condition of emergency, such as rescuing a casualty, fighting a fire or containing the spillage of a dangerous substance.

Sources of help

There are various sources of help and guidance for carrying out assessments, reducing risks of injury in manual handling and giving information, instruction and training to employees. They include the following:

- Your local HSE office (their address and telephone number can be found in your local telephone and/or business directory).
- Abundance Management Services, Abundance House, 17 St Michael's Crescent, Oldbury, West Midlands B69 4RT (tel: 0121 552 2073).
- International Institute of Risk Management, 70 Chandlers Road, Hammersmith, London W6 9RS (tel: 0181 741 1131).

Some useful reading

In addition to the Regulations and Guidance Notes (L23, available from HMSO), a guidance pack *Lighten the Load* (reference C500) is available from your local HSE office. This includes a manual handling assessment check-list as in Appendix 13.

24

Safety in pressure systems

Due to their very nature, pressure vessels and pressurized systems bring with them hazards of various kinds. Various dangers can arise from deterioration of the fabric of the vessels, systems and their components, and substances under pressure can present risks of scalding or poisoning and the effects of gases released into the atmosphere. There can also be chemical reactions of the vessels' contents. These all hold potential consequences for people who are unfortunate enough to be in the vicinity when something does go wrong.

Regulations on pressure vessels came into force on 1 July 1990 and have been implemented in stages until they became fully operational on 1 July 1994. The requirements of those Regulations are summarized here.

The legislation

The Pressure Systems and Transportable Gas Containers Regulations 1989 (PSTGC Regulations) came into force on 1 July 1990. They have been implemented in stages since then and were fully implemented on 1 July 1994 when Regulations 8 to 10 finally came into force and the four years' transitional period for compliance expired.

There is also an ACOP and Guidance Notes, which detail the specific duties and how they can be fulfilled.

The scope of the PSTGC Regulations

These Regulations provide a comprehensive framework, covering all types of pressure vessels and pressurized systems (pressure systems), from compressed air in a small garage or dental surgery to the largest chemical plant and all types of transportable gas containers. This includes all steam systems and any other system in which gases exert pressures of more than 0.5 bar above atmospheric pressure. The PSTGC Regulations also cover all other forms of static or mobile pressurized systems.

Owners and users The PSTGC Regulations are specifically directed at both the owners and users of pressure systems and it is their duty to ensure compliance with these Regulations. The owner or user of a pressure system in this context is the employer or self-employed person (Regulation 12).

Employees Employees are not 'users' of pressure systems in terms of the PSTGC Regulations and are *not* placed under any obligation (except for their duty to cooperate with their employer, as in section 7(b) of the HASWA). The obligation is solely on the employer as owner and user.

Exemptions

There are a few systems excluded from the PSTGC Regulations — mainly mobile systems, such as aircraft, road vehicles and marine craft, that are covered by their own existing legislation. The Regulations do not apply to purely hydraulic systems or liquids in storage tanks that exert a static head pressure. Also, some very small systems have partial exemption.

The requirements of the PSTGC Regulations

The Regulations lay down requirements concerning:

- risk assessments of pressure systems
- written schemes for the examination of pressure systems
- examination in accordance with those schemes
- written reports on cases of imminent danger
- records of inspection procedures
- the duties of designers and installers.

Objectives

The objective of the PSTGC Regulations is to prevent any reasonably foreseeable risk to people from the hazards of stored energy in pressure systems.

'Competent persons'

As with the MHSW Regulations, owners and users of pressure systems must employ the services of a 'competent person' to undertake the duties required by the PSTGC Regulations. Of course, the owner or user may be a competent person themselves. The owner or user must adequately brief a competent person with all necessary information to enable them to carry out their duties. They must also ensure safe access to those pressure systems for the competent person (see Chapter 19 for guidance on this aspect). The competent persons are empowered by the PSTGC Regulations to decide the frequency of examinations made of pressure systems.

Information

Before any duties can be undertaken to comply with these Regulations, it is essential that full information concerning the pressure systems in use must be provided by the designer and installer to the user and/or their competent person. This is equivalent to the product data sheets required for all substances under the COSHH Regulations. The information must include:

- details of the design or construction codes
- details of the examination(s) carried out during construction
- details of methods of non-destructive testing (NDT) carried out.

Pipework In the case of pressurized pipework that is subject to deterioration by corrosion, the following information must be provided by the designer and installer to the user and/or your competent person:

- full drawing, including isometrics (where applicable), detailing:
  —numbered valves with their locations
  —numbered welds with their locations

—supports and insulation details
—maximum, minimum and normal operating temperatures
—pressure and flow rates
—direction of flow
—key monitoring points
—normal monitoring points
- material schedules.

Note that here, 'deterioration by corrosion' includes all forms of cracking and erosion.

Risk assessments

As with most other legislation, and particularly the MHSW Regulations, there is an obligation on the owners and users of pressure systems to carry out assessments of the risks to which employees and others may be exposed as a result of the installation and operation of those pressure systems. Written schemes and the frequency of examination of pressure systems (see below) must be based on those risk assessments.

Risk assessments must be carried out by the competent person, as above (see Chapter 19 for detailed advice on carrying out risk assessments).

Written schemes of examinations

Either the owners, users or suppliers/installers of pressure systems are responsible for ensuring that a written scheme of examination of each pressure system in use is drawn up (Regulation 8). They may appoint a competent person to draw up written schemes on their behalf. There will need to be agreement as to which of these undertake the task, but it is solely the duty of the user to *define the scope* of the written schemes. In the case of mobile systems, the duty is exclusively that of the owner.

The simplicity or complexity of these schemes will depend on the nature of the pressure system itself. Your written scheme of examination must include:

- name and address of the user, owner and/or installer
- exact location of the pressure system
- items to be examined, which will include protective devices in/on the system, its pipework and pipelines
- details of preparatory work required
- the methods of examination required
- the maximum permitted intervals between examinations
- the date following installation by which the pressure system(s) must undergo initial examination
- details of any parts of the pressure system that are difficult to access for examination
- details of British Standards or other codes that are to be used when carrying out modifications and repairs, such as BS5500, the Specification for unfired fusion-welded pressure vessels
- those critical items that must be examined by a competent person when they are modified or repaired before being used again
- the names of the person drawing up the written scheme of examination and the competent person verifying it.

Certification Regardless of who draws up the written schemes of examinations, those schemes must be certified by a competent person.

Review Following the initial drawing up and certification, the user or owner must ensure that the written scheme is reviewed by a competent person on the following occasions:

- at appropriate intervals
- when changes are made to relevant fluids contained within the systems
- when the content of written schemes is modified according to recommendations made by the competent person as a result of reviews.

Examinations of pressure systems

Examinations of all pressure systems must be carried out in accordance with the minimum criteria laid down by Regulation 9 for:

- sequence of examinations
- frequency/intervals of examinations
- types of examinations, that is:
  —visual examination
  —non-destructive testing (NDT)
  —hydraulic
  —pneumatic
  —combined hydraulic and pneumatic

any or all of which can be included in either:

- thorough examination
- working examination.

Sequence of examinations Examinations are carried out in sequence from the time of installation and commissioning. These should be included in the written scheme (above) when it is prepared at the onset, with an in-built mechanism to ensure that they are carried out. The scope of examinations will be determined by your competent person and included in the written scheme. The sequence of examinations is as follows.

- *Initial examination* Carried out *before* the pressure system is used for the first time. This initial examination will ensure the integrity of the system, that is, that the design criteria and manufacture conform to existing British and European Standards. These Standards specify the minimum levels of examination and testing during manufacture.
- *First in-service examination* It is most important that a first in-service examination be carried out, as this will obviate any deficiencies in the design, manufacture or installation and in its use. This examination may include some NDT, as below.
- *Subsequent in-service examinations* These further in-service examinations will obviate any defects or deterioration in the pressure system(s) and will largely be determined in their scope and frequency by the findings of the first in-service examination. If you have a multiplicity of pressure systems, it may be pertinent to install a system of 'sampling', which will permit systems to operate for their maximum periods established by the design specifications and written scheme.

Expansion and contraction devices Where the written scheme of examinations requires it, the examinations should include all components and devices provided to facilitate expansion and contraction of the pressure system.

Frequency/intervals of examinations There are three frequencies, or intervals, in which examinations must take place according to the class of the pressure vessel, as devised by such bodies as the Associated Offices Technical Committee and Engineering Equipment and Materials Users' Association. They are classes A, B and C, indicating differing 'maximum established periods' — A requiring the most frequent examinations and C the least — based on the following data:

- design details
- the methods of construction
- the conditions under which the systems are to be used
- the standards of maintenance required.

Your competent person will determine, in the light of the above four basic factors, the classification and examination frequency for each pressure system.

- *Class A* Pressure systems are allocated to this class when:
  —deterioration is recognized as being possible
  —deterioration has become evident from previous examinations
  —little evidence exists on which to predict a system's behaviour while in service.
- *Class B* Pressure systems that are not expected to deteriorate significantly, but for which there is not sufficient data available to be confident that it is a Class C system, are placed in this class.
- *Class C* Pressure systems that have a low expectation of deterioration and can be examined at intervals up to the 'maximum established period' are placed in Class C.

Intervals between examinations are determined by the nature and speed of deterioration of the system and, of course, systems can be transferred from one class to another, upwards or downwards, according to the findings of the examinations.

Data about 'maximum established periods' and guidance on how to determine them can be obtained from the Associated Offices Technical Committee or Engineering Equipment and Materials Users' Association (for their addresses, see the Sources of help section at the end of this chapter).

Limited-life vessels In addition to classes A, B and C, pressure systems may be allocated one of two other classifications. This is where systems have a limited life due to two factors:

- they are operated at high temperatures and designed using stresses based on creep data related to design life specified in hours
- pressure cycling, caused by process conditions or frequent start-up, which may result in fatigue-cracking should the cyclic life of the vessel be exceeded.

These vessels should be allocated a classification of:

- TL — temperature limited
- CL — cycle limited

in addition to Class A, B or C. Your competent person will be able to advise on these classifications.

Protective devices Protective devices are essential items of equipment (see later in this chapter). These are subject to the same examination and classification criteria, but, because of the multiplicity of protective devices and systems to which they relate, advice on classification should be sought from the Associated Offices Technical Committee.

Significant modification Where there is significant modification to a pressure system, your competent person *must* carry out further examinations and tests *before* the system is brought into use again.

Types of examination There are five basic types of examination (the first five given below), any or all of which can be incorporated into two major examination types, as follows.

- *Visual examination* Only a competent person can effectively carry out a visual examination to properly assess the condition of the system and identify any NOT, chemical and/or metallurgical tests necessary to enable them to certify that the pressure system is up to standard. Visual examination will identify the following:
  —physical damage to the system
  —corrosion in the system
  —cracks in the system
  —any plastic deformation.
- *Non-destructive testing* As the name suggests, this kind of testing tests a system up to but not beyond its limits. This testing will detect surface and internal defects in the system and its fabric.
- *Hydraulic methods* A pressure test using high-pressure oils, which can exert large forces.
- *Pneumatic methods* A pressure test using a high force of compressed air.
- *Combination* A combination of hydraulic and pneumatic tests. The pressures exerted in this and the above tests must be capable of reaching working and test pressure limits.

Any or all of the first five types of examination can be combined in the following two types of examination.

- *Thorough examination* This is a complete, in-depth examination of the whole system. The system must be completely depressurized before the examination begins and the following essential safety precautions must also be taken *before* such examination commences:
  —purge the system (to expel any hazardous substances or fumes)
  —ventilate the system or provide PPE
  —completely isolate the system (to avoid unintentional start-up)
  —remove all external coverings
  —remove all residues of substances
  —descale and polish as necessary
  —open up the system, including opening out for cleaning and examination of fittings and protective devices
  —ensure an appropriate 'permit to work' system is in operation
  —ensure *safe* access is afforded for all internal and external work to be undertaken
  —provide adequate low-voltage lighting
  —remove all internal fittings (to avoid personal injury and facilitate freedom of movement)
  —provide all necessary testing facilities

—provide support personnel where required (to ensure the personal safety of the person carrying out the examination).

● *Working examination* This examination is carried out under operational conditions with the pressure systems at operating pressure and temperature. It should take the form of an external visual examination with the back-up of functional testing of protective devices by the competent person, as required. The following safety precautions must be taken to protect the examiner:
  —ensure that safe access is provided
  —ensure that there are operational/maintenance and NDT personnel available to carry out such functional tests as your competent person requires to see.

Examination of pipework It is estimated that a third of all failures in pressure systems occur in the pipework, often attributable to leakages, bursts, mechanical failure, too great a pressure, defective materials and corrosion. These factors all strongly influence both the placing of pipework in the written scheme and its priorities within it.

New pipework Where *new* pipework is installed and there is a possibility of deterioration by corrosion, certain key points must be established and methods of monitoring agreed with your competent person. The methods of monitoring may include:

● ultrasonic equipment with compression wave probes to measure the thickness of materials
● flash radiography to detect external corrosion under the system's insulation.

The most appropriate NDT techniques should be utilized to test pipework according to the degree of assurance required for the system.

Existing pipework As with main pressure systems, the frequency of testing existing pipework should be determined in light of experience in previous examinations and the levels of deterioration found during modification work. If there is previous evidence of deterioration, then you may need to consider using NDT techniques to predict possible failures.

Frequency of examinations Rates of corrosion in pipework are major factors in determining the *frequency of examination*. Changes in product, catalyst, additives and operating limits can cause acceleration in corrosion rates. In such cases, amendments of the written schemes may be required and your competent person must be informed of these factors.

Methods of examination Pipework examination may be carried out by means of an *in-line* or *off-line examination*.

● *In-line examination* If examination is carried out in-line, it may include the following methods:
  —thickness measurements, using NDT techniques
  —visual examination for external damage, corrosion and leakage
  —removal of insulation or pipe hangers to facilitate access to areas considered liable to corrosion
  —investigation of internal corrosion, using radiographic methods
  —investigation of lining deterioration, using radiographic methods
  —detection of flaws in systems, using NDT techniques
  —monitoring of corrosion and erosion by process steam analysis

—monitoring the growth of defects caused in service.
- *Off-line examination* Examinations carried out off-line may include the following:
  —testing for leakage using compressed air or inert gases at low pressure
  —pressure testing for mechanical integrity
  —thickness measurements, using NDT techniques
  —hammer testing as a preliminary to NDT
  —internal examination by optical examination techniques.

Conditions for the operation of pressure systems Users and owners of pressure systems must ensure that no system is operated or supplied for operation *after*:

- the date specified for completion of repairs, modifications or changes
- the date specified in the written scheme, after which operation of the system must not continue without further examination by a competent person.

Postponement of examination The date by which an examination is due and beyond which the system should not be operated may be *postponed* by written agreement between the user/owner and the competent person, subject to the following conditions:

- such postponement will not give rise to danger
- no more than one postponement per examination is made
- the enforcement authority (the HSE or local EHO) are notified of that postponement *before* the original due date of the next thorough or working examination.

In the case of mobile systems, the date of the next examination or of the postponed date, as appropriate, must be clearly marked on the outside of the pressure system.

Protective devices Protective devices must be adequate by design and in capacity, should be positioned in a safe manner and should not obstruct inlet, vent or discharge piping. They include control and measuring equipment essential to prevent a dangerous condition from arising. These devices will detect the following conditions, which could lead to failure of the pressure system:

- overfilling of systems
- blockage of the system by sediment
- high or low pressure
- excess high pressure
- very low pressure
- corrosion in the fabric, including cracking
- erosion in the fabric
- leakage.

Because the fitness of protective devices for their purpose cannot be determined by visual examination alone, tests should be devised that confirm that the devices are:

- set correctly
- functioning correctly.

Protective devices for pressure systems are of two categories:

- *Category 1* devices designed to protect the pressure system, for example:

—bursting discs
—safety relief valves
—vacuum release valves
- *Category 2* early warning devices to warn of possible systems failures, for example:
  —pressure and temperature gauges
  —protective systems, including 'black boxes' and computer-controlled devices
  —heat input cut-off devices.

Examination of protective devices Following installation and thorough examination, at the discretion of your competent person, a *working examination* may be carried out. Protective devices should be examined not less than once every 12 months after the first thorough (and working) examination. In all other respects, the criteria of examinations for protective devices are as for other devices.

Interlocking devices These are provided to pressure vessels to ensure that the inlet supply cannot be turned on while the door is opened, that is, the door must be fully closed and locked for the supply to be able to flow. Also, an interlocking device ensures that the door cannot be unlocked unless the supply valve is completely closed and the exhaust vent fully open.

Systems that have vessels with quick-opening doors should be examined to verify the presence and correct operation of interlocking devices between door-locking mechanisms and inlet or exhaust valves.

Interlocking devices should also be examined to verify that the device permits the door to be only partially opened, by a small amount, after unlocking it; that device should then have to be released before the door can be fully opened.

Reports of examination
A competent person undertaking examinations of pressure systems must make a written report of those examinations (Regulations 12 and 13), which needs to include the following details:

- details of the examination
- the date of the examination
- reasons given by the competent person for any modification to the written scheme for examination, if any
- the date by which the next examination must be carried out under the conditions laid down in the written scheme for examination (note that the date of the next examination indicates the date of expiry of the period for which the system has been certified)
- a signature or other valid means of authentication.

The competent person must then send the examination report to the user and/or owner of the pressure system.

Records of inspection procedures
Full records of all written schemes for examination and of all examinations must be maintained and be available for inspection by any enforcing authority (Regulation 9). It is the responsibility of the user, owner, lessor or hirer to keep all documentation pertaining to the pressure systems.

Sources of help

Should you need any assistance with the appointment of a competent person, the compiling of a written scheme or the conducting of examinations, the following bodies will be able to assist you.

- Engineering Equipment and Materials Users' Association
- Associated Offices Technical Committee.

25

Control of legionellosis

Up to 200 cases of legionnaires' disease are reported in England and Wales each year. The group of bacteria that cause this and other related diseases are found in fine-spray droplets of airborne water from many sources.

The increased popularity of sports and leisure centres in the past decade has led to the building of many elaborate water-based centres that have all kinds of swimming pools, whirlpool spas and jacuzzis. Hotels are also now increasingly offering these types of facilities. Modern buildings are becoming larger and there are corresponding increases in the numbers of large water storage and supply tanks for such services as hot water and heating.

Recent research suggests that these facilities may present significant hazards to health if they are not properly managed. Water in whirlpools and jacuzzis is kept at the optimum temperatures for these bacteria, is continually agitated and is recycled for varying lengths of time around nutrient-providing human beings. Water in storage tanks is relatively stagnant. All this provides the ideal temperature, moisture, oxygen and food for *Legionellae* bacteria to breed.

Reports of outbreaks of legionnaires' disease and research into *Legionellae* bacteria, their sources and ill-health effects have drawn public and official attention to this potentially lethal family of bacteria.

The terminology

It is helpful to know exactly what is meant by terms used in this legislation.

- *Risk assessment* See Chapter 19.
- *Bacterium* A single micro-organism.
- *Bacteria* More than one micro-organism, either of the same or different types.
- *Legionellae* The group of bacteria in the *Legionella* family. This bacteria can cause fatal, permanently debilitating and less serious illnesses, mostly affecting the lungs.
- *Legionella micdadei* The species of *Legionellae* that the outbreak of Lochgoilhead fever was attributed to, so named after the outbreak that occurred in Lochgoilhead in 1988.
- *Legionella pneumophila* The species of *Legionellae* that causes legionnaires' disease. It can also cause the milder disease Pontiac fever, which is a short, feverish, non-pneumonic illness.

- *Legionellosis* The generic term used for a group of infections caused by the bacteria family *Legionellae,* including legionnaires' disease, Pontiac fever and Lochgoilhead fever.
- *Legionnaires' disease* A pneumonia-like sickness caused by *Legionella pneumophila* that principally affects those who are susceptible due to age, illness, immunosuppression and smoking. Its name was given to it following an outbreak among members attending an American Legionnaires' conference in Philadelphia in 1976. Its symptoms are fever, chest pain, dry cough and breathlessness and may be fatal.

The legislation

The HSE has produced an ACOP entitled *The prevention or control of legionellosis (including legionnaires' disease)*, which came into force on 15 January 1992. This ACOP gives practical guidance on the legal obligations of employers and the self-employed under the following legislation:

- the HASWA — sections 2, 3 and 4 apply to all duties and sections 3 and 6 apply to designers, manufacturers, suppliers and installers
- the COSHH Regulations, issued under the HASWA, Regulations 6, 7, 8, 9 and 12 (as indicated in each main section below)
- the Notification of Cooling Towers and Evaporative Condensers Regulations 1992 (NCTEC Regulations), which came into force on 2 November 1992.

The scope of the COSHH and NCTEC Regulations and ACOP
These apply to the following undertakings and premises:

- those to which the HASWA applies
- those that involve a work activity
- those where, in connection with a trade, business or other premises, large quantities of water are used or stored
- those where there is a means of creating and transmitting water droplets that may be inhaled, thereby causing a reasonably foreseeable risk of legionellosis.

The COSHH Regulations and ACOP cover establishments that have the following water systems, which present a risk of legionellosis:

- cooling towers
- evaporative condensers
- hot water services where the volume exceeds 300 litres (approximately 66 gallons)
- hot and cold water services in premises where occupants are susceptible, such as health-care establishments
- humidifiers and air washers with temperatures above 20°C (68°F)
- fittings and equipment in which warm water is deliberately agitated and recirculated, such as jacuzzis and whirlpool spas
- all other plant and systems in which water is likely to be of a temperature above 20°C (68°F) *and* that are capable of releasing sprays or aerosols during use or maintenance, such as water washing plant and showers.

The first and second systems are also covered specifically by the NCTEC Regulations.

Enforcement
The duties of employers and the self-employed are laid down in the HASWA and the COSHH Regulations. No one can be prosecuted for failure to comply with the quasi-

legal ACOP, but any failure to comply leading to a prosecutable offence would be used as evidence of non-compliance with the law.

Sources of Legionellae

In a Public Health Laboratory Service survey in 1992, of the establishments surveyed, the percentages in which traces of *Legionellae* were found to be present were as shown in Table 25.1.

These figures give some alarming indications. The presence of 'traces' of the bacteria in these systems does not indicate an outbreak, but that there is the *potential* for an outbreak if these systems are not managed properly. Bacteria are literally everywhere and some *Legionellae* will probably be found in all water systems, but the task of management is to control bacteria to prevent multiplication, the production of a spray and the inhalation of water droplets.

Legionellae are common in natural water sources and can enter any man-made system or water service. Once there, they can multiply prolifically under 'ideal' conditions. If there are means of creating and transmitting water droplets (which need only be minute), then people in the vicinity may be at risk from infection by the bacteria. Most outbreaks have been attributable to water services in buildings, whirlpool spas and cooling towers; others have come from humidifier systems, industrial coolants and respiratory therapy equipment.

A survey in 1991 by the Public Health Laboratory Service showed that over 80 per cent of whirlpool spas presented a combination of factors where people had been infected:

- lack of awareness in pool managers of the Swimming Pools and Allied Trades Association's standards for pools
- inadequate training of pool operators
- inadequate monitoring of pool disinfection levels
- practical difficulties in obtaining consistent dosing
- lack of regular attention to pool hygiene.

Who is most at risk?

There are a number of factors: the combination of which will make people susceptible to infection by *Legionellae* include the following:

- *age* particularly people over 50 years old (children are rarely affected)
- *sex* males are three times more susceptible than females
- *respiratory infections* as these make the lungs more vulnerable

Table 25.1 The results of the Public Health Laboratory Service 1992 survey

Establishment	% water systems with traces of Legionella	% water cooling systems with traces of Legionella
Hotels	53	67
Hospitals	70	38
Business premises	75	54
Residential	67	—

- *illnesses* such as cancer, diabetes, kidney disease or alcoholism, which weaken the body's natural defence mechanisms
- *smokers* as people who smoke may have an impaired lung function
- *drugs* those taking immunosuppressant drugs as these inhibit the body's natural defence mechanisms
- *renal dialysis*.

However, in most outbreaks of legionnaires' disease, fewer than 5 per cent have contracted the disease.

Management responsibility

Where there is a reasonable foreseeable risk of legionellosis, every employer, self-employed person or person in control of premises where this ACOP applies (paragraphs 17 to 21) must provide adequate management of that part of the premises affected by this ACOP. The following two persons must be appointed:

- *Appointed person* This is an in-house appointment of a responsible person who will have management responsibility to oversee the fulfilment of the duties under the ACOP and COSHH Regulations (Regulations 8 and 12). The appointed person must be competent, trained in the task and have sufficient ability, experience, instruction, information and awareness to enable them to carry out their duties and responsibilities. They must also be given adequate resources to carry out the task.
  The information and training must also equip them to know:
  —the potential sources of *Legionellae*
  —the risks those sources present
  —measures to be taken, including the protection of people from the risks
  —measures to be taken to ensure that controls are and remain effective.
- *Competent person* There must be a competent person appointed who will undertake assessments and the specialist aspects of control of *Legionellae*. This may be an internal appointment, where a person with sufficient qualities exists, or it may be an external appointment, say, a consultant, if no suitable person exists in the company. A competent person must be suitably qualified and experienced for the role that they will undertake under the ACOP, including being capable of carrying out risk assessments and drawing up written schemes (see later in this chapter and Chapter 19).

Where the external assistance of a competent person is obtained, it is most important that clear lines of communication be established with them, including the levels of authority and responsibility.

Risk assessments (COSHH Regs, Regulation 6)

In keeping with other Regulations, the first requirement on employers is to carry out risk assessments (COSHH Regulations, Regulation 6 and paragraphs 8 to 12 of the ACOP). These assessments must be 'suitable and sufficient' in order to identify the risks of legionellosis arising from the work activities and any potentially harmful water sources. The risk assessments must be carried out by the employer, self-employed person or person in control of the premises (see Competent person, above).

Objectives Risk assessments must enable a valid decision to be made about the following:

- the potential sources of risk
- the reasonably foreseeable risks to health from exposure
- the means by which exposure to *Legionellae* can be prevented
- the measures necessary to minimize exposure, where prevention is not possible or is not reasonably practicable, such as in whirlpool spas.

Your assessments must also demonstrate that:

- all pertinent factors have been considered
- the steps necessary to prevent or minimize the risk and exposure to it are identified and implemented.

If your risk assessments demonstrate that no reasonably foreseeable risk exists or any risk that *is* identified is not significant and unlikely to increase, then no further assessment is necessary, unless changes occur to make a reassessment necessary.

Review Your assessments should be reviewed periodically, on any occasion when there is significant change or when you believe your assessments to be no longer valid. This may include:

- changes to the plant or water system
- changes in the use of that plant or system
- changes to the use of the building in which that plant or system is installed
- new information about the nature of risks or control measures becomes known
- checks on control measures taken indicate that those controls are no longer effective.

Cooling towers and evaporative condensers

Under the NCTEC Regulations, all employers who have cooling towers or evaporative condensers must notify the local authority of their presence (evaporative condensers are found in air-conditioning systems of many large buildings in industrial cooling systems).

The purpose of these new Regulations is to enable local authorities to have knowledge of the locations of cooling towers and evaporative condensers. This will be helpful in the event of an outbreak of legionnaires' disease and facilitate the discovery of its source.

Where such equipment is present on employers' premises, a form for notification can be obtained from the local authority's environmental health department. The form requires the following information to be given:

- the name and address of the premises on which the cooling tower(s) and/or evaporative condenser(s) is located
- the name, address and telephone number of the person in control (as outlined above)
- the number of cooling towers
- the number of evaporative condensers
- their exact locations on the site where they are situated.

Changes Any changes in the information provided to the local authority on the above form must also be notified to them within a month of the change taking place, so that records can be amended. This includes notification that the equipment has ceased to operate.

Transitional period The period of transition expired on 2 May 1993 and, thus, all equipment must now be notified.

Preventing or minimizing risks

Where risk assessments have identified that a reasonably foreseeable risk of *Legionellae* could arise, the first duty of every employer and self-employed person is to seek to *prevent* the risk of exposure from arising (COSHH Regulations, Regulation 7). If prevention is not possible or reasonably practicable, as with whirlpool spas and jacuzzis, the next step is to minimize the risk of exposure.

There are a number of steps or measures that can be taken to *minimize* the risk of exposure to *Legionellae* (paragraphs 13, 14 and 15 of the ACOP).

Written scheme The appointed person (or the competent person) must draw up a *written scheme*. This scheme must outline the steps that will be taken to minimize the risk of exposure. It must be sufficiently specific and detailed to enable implementation of the scheme and for it to be managed effectively. The written scheme should contain the following.

- *Plan* An up-to-date plan of the layout of the plant and/or system, including any parts of it that are temporarily out of use. A schematic plan is sufficient.
- *Description* An explanation of the correct and safe operation of the plant and/or systems.
- *Precautions* Details of the precautions to be taken to minimize exposure to the risks identified in the risk assessments. These precautions must prevent the proliferation of *Legionellae* in the plant or system and minimize exposure to water droplets and spray. The precautions should include the following:
  —minimization of the release of water spray
  —maintenance of water temperatures and conditions that are *not* 'ideal conditions' for the proliferation of *Legionellae* and other micro-organisms
  —prevention of water stagnation (in which bacteria multiply profusely)
  —avoidance of the use of materials that harbour bacteria and other micro-organisms or that provide nutrients (food) for microbial growth and multiplication
  —maintenance of scrupulous cleanliness in the plant or system and of the water in them
  —the use of water treatment dosing techniques, such as calcium hypochlorite (HTH)
  —action to ensure the correct and safe operation of the water system and plant
  —a system for the correct and safe maintenance of the water system and plant (see also Chapter 22)
  —measures to be taken to ensure that the written scheme remains effective, including checks on its operation and the frequency of those checks
  —action to be taken should checks of the written scheme indicate that it is no longer effective.

Having presented the written scheme for minimizing the risk of exposure to *Legionellae*, management have the responsibility of ensuring that the scheme is fully implemented and properly managed (paragraph 16 of the ACOP).

Monitoring

An integral part of all control measures is comprehensive monitoring procedures. These are intended to ensure the effectiveness of your control measures to prevent or minimize risks. Monitoring procedures should include:

- checking your system and its performance against data from the designer, supplier or installer of your system and/or plant
- regular inspection of cooling towers for signs of damage, corrosion or contamination
- ensuring that your water treatment and water quality testing procedures are carefully adhered to, in order to control risks within the standards required.

Even when your monitoring reveals 'negative' results, that is, no contamination, it is essential that regular monitoring should continue so long as your system or plant is in use. *Legionellae* can enter systems and plant from anywhere, at any time.

Records

Why keep records? It cannot be stressed too strongly that doing this is vital. You may have done your job conscientiously and fulfilled all the requirements of the law, but can you prove it? Many a strong defence against prosecution has fallen because of the absence of records. So, good record-keeping is essential.

The ACOP requires records to be kept throughout the period in which they are current, that is, during the operation of the written scheme, and for a minimum of two years after the last date in that period. For example, this would, by implication, mean that where a named person is your 'appointed person', then the records must be kept for the period during which they hold that post and for two years after they cease to do so (paragraph 24 of the ACOP).

Your records should be as detailed and complete as possible. The following information is required by law.

1. *Administration of your written scheme* (paragraph 22 of the ACOP)
   - the name and position of the appointed person(s)
   - details of the risk assessments undertaken
   - the name and position of the person who carried out those risk assessments
   - a full description of the system, with a plan showing all items of plant that are cooled by the system
   - information on water treatment plant or equipment
   - details of the volume(s) of water in your system
   - details of the correct and safe operating procedures for your system and ancillary plant, including water temperatures
   - full details of the written scheme (see page 244)
   - the name and position of the person(s) with responsibility for implementing the scheme
   - details of the responsibilities of the person implementing the scheme
   - an outline of the lines of communication in implementation
   - full records of:
     —when the system or plant is in use
     —when it is not in use and drained down.
2. *Implementation of your written scheme* (paragraph 23 of the ACOP and Regulation 9 of the COSHH Regulations)
   - details of the *precautionary measures* that have been carried out
   - full details of how those measures were carried out, showing that they were carried out *correctly,* including details of water treatment, dosing, cleaning and disinfection, maintenance and inspection measures carried out, and the results of monitoring (above)
   - the dates on which those precautionary measures were carried out

- the dates on which inspections, tests and checks were carried out
- the results of those inspections, tests and checks
- details of any remedial work undertaken
- the dates of completion of that work
- the signature of the person carrying out the tasks or other form of authentication, where appropriate.

Designers, manufacturers, importers, suppliers and installers of water systems and plant

The duties of designers, manufacturers, importers, suppliers and installers are set out in sections 3 and 6 of the HASWA. These are further reinforced concerning water systems and plant by paragraphs 25 to 29 of this ACOP.

These duties are:

- to ensure that risk is avoided or, where this is not reasonably practicable,
- to ensure that the design and construction of the plant and systems is such that it will be safe and without risks to health when used at work
- to provide adequate information about the plant or systems, the risks they present and the necessary conditions to ensure safe and risk-free operation when used at work
- to provide information about aspects of operation and maintenance that have a bearing on risks. This information is to be regularly updated in the light of new information on serious risks to health and safety that becomes available.

Testing

Designers, manufacturers, importers and suppliers of water systems and plant that may present risks of legionellosis must also carry out tests (or arrange for such tests to be carried out) to ensure that the systems and plant will be safe and without risks to health when used at work.

Suppliers of products and services

Suppliers of products and services, including consultancy and water-treatment services the purposes of which are to prevent or control risks of legionellosis, must (under paragraph 27 of the ACOP):

- provide adequate information on the correct and safe use of products, including the circumstances and conditions of their use
- ensure that any limitations in their own expertise, products or services offered are clearly defined and made known to the user or their appointed person, as appropriate
- ensure that their own staff possess the necessary ability and experience and are provided with adequate information, instruction, training and resources to enable them to carry out their duties safely, competently and effectively.

Duties to the public

It must be remembered that many water systems and plant, such as whirlpool spas and jacuzzis, are installed in places that are opened to members of the public for them to use in their leisure time. There is a clear duty of care under section 3 of the HASWA to those who are *not* your employees, just as there is a duty to employees under section 2. The above requirements on designers, manufacturers, importers, suppliers and installers are thus also important so far as the end user is concerned, and employers who receive these systems, plant, products and services take on a dual responsibility, to their employees and customers, or others who may be affected by their operations.

Sources of help

Should you need any assistance in complying with the Regulations and ACOP, the following sources of help are available.

- Your local environmental health officer (their address and telephone number can be found in your local telephone and/or business directory).
- Your local HSE office (their address and telephone number can be found in your local telephone and/or business directory).
- Swimming Pool and Allied Trades Association, 1A Junction Road, Andover, Hampshire SP10 3QT (tel: 01264 56210).
- Chartered Institution of Building Services Engineers.
- Your trade association.

Some useful reading

The HSE's free leaflet *Legionnaires' Disease* (IAC(L)27), contact the HSE's Enquiry Points at Sheffield (0114 275 2539), Bootle (0151 951 4381) or London (0171 221 0870).

Guidance Note, *The control of legionellosis including legionnaires' disease* (HSE, HS(G)70 1991, available from HMSO). This supersedes Guidance Note *Legionnaires' disease* (EH.48 (1987)).

Standards for Commercial Spas: Installations, chemicals and water treatments, Swimming Pool and Allied Trades Association (available from them, see above).

26

Sick building/office syndrome

An area of increasing concern in which experts warn us of the dangers of allergies and sickness is sick building syndrome (SBS) or sick office syndrome (SOS), caused by a cocktail of factors, including problems with the premises themselves and poor working environments.

SBS and SOS are largely the unseen enemy and, because they cannot be seen, they are generally ignored or discounted. While acknowledging the *symptoms* of SBS or SOS, scientists do not fully agree on whether the *causes* of these symptoms lay in the building itself or in the working environment. Yet, SBS or SOS, regardless of their source, can have adverse ill-health effects on employees and, therefore, on your company's cost-effectiveness and profitability.

Following the oil crisis of the early 1970s and perennially increasing fuel prices, there is a need to conserve energy. There is also a need to protect sensitive electronic equipment in clean airtight environments. These needs are often in conflict with the need for good working environments and, thus, there have been reductions in ventilation rates and improvements in the airtightness of buildings.

SBS and SOS are not life-threatening but represent enormous costs to employers in days lost through avoidable illness. Every day of absence and every person who leaves employment due to SBS or SOS is a *cost* to you. A wise employer will recognize and tackle these problems.

The terminology

Sick building syndrome (SBS) is the generic term used to describe the various symptoms of ill-health and lack of well-being experienced by some employees in certain buildings. Sick office syndrome (SOS) is very similar, except that it is more indicative of the problems particular to the working environment in offices. The two are often used synonymously, but even though most SBS or SOS problems are identified with offices, very little being attributed to manufacturing or other environments, the term sick building syndrome (SBS) is used in the remainder of this chapter.

The nature of the problem

There are problems of poor design of premises, including the internal structure or partitioning of them, which lead to high instances of ill-health, general lack of well-being and stress (see Chapter 27). Two reports on surveys commissioned in 1987 and 1992 produced broadly similar findings concerning ill-health effects from SBS.

A survey of office buildings in 1987 (unattributed, but quoted by Paul Appleby and Alistair Rickman in their article 'Sick Buildings', *The Safety and Health Practitioner*, November 1993) lists the following:

- lethargy, 56 per cent
- headache, 45 per cent
- stuffy nose, 43 per cent
- dry throat, 40 per cent
- dry eyes, 30 per cent
- itchy/watering eyes, 22 per cent
- runny nose, 22 per cent
- flu-like symptoms, 15 per cent
- breathing difficulties, 8 per cent
- chest tightness, 8 per cent.

In the *Building Research Establishment (1992)* report commissioned by the HSE, similar findings were produced with the following symptoms reported:

- irritation of the eyes, nose and throat
- itching of the skin
- appearance of rashes
- fatigue
- irritability
- lethargy
- poor concentration
- headaches.

Absence from the offending building usually resulted in the disappearance of these symptoms.

The report also found that sources of stress or dissatisfaction (albeit from the job, organization of work or working environment), while being unlikely primary causes of the disorder, could lead to reporting the symptoms.

If your staff experience and/or consistently report any significant combination of these problems, you should investigate the possible causes as you may have SBS or some other major problems.

Why offices more than factories?
No parallel studies of office and factory workers' health have been carried out, using the same questionnaire and measuring the same data. However, it is suggested that the main differences between factory and office environments are that:

- the expectations of office staff differ from those of factory workers
- factories offer much better ventilation, generally, whereas offices have relatively poorer ventilation than factories, and, of course, do not have large doors that are frequently opened or even left open
- most injuries and ill-health effects in factory environments can be attributed to identifiable causes in the process or substances used, with often no underlying SBS problems being identified
- office staff generally have greater expectations of comfort and are more sensitive to environmental conditions than factory workers, who are generally more active.

What are the causes of SBS?

Despite extensive research, the full causes of SBS are not clearly identified, although it does appear *not* to be associated with other building-related problems. Research suggests that SBS is due to a cocktail of risk factors, including:

- *air quality* there is a widely held view that SBS is caused mainly through poor air quality inside premises
- *carbon dioxide* caused by poor air quality, lack of ventilation and heating systems
- *obnoxious odours* while concentrations of air pollutants from various substances are less in offices than in factories, odour levels in offices can be unpleasant and the cause of complaints
- *ventilation* there is often inadequate ventilation of fresh air from outside, 'ventilation systems' often doing no more than circulating and recycling stale air within an office (offices constructed within factories or large warehouses are typical examples of workplaces that present this problem)
- *radon* a radioactive gas found naturally in many places and which affects many buildings
- *static* static electricity is often a problem caused by carpets, foam insulation materials and metal fittings, so that small electric shocks are given off when the latter are touched
- *temperature* often, environments are either too hot or too cold
- *types of heating* different types of heating can cause problems, especially in combination with poor ventilation, for example:
  —electric or gas central heating, which can cause dry air
  —convector-type heating, which circulates dust if the elements of the heaters are coated in dust
- *humidity* the relative humidity is either too dry or too humid; this can be improved by placing humidifiers above radiators or in appropriate positions in the office (note that EC Directives require correct humidity levels to be attained where visual display equipment is in use — see Chapter 19)
- *air velocity* many illnesses are caused by sitting in draughts
- *lighting* poor lighting (too bright, giving off glare or too low) can cause headaches and eye strain, and buzzing fluorescent lighting is a source of aggravation, causing headaches (this, similarly, is required to be controlled by the DSE Regulations)
- *dust* deposited and airborne dust are frequent causes of sneezing, allergies and other problems (VDUs both attract dust like magnets and emit dust into the atmosphere, and thus correct humidity is especially important where several VDUs are operated)
- *bacteria* bacteria and fungii can cause allergic reactions and infections, especially in old buildings or in premises with poor ventilation and with high levels of condensation
- *noise* noise levels that are too high (dB levels (basic noise level) or dB(A) levels (frequency modulated) or just monotonous noises) can cause problems of fatigue and headaches (see Chapter 13); the DSE Regulations also legislate against aggravating noises in offices where users of VDUs work, such as the noise of printers, telephone switchgear or some copiers
- *smoking* tobacco smoke is an air pollutant, the effects of which on people can be quite adverse, particularly to non-smokers. Smoking and inhaling tobacco smoke has been identified as a cause of illnesses including cancers and bronchial problems, identified by the medical profession, the courts, the HSE and an EC Directive

- *workstations* often, the way in which work is arranged or the physical requirements of the task cause problems.

Office equipment
A source of air pollutants is office equipment, with the main culprits being photocopiers, computers, laser printers and fax machines. For example:

- dry photocopiers and laser printers give off hydrocarbons, ozone and dust
- wet photocopiers give off aliphatic hydrocarbons, ozone and other volatile
organic compounds
- VDUs and faxes give off ozone and volatile organic compounds
- some of the chemicals emitted from photocopiers, printers and fax machines can
be potentially toxic.

Most modern photocopiers and printers are now of the 'dry' type and are quicker in
their operation, so they do not give off such high emissions as some other equipment.
However, although the emissions from *individual* units are less, the cumulative effect
of various types of office equipment (often in a confined space) can cause concern.

Buildings
Newly occupied office buildings often have noticeable odours. This is because newly
constructed premises are chemically unsettled; they contain resins and glues that have
organic solvents in them that have not cured.

Building contents
Many carpets are manufactured with underlay made of latex, matting made of
fibreglass and with adhesives used to join it all together. Furniture and fittings,
including partitioning, shelves and desks, are usually manufactured from plywood or
chipboard composites covered in Formica or veneer. Curtains and drapery are often
made with synthetic fibres, including chemicals that give increased strength, fire-
resistance and smart appearance. All these can present problems as buildings are
constructed and commissioned rapidly with little time for curing to take place during
construction. Also, furniture and carpets are invariably stored and delivered in
polythene wrappings, which store up the emissions from these substances until they
are installed.

External environmental input
Another problem with many workplaces is that the external environment is quite
polluted, so it is high in ozone and other pollutants, such as lead from exhaust fumes.
The World Health Organisation suggests that many European cities have external
ozone levels in excess of 180ppb, whereas it recommends that indoor ozone levels
should not exceed 100ppb over any 1-hour period or 60ppb over any 8-hour period.
Thus, when you open the windows to let 'fresh air' in or have a ventilation system to
the outside air as required by Regulations, you may bring in a *worse* environment
than the one you are trying to get rid of. So, this creates a quandary. In circumstances
where external air quality is poorer than the internal air quality you wish to expel, the
solution may be to install an effective air-conditioning system.

Ill-health effects
Can these emissions cause ill-health and general lack of well-being? The combination
of buildings and contents materials can produce varying mixtures and concentrations

of chemicals and their emissions, but their emissions are much below the maximum occupational exposure standards permitted in industry. In truth, very little is known about the cumulative toxic effects of these emissions in very low concentrations, but they do feature prominently in reports of SBS from new buildings or recently refurbished workplaces. Also, complaints do not arise when a person is *first* exposed to an environment but after some time has elapsed, suggesting that there may be cumulative effects of the working environment and emissions from various substances over time.

What is the cure?

It can be seen from the above cocktail of risk factors that there are many things that, in combination, may cause SBS, including working environmental, chemical, ergonomic, managerial and psychological considerations. While much research still needs to be done into SBS, these factors will require the attention of managers to eliminate or reduce what is an undoubted problem, albeit not a fully understood one.

Pre occupancy

Where possible, buildings should be allowed to cure *during* construction. Before occupying a new building or a refurbished workplace, you should ensure that all windows are fully opened to ventilate thoroughly, as security requirements will permit. If this is not possible, it is suggested that the air-conditioning or ventilation system be switched to maximum outdoor air flow to expel odours.

Furniture

When purchasing new furniture, try to ensure that it is of the type that gives off minimal odour levels and seek to have it cured before delivery. Wrappings should ideally be removed *before* delivery, unless to do so would result in damage or dirtying of items.

Air-conditioning

Ensure that adequate air-conditioning or ventilation systems are installed, properly designed and adequate for the building, its uses and its occupants. If outside air quality is poor (as above), then air-conditioning rather than ventilation will be an imperative.

Ventilation

Where external air quality is good, ensure that the building is well-ventilated by effective use of windows and ventilation systems, while not encouraging draughts.

Maintenance

Regular maintenance of all air-conditioning and ventilation systems is required by law and it is essential to ensure that all pollutants that are filtered are cleaned out from the system, including dust and fibres, which can clog up filters and prevent them from being effective. Poorly maintained systems can *contribute* to indoor ozone rather than *reduce* it, especially if there are electrical spark-overs.

Summary

In general, concentration of effort should be on creating pollution-free working environments with conditions that enhance good staff morale and motivation. This can be helped greatly by good building/office design, effective maintenance systems and management of premises and people.

Information for this chapter has been drawn from various sources, including the author's wide experience, but acknowledgement is given to an article 'Sick Buildings' by Paul Appleby and Alistair Rickman of Building Health Consultants in *The Safety & Health Practitioner* of November 1993.

27

Stress management and corporate health

Stress is a serious problem in industry and is one of the major causes of absenteeism in Britain today. Its cost to the nation is more than 2 per cent of gross national product in the UK (over $20 billion in the USA). Costs to British industry are estimated by Dr Vernon Coleman (in *Stress Management Techniques*) at £1000 per employee per annum, or £400 per day, for an average-sized company of 200 employees. In a lifetime, employees are absent due to stress-induced illness for the equivalent of one and a half years. All indications are that these costs are increasing. It is suggested that one of the best investments a company can make in its human resources is in dealing with stress factors.

Stress is often regarded as a private affair, but it can present ill-health problems that have implications for safety as well as efficiency. Stress in the workplace can cause staff to be demoralized, lose confidence and have poor concentration, as well as cause in them a vicious circle of irritability and aggression. It can have many other adverse effects, including sickness, damaged working relationships, poor performance, poor-quality work, distraction and accidents, and affect life in the home as well as the workplace. Senior executives and busy departmental managers under the pressures of responsibility are very much at risk, while those in boring, repetitive jobs are most at risk. Owner-managers and the self-employed, with the pressures of running small businesses, often coping with most or all of the jobs in their businesses, are also particularly prone to stress.

Stress needs to be managed, so this chapter offers some insights into stress to help you identify it, manage it when it occurs and remedy its effects (whether in others or in yourself).

What is stress?

Not all situations result in stress or in the same type or level of stress for everyone. Two people can respond entirely differently to a given situation, one producing stress symptoms in themselves, the other reacting positively. Stress is, therefore, a person's reaction to a situation, their inability or otherwise to cope with or manage situations that present stressors. The type or level of stress will depend on their mind-set, their view of themselves and how they have programmed their mind to react to situations that present stressors. Not all stress is bad; indeed, we need a certain level of stress (or pressure) to keep us active and alert and many people work well under pressure.

What is a stressor?

A stressor is any situation that has the potential to produce stress in someone, depending on their reaction to it.

What are the symptoms of stress?

There are many symptoms of stress. The presence of only one or two of them in isolation is not in itself necessarily indicative of stress, but a combination of several or many with consistency and persistence is symptomatic. There are many symptoms:

- feeling light-headed
- heavy heartbeat
- stomach churning
- dry mouth
- feeble knees
- irritability
- rapid and uneven breathing
- nausea
- chest pains
- lacking energy
- irrational fear
- tension
- heavy smoking
- cold sweats
- palpitations of the heart
- back pain
- dizziness
- excitability
- breathing difficulties
- constant headaches
- migraine headaches
- constant tiredness
- guilt complexes
- depression
- worry and panic attacks
- drinking alcohol to excess
- memory lapses including the 'tip of the tongue' phenomenon
- drug dependency (most commonly valium and librium)
- regular insomnia, the inability to switch off at night.

But the most common, and strongest, symptom is *anxiety*.

Motivation

Are you or any of your staff lacking motivation? Lack of motivation is not in itself indicative of stress, but a person under stress will invariably lack self-motivation in the job and/or fail to respond to motivation from others.

Road safety

Stress causes many drivers to fall asleep at the wheel, with obvious consequences. There was an incident in 1992 when a driver, caught in a traffic jam on a motorway, fell into a deep sleep and was oblivious of the traffic jam *he* was causing once cars started moving again until the police woke him up. Accidents leading to injuries and death caused by motorists nodding off are rising rapidly and business managers are most at risk. This phenomenon is often due to working longer hours and having fewer staff.

What are the causes of stress?

Personal

Many causes can be traced back over years, perhaps to events the person is not consciously aware of, has forgotten about or suppressed, but which have been reactivated, as it were, by a current stressor, including:

- birth trauma
- environment
- development/nurture
- catastrophe

Other major life changes or upheavals such as:

- divorce
- change of job
- death of a loved one
- abortion or miscarriage

- sale of and/or moving house
- marriage
- injury

are all stressors.

Most sexual problems are symptomatic of relationship problems, many (though not all) of which can stem from childhood.

Family
Events in the family, such as illness or death, marital problems, pregnancy or family discord, are essentially private, but can cause stress and may affect work performance.

Work and finances
These two causes are linked and include:

- overwork
- underwork
- redundancy
- debts
- increased or changed responsibility deteriorating interpersonal relationships (both cause and effect)

- working with VDUs
- the effect of VDUs on the eyes
- emissions of electromagnetic radiation in offices.
- boredom
- impact of retirement
- SBS

The environment
Factors in the environment at home and at work affect all of us, but many people are adversely affected by them. Some factors that have negative effects are:

- noise
- distraction at work
- environmental noise causing sleeplessness
- SBS (see Chapter 27)
- relationships with neighbours
- noisy neighbours (especially those who are noisy late at night)
- physical environment
- the atmosphere.

Disasters
People involved with or in disasters or major incidents, such as explosions, fire, air disasters and multiple vehicle crashes, often require psychological treatment as a result of that experience.

The direct shock of the situation, the number of casualties to be rescued and transported as well as the number of people involved both directly and indirectly affect the impact such events have on individuals. The results can include nervous shock and post-traumatic stress disorder. Although mental well-being is not *specifically* dealt with in the HASWA, it may be *implied* under the employer's general duty to ensure the health, safety and *welfare* of employees at work under section 2(1) of the Act.

Shiftwork

The HSE's report *Contract Research Report* (31/1992) deals with the health and safety aspects of shiftwork. This report suggests that shiftwork may render employees involved susceptible to increases in cardiovascular disorders. These conditions are possibly induced by increases in body mass, blood pressure and smoking that, in turn, may be caused by disruptions to the normal daily metabolic routines. The report also evidences increases in digestive disorders and ulcers. Sleep loss has been accepted as being a major problem and is known to be a cause of depression. Shifts that last longer than eight hours are associated with poor performance, especially if the job is physically or mentally demanding or is repetitive.

A stress test

You or your staff can conduct your own stress test using the questionnaire given in Table 27.1.

People's responses to stress

Different people respond differently to stress. Three main responses are as follows.

- *Physical* People experiencing stress will engage in either 'fight or flight' behaviour (see The stress response, below). Constant firing of the fight or flight mechanisms in the body can result in an adaptation syndrome, leading to the malfunctioning of glands and organs. There may eventually be heart disease, heart attack, stroke or even cancer.
- *Psychological* Psychological responses are difficult to measure. Anxiety features prominently and a stressed person may often be irrational. They may also experience:
  —fear
  —anger
  —apathy
  —excitement
  —frustration
  —withdrawal/catatonic behaviour
  —conflict
  —skipping or rushing meals
  —overeating
  —short-temperedness
  —lost self-esteem
  —phobias about many things (such as of the telephone ringing, mail, going outdoors).
- *Work performance* The effects of stress seen in work performance may include the following:
  —ineffectiveness
  —incapability
  —inefficiency
  —procrastination
  —lack of motivation
  —wasted energy
  —lost sight of goals
  —poor time management
  —conflicts in the workplace.

Table 27.1 Stress test

Which of the following experiences or events listed have affected you/them in the past 12 months? (put circles round the scores of the events that have occurred during this time)

Experience/event	Score
Death of spouse	100
Broken engagement	80
Divorce	73
Separation from spouse or end of relationship	65
Jail term	63
Death of close family member	63
Personal injury, illness, miscarriage	53
Marriage	50
Dismissed from employment, including redundancy	47
Marital or relationship reconciliation	45
Retirement	45
Change in family member's health	44
Pregnancy	40
Sexual problems	39
Addition of new family member (birth/adoption/foster/etc)	39
Business readjustment (merger/reorganization/bankruptcy)	39
Change in financial status	38
Death of close friend	37
Change to different type of work	36
Increase in number of marital arguments	35
Mortgage or loan of over £25 000	31
Foreclosure of mortgage or loan	30
Change in work responsibilities	29
Son or daughter leaving home	29
Trouble with in-laws	29
Outstanding personal achievements	28
Spouse begins or stops work	26
Starting/finishing school, college or university	26
Change in living conditions	25
Revision of personal habits	24
Trouble with the boss	23
Change in working hours or conditions	20
Change in residence	20
Change in school, college or university	20
Change in main form of recreation	19
Change in church activities	19
Change in social activities	18
Mortgage or loan under £25 000	17
Changes in sleeping habits (not insomnia)	16
Change in number of family gatherings (mostly increases)	15
Holiday	13
Christmas season	12
Minor violations of the law	11
Total score	

Evaluation

If you have scored 300 or more, you are twice as likely to suffer from stress as someone with a score of less than 300. If you scored between 200 and 300, take care, stress may catch up on you.

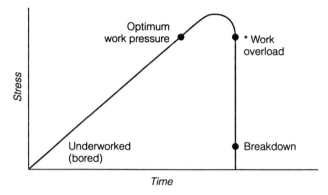

* The point at which extreme extroversion 'flips' and nervous
breakdown occurs.

Fig. 27.1   The work curve of stress

Figure 27.1 shows what happens to cause stress in the form of a 'work curve',
especially in a person who is very extrovert. At the point of overload, extreme
extroversion 'flips' and nervous breakdown occurs. The work curve can also be
applied to pressures in relationships and events.

The stress response
The stress response is a series of physical changes initiated by the endocrine and
sympathetic nervous systems. These physical changes optimize the body's ability to
cope with (spiritual, psychological, physical or social) danger. They are:

- *increased neural (brain) excitability* at best, this initiates active thinking, active
  attention and active problem-solving; at worst, it initiates panic
- *increased heart rate and blood pressure* this optimizes the availability of essential
  chemical compounds and the disposal of waste products; at worst, it is experienced as a pounding heart
- *breathing rate increases* this optimizes the availability of oxygen. Incorrect
  breathing can lead to hyperventilation (rapid and excessive deep breathing,
  which can cause buzzing in the ears, fainting and so on), which will cause
  increased anxiety
- *all necessary organ activity slows* to ensure that the body's defence mechanisms
  can make full use of all available energy
- *perspiration increases* to cool the body and allow it to burn more energy (cold
  sweats, therefore, can be a response to stress)
- *increase in sodium retention* to allow for better heat and waste dissipation (this can
  cause increased fluid retention, affecting blood pressure)
- *increased muscle tension* in preparation for important action (stiff neck or tension
  in the shoulders can, therefore, be stress-related, including that arising when
  working with VDUs)
- *sugars, fats and proteins are mobilized* to provide fuel for quick energy (it is
  amazing the endurance and strength people can muster — think of the athlete
  who runs beyond normal endurance levels and then collapses after passing the
  finishing tape or the soldier in the midst of battle who shows great heroism he
  would never have dreamed of and then collapses in a cold sweat afterwards)

- *chemicals are released* to make the blood clot more rapidly (if you are injured, this clotting can reduce blood loss, but if this reaction is triggered over the long term, the clotting can lead to a stroke)
- *increased sensitivity* of all the senses, which optimizes alertness.

There is much more one could say about the stress response, but the foregoing summarizes the fundamental features.

Stress and personality types
A study in California in the 1960s concluded that there are two personality types:

- *type 'A'* people who are very easily stressed
- *type 'B'* people who handle pressure with ease.

This is because type A people are:

- ambitious — strongly reactive
- time-urgent — their blood pressure is up
- competitive — incidence of coronaries is up for these people
- self-driven — suffer job dissatisfaction

whereas type B people are:

- relaxed
- uncompetitive.

Table 27.2 is a personalized character test to find out which type, A or B, more closely fits your personality and how likely you are to become a victim of stress.

Executive stress

Stress occurs most frequently in those executives aged between 30 and 60. The stress is often related to work pressures and responsibility or there may be changes in working arrangements, such as a new department, promotion, enlarged job or redundancies to implement. Many people do not like change. For example, a person attending a seminar the first day chooses a particular seat and location in the room; on following days they keep to that seat and are upset if someone else sits in it!

There will be *time* pressures (such as telephone interruptions, increased correspondence, perpetual meetings). Perfectionism can lead to stress, whether perfection is achieved or, worse, not achieved. Relationships may be strained and there may be perceived competition for success (often imagined and irrational), seeing others as a threat to one's own success — particularly well-qualified subordinates.

Anger
Becoming angry and blowing your top is a major cause of raised blood pressure, which is one of the main causes of heart attacks. Managers who have type A personalities have long been urged to relax in order to reduce their high blood pressure, but now curbing one's temper is regarded to be at least as important.

In 1990/91, psychologists at the University of Wales, Cardiff, carried out a study of 63 type A men who had mild blood-pressure problems. They found that counselling them to overcome their anger together with relaxation therapy, brought a considerable reduction in their blood-pressure levels. Their report, in the *Journal of Psychosomatic Research*, states that people in the risk categories need to be taught how to deal with anger and hostility and how to relax in order to protect their health.

Table 27.2 Character test to assess whether you are personality type A or B

Study the statements below and score them as follows:

- if the description on the *left* is completely you, give it a score of 1
- if the description on the *right* is completely you, give it a score of 10
- if *neither* is completely you, give it a score of from 2 to 9, as appropriate.

I am:

Casual about appointments	Never late for appointments
Very casual in approach to work	Very eager to get jobs done
A good listener	Interrupt people in mid sentence
Never feel rushed	Always am rushed
Express feelings easily	Hide feelings from others
Can be very patient	Impatient when (kept) waiting
Take matters one at a time	Try to do many things at once
Have many interests	Have few interests outside work
A slow and deliberate talker	Emphatic in my speech
Slow in doing things (eating, walking)	Fast
Quite unambitious	Very ambitious
Very easy-going	Hard task-master to myself

Scoring
A total score of about 75 would indicate a fairly balanced personality type between A and B.

The nearer a total score is to 120, the more firmly you can be classed as type A, with its possible problems.

A total score of around 35 would indicate a probable type B personality.

A total score at or very near to 12 indicates that you need to wake up from your sleep!

Evaluating personal executive stress
In Table 27.3 is a stress evaluation scale. Each statement is scored to show how true it is *or* the amount of time you believe that each statement is true for you.

Prevention, or remedying, of stress

Stress can be prevented. If it exists, determined action will need to be taken to remedy it. The hints here can be applied to yourself or will assist you in finding solutions for colleagues' or employees' stress.

Priorities
There is a need to establish priorities. First, try sorting out your workload into four separate files or lists:

1. *priority 1* urgent and essential — those proactive tasks essential to your work/ business, task achievement and/or earning money
2. *priority 2* important, but less urgent — tasks that must be done but can wait a while, which may be proactive or reactive, like completing statutory returns by a certain date

Table 27.3 Stress evaluation scale

Score the statements below as follows:

0 = not at all true for me
1 = somewhat true for me *or* true for me only part of the time
2 = fairly true for me *or* true for about half the time
3 = mainly true for me *or* true for most of the time
4 = true for me *or* true *all* the time.

Statement	*Your score*
I feel inferior and inadequate compared to others	
I feel unworthy and guilty when criticized	
I am easily frustrated	
I have a compulsive need to prove my worth and importance	
I am anxious about my future	
I have difficulty making decisions	
I am afraid of death	
I am easily angered	
I resent people who don't do what they should	
I am badly upset by disappointed expectations	
I have a strong need to dominate and control others	
I blame myself for my mistakes and defeats	
I have a strong need for confirmation and agreement	
I habitually put off doing what I know I should do	
I have an intense need for approval and acceptance	
I am fearful of undertaking new endeavours	
I am sensitive to social pressures	
I have an intense fear of failure	
I have trouble admitting I am wrong	
I worry about my loved ones	
I am pressured by responsibility	
I am afraid to let others see the *real me*	
I have a compulsive need to meet others' expectations	
I have a compulsive need to sin	
I am impatient and worry about getting things done on time	

Scoring
Add up all your scores to find out what your personal executive stress factor (PESF) is:

- a PESF of 5 indicates an essentially stress-free life
- a PESF of 15 is a definite handicap to your emotional well-being
- a PESF of 25 indicates a severe handicap
- a PESF of 50 or more indicates serious emotional problems and a definite threat to your health.

3. *priority 3* routine — those things that are important but which can wait until priority 1 and 2 things are out of the way
4. *priority 4* those interesting but non-essential bits of paper that people ask you to action or those market research forms that everyone wants you to fill in today or now.

Ask yourself these questions:

- 'Will it matter in three or six months' time?' If the answer is 'No', leave it in the file marked priority 4, then, in three or six months' time, when no one has asked you for it, throw it away!
- 'Can I delegate some of those priority 1 and 2 tasks?'

Delegation

So many busy executives, frankly, waste their time doing those things they could delegate or simply occupy time but do not produce results — except stress. So, *delegate* tasks to subordinates and train them to be able to take tasks away from your desk (my book *The Employer's Survival Guide* gives guidance on delegation).

Reprogramming

Our minds are like computers or tape recordings. Stressed managers need to reprogramme their mind-sets. There are a number of ways of coping with and remedying stress in this way that a stress management seminar would advocate, including the following:

- establish a *vision* with goals for your own life (the future is limited only by your imagination)
- *relax* — if you feel stressed, stop, take two or three deep breaths and relax
- don't be anxious about the telephone — filter calls, install a machine that enables you to choose who to answer, or if you have an assistant, get them to filter your calls
- don't anxiously rush for the mail — leave letters for a while
- don't grab the telephone — let it ring three times (or a maximum of five) before answering
- don't slam the telephone down — replace the receiver gently — slamming is an aggressive move that creates tension in you as well as your listener
- be assertive rather than aggressive or submissive
- learn to say 'No' firmly but politely
- don't allow others to pressure you into impossible objectives or be detracted from those important tasks and objectives
- take breaks during your work — get up, walk around, take a tea or coffee break, especially if you are engaged in telephone sales or in intensive discussions
- don't worry about mistakes — there is no such thing as failure, only learning experiences along the road towards the achievement of your goals (Edison did not have 1200 *failures* in designing the tungsten filament lamp, he discovered 1200 ways in which his idea would *not* work, which led him to the one that *did* work)
- take ten minutes in each day (lunch-time is a good time) to just lay back, close your eyes, forget about work and all those pressures and *relax*
- obtain therapeutic body massage, but only from a professionally qualified therapist, to relax you
- additionally, use relaxation techniques and consciously relax each part of your body, beginning with your forehead and moving down to your feet (a stress counsellor can help you learn how to do this)

- spend time with your family and/or friends
- think positively: think pleasant thoughts, talk positively to bring about positive events — say good things about yourself, others, your job or your business, and a positive confession can change perceptions for the better
- anchor good and pleasant feelings from other situations and hold them in your mind when you face potentially threatening or stressful situations
- find a creative pastime or hobby, something different (if you are a car mechanic, don't make mending your car your hobby)
- take a holiday — don't leave a number with your secretary* as an efficient business or department will run efficiently when the boss is not there (no one is indispensable, but your health and life *are*) (*unless yours is a hazardous industry, say, in chemicals)
- adopt a role model — someone who is an achiever with qualities you admire — then emulate them
- exercise regularly — a daily, brisk two-mile walk will do wonders for your health.

Finally, discuss (or get your affected employee to discuss) the stress problem with someone — preferably a trained counsellor. Avoid isolation, share things with someone you can trust and avoid the '12 hours a day, 7 days a week' syndrome. Also, ease off on the perfectionism many senior executives, specialist professionals and owner-managers are often guilty of expecting of themselves and others.

Avoiding stress through good stress management and remedying stress with qualified counselling will not only improve motivation, effectiveness and profitability of management and employees, but will greatly enhance the health and safety record of your company.

Sources of help

The following organizations are available for contact when assistance or advice is needed on stress.

- Abundance Management Services, Abundance House, 17 St Michael's Crescent, Oldbury, West Midlands B69 4RT (tel: 0121 552 2073) for stress management training and professional counselling.
- Care Assist Group Limited, Care Assist Court, Wheatfield Way, Hinckley Fields, Hinckley, Leicestershire LE10 1YG (tel: 01455 251155). A provider of employee assistance programmes, which give access to professional counsel and legal services to employees.
- Corke, Carr Associates, 28 Rochester Square, London NW1 9SA (tel: 0171 267 2208). For stress management and motivation training, for corporate, public and private sectors.
- Stress and Motivation (UK) Limited, Suite 11, Balmoral House, Windsor Way, Brook Green, London W14 0UF (tel: 0171 603 2846). Corporate stress management and motivation advisory and training services.

28

Health and safety in Training for Employment schemes

The life-blood of industry's future manpower is its young people — understudies in all the many occupational skills for which they undertake training.

Young people are, however, invariably lacking in knowledge, skills and experience, which causes them to be unaware of the hazards in the workplace. Add to this their often high-spirited natures and the combination can have potentially lethal implications for their health and safety. For this reason, managers of placement companies involved in government Training for Employment (TFE) schemes receiving young people for training have a particular duty of care towards them.

Older people in training, too, often have preoccupations, familiarity or attitudes formed by experience that can result in unsafe acts and omissions, so that special duty applies in such cases also.

It may be thought that a trainee who is seconded to a placement company for work experience and training via TFE is not the responsibility of the placement company manager, but the law takes a different view. We hope that the advice given in this chapter will assist those responsible for the training of people via TFE to fulfil both their legal and moral obligations.

General duties of the employer

All those who provide training for employment, under such government-sponsored initiatives as Investors in People (IIP), have a duty to ensure, so far as is reasonably practicable, the health, safety, hygiene and welfare of all their trainees, while they are:

- on their own premises
- the premises of placement companies (placements)
- the premises of subcontracted training establishments (subcontractors) who provide off-the-job training on behalf of the main provider
- colleges of further and technical education (colleges).

All IIP and/or TFE schemes are administered by the Training and Enterprise Councils (TECs) in England and Wales, and by the Local Enterprise Companies (LECs) in Scotland.

The duties in this respect are laid down in the Health and Safety (Training for Employment) Regulations 1990 (TFE Regulations), which afford all trainees the same protection and rights as other employees enjoy under the HASWA. This duty has been reinforced by a European Community (EC) Directive designed to protect young people at work, which became effective on 31 December 1993. This EC Directive extends to *all* young people, regardless of what type of training they may be undergoing. So, the protection of the TFE Regulations extends to trainees on Initial Training (IT), Youth Training (YT) or Employment Training (ET) schemes and other types of training for employment as appropriate to various initiatives such as Job Club, Job Search and so on.

Status of trainees

There are two classes of trainees:

- *employed status* trainee employees of the placement company
- *non-employed status* employees of the main TEC-funded training provider.

Under the TFE Regulations, all trainees who are undergoing training for employment under any government initiative, including IT, YT, ET, Job Club, Restart, Employment Action and other schemes, are to be regarded as *employees* by the main provider company, placements, subcontractors and colleges, for the purposes of health, safety, welfare and hygiene. They are to be afforded full protection as is given to other employees.

Responsibility and accountability

The main provider company, its managers and supervisors, including field staff and tutors, have a *special duty of care* to those trainees in their care who are under the age of 18 years, in addition to the specific duties imposed upon them under sections 2(1) and 2(2) of the HASWA and other associated Acts of Parliament's Regulations concerned with health, safety, welfare and hygiene.

This same responsibility extends to managers and staff in placements, subcontractors and colleges that have trainees placed with them for training and/or work experience.

Field staff of the main provider company (usually called the training agent) are responsible for ensuring that stated conditions in a contract for training are complied with, including taking personal action where appropriate. Where trainees are the direct employees of a placement, field staff of the main provider are responsible for assuring health, safety and welfare, but have no legal powers of enforcement. They must, however, assure themselves and their own main provider company that standards are met, taking such action in cases of non-compliance or refusal to comply as outlined in Appendix 8.

The conduct of staff Managers, field staff, contractors and staff acting on behalf of the main provider company must, at all times when in training and work experience establishments, conduct themselves in such a manner as to protect the health, safety, welfare and hygiene of trainees and of managers and employees of placements, subcontractors and colleges.

The requirements of the TFE Regulations

Registration

All placements, subcontractors and colleges in which trainees are placed for training and/or work experience must be registered with the appropriate legal authority (the HSE or an EHO)as appropriate. Registration includes:

- Notification of premises as a place of employment on:

—HSE Form F9 (for factory premises) to the local HSE office
—EHO Form OSRI (for offices, shops, railway premises) to the local EHO
- registration of premises used for the processing, production, preparation, storage, distribution, sale and/or serving of food for human consumption, as required by the Food Safety Act 1990 (this is done by filling in forms available from your local EHO; note that all catering and food service establishments that have trainees are included in this requirement).

Health and safety policies

All placements, subcontractors and colleges that employ five or more persons, including the director(s), manager(s) *and any trainees*, must produce a written statement of their policy on health and safety. If, for example, there are a director/manager and three employees, the addition of just *one* trainee will bring the number of employees to five and a written policy is then required. Establishments employing fewer than five employees including trainees are *not* legally required to have a written policy, but should demonstrate that there *is* a policy in operation and should be encouraged to commit this to paper.

It is often helpful for field staff to make suggestions as to the design and content of health and safety policies in placements, subcontractors and colleges, where considered appropriate, for example, where they have no health and safety specialist of their own.

The main provider's policy The main provider's health and safety policy should contain policy statements on the safety of trainees in each respective occupation for which training and/or work experience is provided. Extracts of the main training provider's health and safety policy document should be provided to managers of placements, subcontractors and colleges. Each section extracted should be pertinent to the activity being undertaken, such as food safety and hygiene for catering establishments, VDU operations in secretarial placements, bricklaying or woodworking safety in construction and fire safety for *all* placements.

The placement or subcontractor's policy Field staff of the main provider company should peruse the health and safety policy document of the placement company, subcontractor or college to assess whether it affords the appropriate protection to trainees and reflects all statutory requirements, according to the particular occupation for which the trainee is in training and/or receiving work experience.

The implementation of a policy During the monitoring process, field staff should assess that the health and safety policies of both main provider and placement/subcontractor are being implemented, for example, checking if:

- the policy states that a particular item of protective wear is to be worn, that it is in fact being worn
- certain fire safety standards are laid down, that they are complied with.

Fire certificates

All placements, subcontractors and colleges *must* apply for and obtain a fire certificate from the local fire authority, under the Fire Precautions (Application for Certificate) Regulations 1989, in the following situations:

- where there are *more than* 10 persons, including trainees, employed below ground-floor level (say, in basements)

- where there are *more than* 20 persons, including trainees, employed at ground-floor level
- where, *in aggregate*, there are *more than* 10 persons, including trainees employed on all floors above ground-floor level, (for example, if there are 2, 5 and 4 persons deployed on the first, second and third floors, respectively, a fire certificate is required.

No trainee should be permitted to work where a fire certificate is clearly required and has not been obtained or applied for.

Some fire authorities, however, for their own reasons, refuse to recognize trainees on IT, YT or ET schemes *as* trainees, mostly in small firms where the number of managers and staff excluding trainees is less than the numbers given above. This does not accord with the Regulations, though, and so the main provider or placement staff should both ask for a fire certificate, if appropriate, and keep a written record of any such refusal.

Fire safety and fire precautions
Field staff should ensure that all the requirements of the following Acts and supporting statutory instruments are complied with in placements, subcontractors and colleges, in so far as they affect trainees, as follows:

- Fire Precautions Act 1971
- Fire Precautions (Places of Work) Regulations 1995 (FPR 95)
- Management of Health and Safety at Work Regulations 1992 and its subsidiary Regulations (see Chapter 19)
- NHS and Community Care Act 1990
- For as long as they are in force, other fire Regulations issued under the Factories Act 1961 and Offices, Shops and Railway Premises Act 1963.

The requirements include the provision of:

- adequate means of escape (MOE)
- protection of the MOE by fire-resisting construction
- maintenance of MOE in safe condition, free of all obstructions
- adequate means for fighting a fire, normally portable fire extinguishers, with access to them kept clear at all times (note that the use of halon 1211 extinguishing agent is to be banned completely as from 1995 and suitable alternatives, such as CO_2 gas, used instead — see Chapter 12)
- fire drill notices in full compliance with FPR 95
- information, training and instruction in the safe and correct use of firefighting equipment, including which extinguishing agents are to be used on particular types of fire and which are *not to be used*, for example, do not use water on electrical fires
- a system of checking/clocking-in and out
- practise fire drills not less than once every six months or as stipulated by the fire certificate (if held)
- a system of carrying out assessments of fire safety and fire precautions under FPR 95.

If any placement, subcontractor or college has difficulty in fulfilling these obligations, you should refer them to a competent specialist advisory service, which may (subject to agreement) be the main provider company's own health and safety adviser.

Prohibited and dangerous machinery

Prohibited machinery

Under the Provision and Use of Work Equipment Regulations 1992 (Wk Eqpt Regs), no person under the age of 18 years is permitted to operate or be employed on or near any prohibited machinery. There are many types of machinery that young people under the age of 18 years are prohibited from operating and the appropriate Regulations pertaining to the particular occupation should be consulted. Included is such machinery as power presses, industrial guillotines, chainsaws, circular saws, meat slicers, dough mixers, certain chemical plant and so on.

Dangerous machinery

The Wk Eqpt Regs also prohibit any trainee (of whatever age) from operating dangerous machinery without close supervision, unless they have been adequately trained by a competent person. A register and certificate of training in the appropriate machines should be maintained by the placement, subcontractor or college. There are many types of dangerous machinery, but they include drilling, milling, grinding and boring machines, centre lathes, power drills, compressed-air lines, compressors, high-voltage electric charging machines and fork-lift/power trucks.

Guarding and fencing of dangerous machinery

Field staff should ensure that all dangerous machinery in operation on placement, subcontractors' and college premises is adequately guarded and/or fenced, including fail-safe devices, as required by section 14 of the Factories Act 1961. Such guarding must be to at least the minimum of British Standard BS 5305 (1988).

Instruction Trainees must be instructed that they must not, at any time or for any reason whatever, remove or otherwise tamper with or interfere with any guard, fence, fail-safe device or other item provided to protect them and other employees from the dangers of operating machinery. Trainees must follow the safe method of operation as instructed, including the use of guards, fences and fail-safe devices, and must not take short-cuts in the interests of speed.

Bearing in mind the special duty towards people under 18 years of age, if field staff consider that a trainee has not received or is not receiving adequate instruction and training in the safe use of machines, including guarding and fencing, or that supervision is not adequate so as to assure their safety, action (as outlined under Action to take for non-compliance with Regulations, later in this chapter) should be taken.

PPE

Placement companies, subcontractors and colleges are responsible for providing all trainees placed with them for training and/or work experience with those items of PPE as required by statute and local policy. The main provider company may insist on particular items of PPE being provided, according to the nature and circumstances of the training and/or work experience. Where PPE is prescribed by statute or policy, the training or work experience establishment *must* provide such items free of charge and enforce the wearing of them. Note in this regard that section 9 of the HASWA renders it an offence to charge employees, including trainees, for any item of PPE required by statute or a company's health and safety policy.

Literature

Placements, etc

Field staff should ensure that all placements, subcontractors and colleges are issued with or have obtained the appropriate Training for Employment literature from the TECs or LECs; also, that other relevant literature relating to placement safety and managers' responsibilities towards trainees is given to them.

Trainees

Field staff should ensure that all trainees placed with placements, subcontractors and colleges are issued with appropriate general health, safety, welfare and hygiene literature, as appropriate and as amended from time to time, concerning their rights, duties and responsibilities in relation to their own and others' health, safety, hygiene and welfare. They should also be issued with literature appropriate to placement and occupational safety issued by the TECs or LECs and Department of Employment, plus other HSE, EHO or other literature pertinent to the particular trade or occupation for which the trainee is undertaking training and work experience.

Legal documentation

It is important to ensure that all placements, subcontractors and colleges have complied with legal and other requirements in relation to health, safety, hygiene and welfare documentation. They must have:

- obtained employer's liability insurance (ELI) cover and display a copy of their corresponding certificate prominently where all employees including trainees can see and read it daily (as per the Employer's Liability (Compulsory Insurance) Act 1969) — having it in the manager's office or desk drawer is *not* adequate
- obtained public liability insurance cover, a current, valid certificate of which is being held and available for inspection (this is important for the protection of non-employees, including the main provider company's managers, representatives and field staff)
- obtained and displayed a copy of the HSE's poster *Health and safety law — what you should know* (ISBN: 0.11.701424.9, available from HMSO), and have it displayed where it can be seen and read daily by all employees, including trainees
- in use, a book for recording all accidental injuries, no matter how slight (accident book, DSS Form BI510 (available from HMSO — ISBN: 0.11.761384.3) is recommended for this purpose, but it is not compulsory) and field staff should ensure that, where an accident book of the company's own design is used, it contains at least the minimum content laid down by the Reporting of Industrial Diseases and Dangerous Occurrences Regulations (RIDDOR) (1985) as amended
- obtained for use, if and when needed, pad(s) of HSE Report Form F2508 (ISBN: 0.11.883853.9) and F2508A (ISBN: 0.11.883854.7) (both available from HMSO; Forms F2508 are to be used for all dangerous occurrences and injuries resulting in absence from work of four days or more, while Forms F2508A are to be used for notifiable diseases — particularly important where catering trainees are employed)
- obtained and displayed those abstracts of Regulations (not the Factories or Offices, Shops and Railway Premises Act) appropriate to the activity in which trainees are involved in training or work experience, such as the Abrasive Wheels Regulations 1970 (Form F2345) and Woodworking Machines Regulations 1974 (Form F2470).

First aid provision

It is important that all placements, subcontractors and colleges have adequate provision for first aid in accordance with the Health and Safety (First Aid) Regulations 1981 and the 1990 ACOP. The biggest problems are normally failure to keep first aid boxes adequately stocked after items have been used and failure to display notices giving the names of first aiders. See Chapter 7 for details of first aid requirements.

Occupational safety

TFE covers a multiplicity of occupations and skills so it is not practicable to include specific advice on each here. However, placements, subcontractors and colleges are responsible for ensuring that all relevant health and safety standards are met. Main provider companies have a responsibility to ensure that the former do actually fulfil these requirements (see the relevant chapters in this guide for specific advice on what is required in particular occupations and skills).

Monitoring health and safety

Field staff should assure themselves that placements, subcontractors and colleges comply with all the statutory and other (such as TEC or LEC) requirements for health, safety, welfare and hygiene. To this end, field staff should carry out regular, frequent, planned, and surprise *ad hoc* visits to establishments in which their trainees are placed, to assess the level of health, safety, welfare and hygiene, including fire safety, fire precautions and food safety and hygiene.

A check-list covering all those points included in these requirements should be devised and used when monitoring establishments. Field staff should seek *evidence* of compliance, that is, by personal inspection or sight of documents. Do not simply take it for granted nor accept a manager's word that they are doing these things — check that they are.

On-the-job training Monitoring of on-the-job training on subcontractors' premises and colleges should be undertaken by visiting the trainee's actual place of training (whether it is an internal workshop, kitchen/restaurant or an external site). This should include a review of the presentation of training. Reviews of trainees' progress should include checking the practical work undertaken and log book entries, including health and safety aspects. Comments of appraisal should be entered regularly in each trainee's log book with a record in the field staff member's own records being maintained.

During the monitoring process, the establishment manager or supervisor and trainee(s) should be interviewed on each occasion to assess and confirm the standards being achieved and maintained. Field staff should not, for example, simply accept that health and safety training took place but should assess the effectiveness of that training by questioning the trainees' knowledge and understanding of that training.

Records

Main provider companies should compile and maintain detailed records of the following:

- trainees' names, ages, addresses, trades/occupations, supervisors and so on
- systems for communication and complaints concerning health and safety
- placements, subcontractors and colleges providing training

- training given to trainees
- details and confirmation of monitoring visits
- details of any deficiencies in health, safety, welfare and hygiene standards in establishments
- details of action taken (if any) to seek to encourage or persuade establishments to achieve and maintain standards, together with any advice given
- details of any restrictions placed on the deployment of trainees and/or the activities in which they may partake
- details of sanctions applied, if any.

Action to take for non-compliance with Regulations

It should be noted that neither the management of main provider companies nor their field staff or tutors have any legal power or authority whatever to seek to *enforce* health, safety, welfare and hygiene standards in placements, subcontractors and/or college. Only HSE inspectors, environmental health officers and fire officers have any powers of enforcement. In cases of non-compliance or refusal to comply, any of the following options could be exercised at the discretion of the management or field staff of the main provider company:

- advise the director/manager of the establishment of the minimum standards that are required in the particular area of concern — with information about the appropriate legislation (Fire Precautions Act 1971, Food Safety Act 1990 and so on) and request them to conform — and the managers should be advised that continuance of trainees within their operations is conditional on these standards being met and maintained
- restrict the areas in which trainees may be permitted to work or to have access
- withdraw the trainees
- inform the local HSE office or EHO by telephone; this may be done anonymously, if desired
- inform the local TEC or LEC.

Field staff sometimes fear losing a placement if they insist on minimum standards being attained. However, on no account should the life, health or safety of any trainee be placed at risk due to unsatisfactory health, safety, welfare or hygiene standards, even where there is a possibility of losing that placement or other establishment as a result of trying to persuade them to comply or taking action in cases of non-compliance. The trainees' lives and health and safety are paramount.

Training

The quality of health and safety provision and training standards is only as good as the staff and tutors of provider companies. It is thus essential that all field staff and other members of management and staff involved in training and the monitoring of placements, subcontractors and colleges should receive adequate information, training and instruction in:

- health and safety legislation, including the HASWA, fire precautions legislation, the Food Safety Act 1990, Food Hygiene Regulations, EC Directives, DSE Regulations, RIDDOR, Manual Handling Regulations, PPE Regulations, and so on
- the management of health, safety, welfare and hygiene, and companies', managements' and employees' duties and responsibilities under various laws — what to

look for and how to know that it is to the minimum acceptable standards required
by law
● methods of monitoring, assessing and attaining health, safety, welfare and
hygiene standards in placements, subcontractors and colleges, including the
design and use of check-lists
● particular health, safety and hygiene standards pertaining to specific trades and
occupations within their spheres of operation.

In addition to the legal aspects, the information in this chapter is gleaned from wide
experience of IIP and TFE and is intended as a guide only. It is the prerogative and
responsibility of the main provider, placement company, subcontractor and college
involved to devise their own schemes. We hope this chapter will assist.

A suggested health and safety check-list for monitoring placements is given in
Appendix 8. This may also prove useful to placement providers as a means of
assessing for yourself how well you comply with all that is legally required when you
take on trainees. The check-list is also useful to any company for checking compliance
with health and safety requirements.

29

Health and safety training

There are many sound commercial reasons for training employees — the need for efficiency, productivity, cost-effectiveness, improved quality, reduced wastage and rework and, of course, profitability, are sufficient reasons alone. However, since the implementation of the HASWA and later Regulations, legal obligations have been placed on employers to train employees in the various aspects of health and safety. These obligations have been extended by 1992 Regulations.

The primary objective of health and safety training is accident and ill-health prevention. Employees need to be informed of the duties of themselves and their managers concerning health, safety, welfare, job safety, hygiene and the hazards in the workplace, including hazardous substances. Many employees regard their health and safety as being a matter of simple common sense, but, apart from the questionable validity of such an assumption, employees can only apply common sense to knowledge and skills in health and safety that they can only receive through training.

The legislation

Numerous laws impose legal obligations on employers to provide training in health and safety, including:

- section 2(2)(c) of the HASWA
- the COSHH Regulations and its ACOP
- Approved General Code of Practice (ACOP)
- the 1992 ACOP on carcinogenic substances, issued under the COSHH Regulations
- the 1991 ACOP on legionnaires' disease, issued under the COSHH Regulations
- the Control of Noise at Work Regulations 1989
- the Control of Lead at Work Regulations 1980
- the Control of Asbestos Regulations 1987
- the Management of Health and Safety at Work Regulations 1992 (MHSW Regulations)
- the Workplace (Health, Safety and Welfare) Regulations 1992
- the DSE Regulations
- the Manual Handling Regulations
- the PPE Regulations
- the Work Equipment Regulations
- the Fire Precautions (Places of Work) Regulations 1995
- the Food Safety Act 1990

- the Environmental Protection Act 1990
- the Electricity at Work Regulations 1989.

Quite a formidable list! But with accident statistics at consistently high levels, with no signs of significant improvement, training is an *essential* management activity — as important as managing any other part of your organization.

The terminology

A recurrent theme in legislation is the requirement to provide 'adequate information, instruction, training (and supervision)'. Section 2(2)(c) of the HASWA states that:

> . . . the matters which that duty [referred to in s 2(1)] extends include in particular —
>
> (c) the provision of such information, instruction, training and supervision as is necessary to ensure . . . the health and safety at work of his employees

This requirement for information, instruction and training is reinforced by the MHSW Regulations (see Chapter 18).

But, what is meant by the terms 'information', 'instruction' and 'training'?

Information
Data important to the safety and health of employees, including:

- safe systems of work, methods and procedures
- materials being made and in use during manufacture
- hazards in the workplace
- hazardous substances in use in the workplace
- fire safety and precautions procedures, including fire drills.

Instruction
On-the-job instruction in the practical aspects of job safety in the workplace. This includes procedures, processes and the safe operation of machinery. Practical instruction may often include off-the-job instruction in areas established away from the factory/production environment, but this is, none the less, practical, such as apprentice training centres.

This should not be confused with *written* instructions, which may be printed on paper or in labels on machinery and containers.

Training
Off-the-job training in the theoretical aspects of health and safety. This will include training in:

- aspects of the law, such as the duties of managers and supervisors
- legal aspects of the COSHH Regulations, lead, asbestos, VDU safety and so on
- design of machinery and guarding
- company safety policy
- accompanying theoretical training to practical instruction.

Just to confuse you, the term 'training' is often used synonymously with practical off-the-job instruction in such matters as manual/kinetic handling or firefighting. Also, the term 'on-the-job training' may be used in connection with practical instruction.

In this chapter are the main health and safety subjects about which the law requires employees to receive information, instruction and training.

The requirements of the legislation

Managers' and employees' duties

The aspects of health and safety to be included in training under the requirements of section 2(2)(c) of the HASWA include:

- the duties of directors and managers, as found in sections 2 to 6 and 9 of the HASWA
- the duties of employees (including directors and managers) under sections 7(a), 7(b) and 8 of the HASWA
- the implications of other sections of the HASWA, including legal sanctions, as they affect managers and employees.

Remember that directors and managers are also employees of their respective companies and, thus, have dual responsibilities.

You should refer to the details given in the chapters covering the subjects mentioned under The terminology, above, for guidance on the health and safety training that should be given in them. To avoid repetition of this information, in this chapter there is simply a summary of each of the above legislative requirements so that you have a brief check-list.

The COSHH Regulations and ACOP

There are many substances in the workplace that are hazardous, including chemicals, gases, oils and powders. All employees must receive information concerning such substances, including:

- *classifications* toxic, harmful, irritant, flammable, corrosive, explosive, radio-active, oxidizing and so on, according to the Chemicals (Hazard Information and Packaging) Regulations 1993, which replaced the 1984 Regulations
- *substances* the hazardous substances in use or manufactured in the workplace, including:
  —their common names
  —their chemical names
  —their ingredients
  —the specific hazards of each substance
  —their safe method of storage
  —their locations of storage relative to each other
  —their transportation
  —their correct and safe uses
  —the safe maximum exposure limits (MELs) and occupational exposure standards (OESs)
  —the methods of protection against exposure, such as PPE
  —first aid and medical treatment in the event of being exposed to substances by contact with the skin or eyes or by ingestion
- *danger areas and emergency procedures* details of areas where hazardous substances are stored and the emergency procedures in the event of a spillage, fire or explosion.

See Chapters 10 and 18 for further details.

Carcinogens and Legionellae

Employees should be made fully aware of any carcinogenic substances that are either used or produced in the workplace (Regulation 11). They should also be made fully aware of any risks of *Legionellae* bacteria entering any water systems or plant (Regulation 26). They should receive information on:

- who the 'responsible person' is for each carcinogenic substance or *Legionellae*
- what those carcinogens are
- what those risks of *Legionellae* are

and in relation to either or both:

- what the particular hazards are
- what steps you have taken to eliminate or minimize the risk of exposure to those substances/bacteria
- what control measures you have put in place
- what employees must do to comply with those control measures
- what health and safety precautions they are required to take by statute or by company policy, including the use/wearing of PPE
- what control measures are in place
- their duties to you as the employer to enable you to fulfil your duties under the law.

See Chapters 11 and 26 for further details.

Noise

Employees must be made aware of their rights and responsibilities where there is a noise problem or one is suspected.

Rights

If they suspect that the noise level is at or above 85bD(A), they may request and be provided with PPE, subject to confirmation by noise measurement instruments.

Responsibilities

If noise levels are confirmed by measurement to be at or above 90dB(A), they must be issued with PPE and they must wear it. They must know what to do if items of PPE are lost or damaged.

Controls

They must know what control measures the company has instituted and how they must comply with them; also, what they must do in order not to *increase* noise levels, for example, not bring in ghetto blasters.

See Chapter 13 for more information on this subject.

Lead

Information

Employees must be informed where there is lead in use or produced during the work process, including full information about the lead, its nature and concentrations and what the exposure limits are for those working with lead.

Young people and women

There are restrictions on young people under 18 years of age and women concerning working with lead. For example, there must be no more than a 10 per cent concentration of lead in the substance being worked with.

Controls

Employees need to be informed about what their responsibilities are in relation to:

- handling and working with lead
- what control measures are in place
- personal hygiene standards they must observe
- what PPE they must use/wear
- what medical surveillance they must undergo.

See Chapter 16 for further details.

Asbestos

One of the problems with asbestos is that people do not appreciate the hazards associated with it — until many years later when an unsuspecting ex-employee falls prey to an asbestos-related disease. Information, instruction and training are therefore very important in places where asbestos is worked with, is or may be present in a workplace and concerning the markings (where known) to use to indicate the danger to employees and others.

Information

Affected management and employees should be given full information on the three types of asbestos and their relative hazards. They must also be informed of the likely places where asbestos may be found in the workplace.

Instructions

Management and employees must be given written and verbal instructions on the action they *must* take if they discover asbestos in a workplace, for example, when undertaking renovation or demolition work (they must contact the HSE).

Training

Employees must also be trained to be able to recognize asbestos when it is found, though identifying exactly what type it is (blue fibre, brown fibre, white powder) can only be reliably done by means of laboratory analysis.

Controls

Managers and employees must be informed of the control measures to use to prevent any emission of asbestos fibres into the atmosphere and, when it is unavoidably disturbed during any work operation, how to prevent exposure to it.

Note that only HSE-authorized contractors are permitted to undertake work that involves demolition, refurbishment or other work where blue and/or brown asbestos is to be disturbed or removed. Employees (except those of licensed contractors) must *not* touch asbestos materials, except the less hazardous white powder type and then only with the use of suitable protective face masks.

Where there is to be exposure to asbestos, employees need to know what items of PPE must be worn (on the advice of the HSE) and, for approved contractors, what decontamination procedures are in place. See Chapter 17 for more information about asbestos in the workplace.

Workplace

Employees should be given training in all the various aspects of health and safety in the workplace itself, including the buildings, their layout and contents. Engineers, for example, should be given training in the minimum standards required in the design, construction, fabric and layout of contents of a workplace. See Chapter 21 for more about these subjects.

VDUs

Employees who operate VDUs must be informed of the nature of the hazards associated with them, including emissions, possible effects on eyes and eyesight, the effects of the workstation, its design and arrangement and so on.

Rights

Employees should also be informed of their rights concerning the use of VDUs, for example, eye and eyesight tests, minimum breaks from workstations, minimum lighting standards and so on.

Responsibilities

They must be told about their responsibilities, what they must do to minimize the effects of prolonged working with VDUs, including how they can avoid eye strain and fatigue and how they must cooperate with their employer's policy on VDUs and health and safety.

See Chapter 20 for more details.

Manual handling

Manual handling is statistically the most hazardous occupation, with seemingly harmless actions resulting in some of the most serious consequences experienced by people at work.

Information

Important pieces of information employees need to know are the potentially serious effects of incorrect manual handling and that about 34 per cent of injuries occurring at work result from manual handling work. Employees must also be informed of the nature, size, weight, contents and hazards of any load that they are asked to handle manually.

Handling methods

It is essential that all employees engaged in manual handling are instructed in kinetic handling methods and the best ways of avoiding accidents and injuries.

PPE

Employees should be trained in what PPE may be necessary in order to eliminate risks from manual handling by, for example, avoiding or being aware of sharp or jagged edges or preventing slippery surfaces or hands, which lessen the ability to grip and result in injury.

See Chapter 24 for more information about this area of work.

PPE

The wearing of (or failure to wear) PPE is perhaps the second most contentious problem affecting management in industry. Often this is because of costs, but also because of employees' attitudes towards PPE. Not wearing it has obvious consequences in terms of injuries and ill-health effects.

Information
Employees must be given information on the various hazards that may exist, the company policy on those hazards and what items of PPE they must use or wear to protect themselves from them.

Instruction and training
Employees must be given instruction and training in which items of PPE are appropriate to particular hazards and instructed in their correct use and wear.

Controls
Employees must be trained in the procedures to follow when an item of PPE becomes lost or damaged. They must also be informed of the control measures for ensuring compliance with company policy on PPE and of the consequences (both personally in terms of possible injuries they could suffer if they don't wear it and in terms of disciplinary procedures) in the event of non-compliance.

See Chapter 21 for more information on this subject.

Work equipment
Information
Where there are items of plant, equipment and machinery in the workplace, employees must be given full information about:

- what those items are
- what their particular hazards are
- what guards and/or fencing have been provided in the interests of health and safety.

Training
Employees must be trained in:

- the health and safety precautions in relation to plant, equipment and machinery
- the legal requirements for guards and fencing to be in place at all times, unless authorized by management, say, for the purposes of maintenance, repairs and cleaning
- what fail-safe devices are installed for employees' protection
- the duty not to interfere with or abuse these items in any way.

Engineers
It is important that engineers be trained in the minimum standards of anchoring, bolting, maintenance, repairs and servicing of plant, equipment and machinery, as appropriate.

Controls and records
All employees must be informed and instructed in the requirements to control health and safety matters in relation to work equipment and the records required for its installation, use, engineering maintenance and repairs. This should include training in all necessary certification, such as test and hand-over certificates for power presses.

See Chapter 22 for further details.

Fire safety
Another top priority in safety training is fire safety. Employees must receive information, instruction and training in:

- *fire safety* what measures are in place to prevent fires from occurring and what precautions employees must take in this respect
- *fire precautions* what precautions the company has in place to protect the safety of employees in the event of fire, including:
  —what action to take on discovering a fire
  —what the fire procedures are, including carrying out regular fire drills and the location of safe assembly points
  —what first-aid firefighting equipment is in place, including:
  what types are in place,
  what their uses are (that is, which to use on what types of fire),
  what types of fire particular extinguishers should *not* be used for (water on electrical fires, for example),
  what action to take if a fire extinguisher is set off or used, either deliberately for fighting a fire or accidentally)
- *fire precautions manual* those concerned with managing fire safety should be trained in carrying out fire safety checks and completion/maintenance of the fire precautions manual.

See Chapter 12 for more on this important subject.

Food safety and hygiene
The potential for food poisoning of employees and non-employees, including the public, is enormous. The problem with bacteria is that they are not visible to the naked eye and so people do not appreciate the presence of the hazards associated with them.

Information
Employees must be informed of the types of bacteria, the potential sources of and vehicles for bacteria there are, including themselves. This is particularly important for those engaged in food manufacturing, processing or serving, whether in food factories, restaurants, cafés, company restaurants and canteens or roadside food bars. The depth of the information given will depend on the nature of a person's work (you do not need to talk to a typist in a food company about types and names of bacteria, but a chef or food processing operator does need to know them).

Controls
What control measures are in place to ensure food safety and hygiene and prevent contamination of products needs to be conveyed to employees. This will include matters of due diligence and hazard analysis and critical control points systems (HACCPS).

PPE
Remembering that PPE is used mainly to protect the food product from the *employee* (not the employee from the *food*), employees need to know if and what PPE must be worn; also, where appropriate, what PPE must be worn for employees' own protection.

Environmental protection
Employees should be trained in the steps that are necessary to prevent pollution of the environment, including the atmosphere, rivers, drains, surrounding land and countryside. This should include such things as litter on adjacent land, litter on firms'

premises that could spread to other land and so on. The law on litter even mentions shopping trolleys from supermarkets and litter left on or outside firms' premises by customers, such as entertainment centres and chip shops, so be warned.

See Chapter 14 for further information on this area.

Electricity

Employees should be trained in electrical safety in the workplace, such as that:

- they should not tamper with any electrical item
- only a qualified electrician or electrical/electronics engineer is permitted to carry out any repairs or maintenance for electrical items
- what hazards are posed by electricity in the workplace, including fire and the dangers of overloading electric circuitry.

See Chapter 15 for more on this subject.

Others

The list of health and safety matters that carry legal obligations to provide information, instruction and training is seemingly endless, but if you apply the advice given in this chapter and the others mentioned, you will be able to fulfil all your legal and moral obligations.

Sample seminar programmes

In Appendices 14 and 15 are sample health and safety training programmes for management and other employees respectively. Adapt and extend these as necessary so that they fit your particular requirements.

30

Registers, certificates and records

All employers are required to keep and maintain in up-to-date state certain registers, certificates, records and forms, which ones depending on the number of employees and the nature of the undertaking.

Having done all you can to comply with the legal requirements for health, safety, welfare and hygiene, making and maintaining records is not just a legal duty but essential for your own peace of mind. Many a valid defence against prosecution has failed because the defending company did not back up its health and safety compliance with adequate records. As said earlier, no records means no defence.

Following are the main legal requirements for certificates, registers and records. What is applicable to you will depend on the nature of your undertaking and product or service. Remember that when you are counting the number of employees to see which certificates and so on your company qualifies for, the director or owner-manager is also included.

Registration

In all places of work in which two or more people are employed (the owner or manager included in this figure, plus self-employed persons), that employer is required to register those premises as a place of employment with the relevant authority, as follows:

* *offices and shops* with the local environmental health officer (EHO) on Form OSR1 (OSR being the abbreviation for the Offices, Shops and Railway Premises Act 1963)
* *factories and workshops* with the local HSE office on Form F9 (the 'F' standing for factories)
* *building or engineering construction* with the HSE on Form F10
* *catering establishments* with the local EHO on a form obtainable from their office (this requirement may be dispensed with in the near future, as registration does not mean licensing and so it is not considered to be of great value).

General registers
The occupier of every factory premises must maintain a general register (Factory Form F31, available from HMSO). It must be kept up to date and preserved for inspection by an authorized inspector for a period up to two years after the final date

of entry in it. (This requirement does not apply to premises under the Offices, Shops and Railway Premises Act 1963.)

Abrasive wheels

Every factory or workshop that has abrasive wheels in use must, by law, ensure that only those persons who are authorized and have been properly trained under the Abrasive Wheels Regulations 1970 are permitted to mount abrasive wheels. There are a few exemptions to this requirement, for which exemption certificates are issued. A register of those authorized and trained persons must be maintained in Register Form F2346.

Insurance

Employer's liability insurance (ELI)

Every employer, including the self-employed, who employs one or more people (worked out as given in Registration, above) must obtain employer's liability insurance cover for a minimum of £2 million arising out of one occurrence. This cover must be obtained from an 'authorized insurance company' given in the *Insurance Business Annual Report*.

Certificate of employer's liability insurance

Every employer must display a valid, up-to-date ELI certificate in a position where every employee can see and read it. The HSE or EHO have the right to require a copy to be sent to them for inspection. The penalty for failure to obtain ELI is up to £1000, plus prosecution of the directors or managers where failure to obtain a certificate is due to connivance or wilful neglect. Failure to display a valid, up-to-date ELI certificate attracts a fine of up to £400 per day.

Public liability insurance (PLI)

Every employer should obtain suitable PLI and maintain a certificate of PLI to cover those who are not their employees but who may be affected by their undertakings. There are no legal requirements to display the PLI certificate.

Fire

Fire certificate

Employers (or owners of premises where there is multiple occupancy) are required to obtain a fire certificate from the local fire authority in the following circumstances:

- where there are *more than 20* persons regularly employed on the ground floor
- where there are *more than 10* persons regularly employed either below ground level (say, in basements) or on floors above ground level.

Note that the 'above ground level' figure includes *all* floors. Thus, if you have just 10 people on first-floor premises, you do *not* need a fire certificate, but if you have, say, five, four and two people employed on the first, second and third floors, respectively, you *do* need a fire certificate.

Remember that these figures are to include trainees and anyone employed on short-term contracts, but not self-employed people, visitors, customers or members of the public.

Where no fire certificate is required because the numbers of people employed are fewer than those above, the employer (or owner of multiple-occupancy premises) must comply with all the requirements of the Fire Precautions Act 1971 and the Fire Precautions (Places of Work Regulations) 1995. The absence of a requirement for a fire certificate is not a licence to ignore the Act or the Regulations.

Fire precautions manuals

Every employer is encouraged to draw up and maintain a fire precautions manual in which to record all the necessary fire safety and precautions actions that are carried out. This is a legal requirement of the fire certificate where held, but is strongly recommended for all employers, especially in multistorey buildings. An example of a fire precautions manual is given in Appendix 4.

Dangerous substances

Regardless of the numbers of people employed, occupiers of premises where dangerous substances (such as volatile chemicals, explosives and so on) are used and/ or manufactured are required to register that fact with the local authority and/or local fire authority.

Accidents

Accident books

Every employer must maintain an up-to-date accident book (DSS Form BI510, available from HMSO).

Accident reports

Every employer must complete an accident report (HSE or Form F2508) for every dangerous occurrence (such as a fire, explosion or major collapse), death, and major or serious injury where an employee is off work for more than three days. This form is to be forwarded to the local HSE office or EHO as appropriate and a copy held by the employer. In the case of a death or dangerous occurrence, notification must be given immediately by telephone and followed up within seven days by a completed Form F2508.

Notifiable disease report

Every employer must complete and submit HSE Form F2508A to the local authority in every case where an employee is found to be suffering from any of the 28 diseases specified in Schedule 2 of the Reporting of Injuries, Diseases and Dangerous Occurrences Regulations 1985. These include:

- various poisonings by industrial substances
- various skin diseases
- lung diseases
- certain infectious diseases
- various cancers.

Food-contaminating infections

There is a legal requirement under the Food Safety Act 1990 and the Food Hygiene Regulations 1970, as amended, to notify the local environmental health department of any outbreak of food poisoning or infectious diseases in food handlers in a company that is engaged in the manufacture, preparation or serving of food products. These include:

- any staphylococcal infection likely to cause food poisoning (such as septic cuts, boils and throat or nasal infections)
- typhoid fever
- paratyphoid fever
- other salmonella infections
- amoebic dysentery
- bacillary dysentery.

HSE Form F2508A should be used for notification.

Infectious diseases

In addition to those diseases that may infect food and cause poisoning (above), all employers are required by section 29 of the Public Health (Control of Disease) Act 1984 to notify their local environmental health department (by telephone, followed up by letter or HSE Form F2508A) of any of the following infectious diseases suffered by any employee:

- acute encephalitis
- acute poliomyelitis
- amoebic dysentery
- infective jaundice
- typhoid fever
- leprosy
- whooping cough

- acute meningitis
- diphtheria
- bacillary dysentery
- anthrax
- paratyphoid fever
- leptospirosis
- scarlet fever.

First aid

A register of appointed first aid attendants who have been trained by HSE-approved bodies or who have other approved qualifications, with notices posted in the workplace giving the name(s) of first aider(s) (see Chapter 7).

The COSHH Regulations

The following are required:

- records of all assessments of hazardous substances carried out under the Regulations (see Chapter 10)
- written scheme and records of all carcinogenic substances and control measures implemented as required by the Regulations, including the control measures taken (see Chapter 11)
- written scheme for the control of *Legionellae* and records of all control measures implemented (see Chapter 25).

Noise

Records need to be kept of all assessments of noise under the Control of Noise at Work Regulations 1989. These must include initial assessments, even if these show a nil return, plus periodic reviews of those assessments as necessary.

Due diligence

Under the Food Safety Act 1990, the *only* defence against a prosecution for supplying food that is injurious, unfit for human consumption or heavily contaminated or for failure to supply food that is of the correct specification is *due diligence*. This means maintaining detailed records of all that occurs in the total process, from the reception of raw food material to the final despatch of finished food products, whether to the table or by vehicle to a customer.

Even if you have complied with all legal requirements and have most conscientiously taken all reasonable precautions to comply with those requirements, if you have not maintained full written details of every action in the food processing cycle, then, in the event of a prosecution, you will have no defence. So, good records are essential.

Hazard analysis and critical control points system (HACCPS)

Though not a legal requirement, part of the due diligence process is to implement and follow HACCPS.

Pressure vessels

Records of all tests and maintenance of pressure vessels need to be kept (see Chapter 24).

Power presses

If you have power presses, under the Power Presses Regulations 1965, as amended in 1972, a register of all power presses must be maintained on Register Form F2198. You must also maintain copies of all certificates of testing and thorough examinations of power presses and associated safety devices on Form F2197. Records of all maintenance and hand-over certificates as well as records of training for competent and authorized employees must also be maintained.

Maintenance

Full records must be maintained of all maintenance carried out in the workplace (see Chapter 20), work equipment/machinery (see Chapter 22). Maintenance of other plant, equipment and machinery must be recorded as outlined above. Also, under sections 22, 33, 35 and 36 of the Factories Act 1961, examinations of plant must be recorded on the respective form for each one, including:

- hoist or lift on HSE F54
- steam boiler on HSE F55
- steam boiler (under pressure) on HSE F55A
- steam boiler (heat exchanger) on HSE F55B
- steam boiler (normal pressure) on HSE F55C
- economizer (cold) on HSE F56
- superheater (cold) on HSE F57
- steam receiver on HSE F58
- steam receiver (when cold and with exemption certificate) on HSE F56A
- steam receiver (normal pressure with exemption certificate) on HSE F58B
- air receiver on HSE F59
- steam or air receiver on HSE F60.

31

Sanctions and penalties

Although summonses, convictions and the levels of fines have increased considerably in recent years, enforcement officers (also known as inspectors) will seek to resolve health and safety problems by other means first, with prosecutions under health and safety laws always being regarded as a last resort.

Inspectors have considerable powers. There are procedures according to which they normally operate, outlined here so that you may be directed towards (and be kept on) the right side of the law.

Who to call for advice

There are three enforcement authorities for health, safety, welfare, food hygiene and fire, which are:

- the HSE and its enforcement officers (also called inspectors)
- local authorities' environmental health departments and their environmental health officers (EHOs)
- local fire authorities with fire officers.

If you call an inspector, EHO or fire officer *before* a serious health, hygiene or safety situation is allowed to develop, this will get them on your side. They would rather help than prosecute because their primary role is accident and fire *prevention* and saving lives, *not* prosecution.

Your local telephone directory contains the numbers of your local HSE inspector's, EHO's or fire officer's offices from where a duty inspector or officer will be happy to give advice or pass you to an inspector who specializes in your type of industry.

The authorities' powers

An inspector or EHO can enter any workplace at any reasonable time without prior warning. They must only advise a member of management of their presence, but must show their identity card if requested (do ask for it). A 'reasonable' time means during your normal working hours. So, if you work a 24-hour shift, then 3.00 am is reasonable, but if you work the basic nine to five, Monday to Friday hours, then 3.00 am on a Sunday is *not* considered reasonable, unless there is an emergency.

The inspector can go anywhere on the premises (without being guided or steered) and speak to anyone considered appropriate to their function but bearing in mind their own responsibility under section 3 of the HASWA.

They can demand to see any documents, records or registers considered relevant to the particular health and safety concern and can take (or require) copies of any relevant documents. Items of relevance, including food articles, perhaps an exhibit for evidence or a prohibited substance, can be confiscated.

The inspector can take with him/her into the workplace a police officer or 'any other person duly authorized by the enforcing authority', say, a gas or electrical engineer, explosives expert, medical practitioner or food or hygiene specialist.

Investigations

Inspectors may investigate any serious incident and may demand the cooperation of any person who was involved, was a witness or may be able to provide helpful and relevant information. They may interview anyone (alone or accompanied) and require documents, forms, registers and anything to be produced that will help in the conduct of their investigation.

Enforcement

An inspector will employ any one of the following three means of enforcement, according to the situation and the danger and/or urgency.

- *Persuasion* If, after an inspection, certain hazards that are a risk to health, safety and/or welfare are found, the action required to remedy the situation may be set out in a formal letter. Failure to comply with such a request is not, in itself, an offence, but failure to fulfil one's duty as an employer/employee *is* an offence and may lead to the issue of *enforcement notices*, which are either of the following, as appropriate:
- *Improvement notice* A notice stating that certain improvements are required may be issued. It will state what the problem is, what is expected to be done to rectify it, the date by which it must be done and who is responsible for ensuring that it is done. Failure to comply with an improvement notice is a serious offence — one for which directors have been sentenced to suspended terms of imprisonment.
- *Prohibition notice* If either an improvement notice has not been complied with or the situation is too dangerous to permit work to continue, a prohibition notice may be issued. It will contain the same details as the improvement notice and will either say that it is to be:
  —*with immediate effect,* in which case you *must not* operate the machine or process or permit the named employee to continue working, unless and until the requirements of the notice are complied with (if it is an *absolute* prohibition, you must neither operate the machine or process nor must you sell it to another person (except as scrap), as to do so would contravene the Trades Descriptions Act and section 6 of the HASWA)
  —*with deferred effect,* to allow for work to be carried out or the process to be completed (if a period of grace is given and the requirements of the notice are not fulfilled by the date specified, then the notice will come into immediate effect on that date).

As with improvement notices, failure to comply with a prohibition notice is a serious offence, which can bring stiff penalties (see below).

An improvement or prohibition notice may be issued against a director, manager, employee, building, machine, process, material or anything affecting health, food safety and hygiene, safety and/or welfare. In the case of a prohibition notice against an employee, you would have no option but to transfer them to another job or to dismiss them (they would have no recourse to a tribunal).

Right of appeal

Under section 24 of the HASWA, there is a right of appeal at an industrial tribunal against any enforcement notice. In the case of an improvement notice, operation of the notice would be suspended until the hearing and decision of the tribunal, but, in the case of a prohibition notice, the order remains fully in effect unless and until directed otherwise by the tribunal. So you *must* obey the conditions of the notice until the hearing.

Prosecution

If an offence under the HASWA has been committed, or an enforcement notice has not been complied with, then the inspector may prosecute. They do not need the services of the police (except for arrest), a solicitor or a barrister, but an HSE inspector will conduct their own case with the full knowledge of the case, having investigated it themselves (section 39(1) of the HASWA; not applicable in Scotland).

It is worth reiterating here that it is for the accused person to prove their innocence, that is, that it was *not* reasonable or practicable for them to comply with requirements or that it was not reasonable to use the best practical means. It is not for the inspector or officer to prove that it was (section 40 of the HASWA).

Statements

If an inspector requests a statement from a person *without* preceding that request with a caution, that person *must* give that statement; it is compulsory. This is an important point as to refuse to give a statement can constitute the offence of impeding an inspector in the execution of their duty.

If, on the other hand, an inspector requests a statement from a person, and precedes the request with a caution, that is, words to the effect 'I must caution you that you are not obliged to say anything, but anything you do say will be taken down and may be used in evidence' (not necessarily against the person spoken to), then that person is not obliged to incriminate themselves or anyone else, and may decline to give a statement. Then it is voluntary.

Penalties

The HSE has indicated that, because of indifference to health and safety in many places, despite prosecutions, they intend to pursue prosecutions in the higher courts. There is also a growing trend for prosecutions of individuals and employees under sections 3 and 7 of the Act.

The degrees of penalties imposed are determined by the circumstances and nature of the offence, the particular legislation involved and the status of the court, as shown in Table 31.1.

Specific laws also provide for similar fines and terms of imprisonment to those given in Table 31.1. These may presently be referred to the higher courts where magistrates feel that fines in excess of their limit are justified, and include the following maximum fines for the particular pieces of legislation listed:

- Fire Precautions Act 1970, £20 000

Table 31.1 The penalties imposed for non-compliance with the HASWA

Court	Fines	and/or	Imprisonment
Magistrates' court	Up to £5000* for ss. 7 onwards *or* up to £20 000* for ss. 2 to 6		Up to three months
Higher court	Unlimited (all sections)		Two years

*Fines are for each offence, which will explain some apparently high levels of fines in magistrates' courts. The Criminal Justice Bill 1991 increased the level of fines a magistrate can impose to £20 000 for each offence from October 1992.

- Food Safety Act 1990, £20 000
- Food Hygiene Regulations, £5000
- Environmental Protection Act, £20 000
- Employer's Liability (Compulsory Insurance) Act 1969, for failure to have employer's liability insurance cover, £1000; for failure to display a certificate of this insurance, £400 per day
- Regulations issued under the HASWA (such as the COSHH, MHSW, Manual Handling Regulations), £5000
- *plus* up to three months' imprisonment (in magistrates' courts) or up to six months' imprisonment (in higher courts) and unlimited fines in higher courts.

Some examples of higher penalties
Here are some of the notable fines awarded for offences under health and safety laws in recent years:

- British Petroleum, 1989, £750 000
- British Rail (Clapham), 1991, £750 000
- SOGAT, £550 000
- TML (Channel Tunnel), 1993, £200 000
- J. Murphy (Construction), 1993, £160 000
- Nobels Explosives, 1991, £100 000
- Nobels Explosives, 1991 (second time), £250 000
- Atlantic Drilling (Aberdeen), 1992, £101 000
- Tate & Lyle, 1991, £100 000
- Lyme Bay Activity Centre, 1994, £60 000
- Caird Environmental (Birmingham), 1992, £50 000
- company director, St Albans, 1992, £30 000
- consulting engineers, Nottingham, 1991, £20 000
- Gainsborough Carpet Company, 1993, £10 000
- well-known country house hotel: failure to fit a guard to a band-saw in a kitchen, £5500; and to notify of an accident (RIDDOR), £500

- two companies, 1993: failure to provide eye and eyesight tests for VDU users, £2800
- college lecturer, 1993, £750
- two supervisors at Rover, 1993, £2600 and £2350
- college lecturer, 1993, £750
- company director, 1992, £5000, plus disqualified from being a company director for two years, for ignoring a prohibition notice
- plus many others between £200 and £25 000.

All of the above sums had legal costs added to them and, in some cases, these were up to 375 per cent of the fine itself (for example, £75 000 costs added to a £20 000 fine).

The following are some examples of terms of imprisonment transgressors received in the courts:

- director of a company in Stockport, two years, suspended (an employee died in a plastic shredder)
- company director, one year, suspended, plus £47 000 fine (manslaughter in works accident)
- company director, six months, suspended (failure to comply with improvement notice)
- company director, three years to serve from December 1994 (corporate manslaughter by criminal negligence — section 37(1) of the HASWA)
- company director, six months, served (illegal deposit of industrial waste).

Welcoming the advent of new penalties, John Rimington — Director-general of the HSE — said:

> Of course, we are glad to be able to bite harder where we need to. We were getting to the situation where the law was specifying higher penalties for the death of bluebells than people.

Conclusion

Human and financial losses are inevitable where there are failures in health and safety management. However, they can be successfully avoided by applying the advice contained in this guide.

There are no short-cuts or easy routes to the successful and effective management of health and safety. It cannot be side-stepped or delegated out of sight. Sincere and firm commitment from top management is beneficial and worth while, but it is also essential.

Successful health and safety management systems essentially incorporate planning, objective-setting, organizing, assessing, auditing and reviewing of health and safety performance. These efforts will go a long way towards complying with statutory instruments, ensuring the implementation of your health and safety policy and towards achieving accident prevention.

Appendix 1: An example of a health and safety policy

This is an example only. You should follow the Statement of policy and the General statement of intent parts fairly closely, according to your situation, ensuring that you include the signature of the chief executive, then adapt the remainder as appropriate to your company's requirements. The text in parentheses should be worded in a way appropriate to your company's structure.

After the Statement of policy and General statement of intent, headings are given of the types of subjects that could be included. It is impossible in this appendix to go into full details on every subject to cover every eventuality. Thus, under certain headings some detail has been given, but, for most subjects, you will need to delete or expand the content according to your particular situation.

ABC GROUP LIMITED

At this address

Health and safety policy

ABC Limited, in all its operations and locations, is hereinafter called 'the Company'. **Employees** of ABC Limited in all its operations and locations are hereinafter called 'the employees'. All **contractors**, **sub-contractors**, self-employed **installers**, **service engineers**, **advisers and consultants** are hereinafter called 'the contractors'.

1. Statement of policy

Corporate responsibility Overall control of the operations of ABC Limited is vested in the (Board of Directors). Responsibility for the executive control and implementation of this health and safety policy (throughout the Company) rests with the (Managing Director).

Responsibility for the workplace and working environment The (Board of Directors) recognizes the importance of achieving a safe place of work and a healthy working environment. The Company accepts its responsibilities to all its employees and others (contractors, customers) who are affected by the Company's operations, for ensuring that safe and healthy working conditions and practices exist.

Plant and equipment The Company policy includes health and safety considerations in the purchase, maintenance and updating of plant and equipment, with the requirements of health and safety legislation taken as the minimum requirements for the Company's own practices.

(Unit's safety practices) It is the personal responsibility of managers of the separate (units) (factories) (shops) (offices) (business centres) and (branches) to study and publish that part of this policy document relevant to their individual locations and operating circumstances. It is also their personal responsibility to train their subordinates (and contractors) in that policy, and to ensure that relevant policy is carried out in their respective locations.

A. B. Ceedee
Managing Director
March 1992

2. General statement of intent

It is the policy of this Company that the Company will ensure, so far as is reasonably practicable:

(a) the health, safety and welfare of all its employees while they are at work (in whatever operation or location, whether on site or in transit on authorized business), of visitors to company premises and operations, and of others who may be affected by its actions

(b) the provision of systems of work that are safe and without risks to health, with necessary supervision and control mechanisms to ensure health and safety

(c) the maintenance of a working environment that is safe and without risks to health and the provision of adequate facilities and arrangements for welfare at work

(d) the provision of plant, machinery, equipment and vehicles (whether owned or hired) in conditions that are safe and without risks to health and to provide systems for inspections and preventative maintenance to ensure safe conditions

(e) that arrangements are in place for ensuring safety and absence of risks to health in connection with the use, handling, storage and transportation of articles and substances

(f) the provision of such information, instruction, training and supervision necessary to ensure the health and safety at work of employees, and information to contractors and others who may be affected by the Company's operations or products

(g) the provision of a safe means of access to, movement within and egress from places of work

(h) cooperation with, and involvement of, employees in meeting health and safety objectives.

The necessary resources and input will be afforded to the achievement of the foregoing policy, and to this end the Company will:

(i) ensure that all requirements of the Health and Safety at Work, etc. Act 1974, Regulations and Approved Codes of Practice issued under the Act, and other relevant Acts that apply to the Company's operations, are complied with

(ii) provide the necessary management information and involvement, financial resources and safety engineering input, so far as it is reasonable and practical to do so, to achieve the standards laid down in this policy

(iii) maintain necessary up-to-date knowledge; maintain contact with relevant outside bodies, including health and safety advisory and specialist services; and keep up to date with developments in health and safety legislation, codes of practice and other technical or guidance material relating to the Company's operations

(iv) disseminate such information within the Company to employees, contractors and visitors, as such information affects them

(v) ensure that all health and safety factors are taken into account when new and revised systems of manufacture, operation, storage, materials handling, etc., are planned and effected. Further, the Company will, when considering the reorganization of its operations or new premises from which to conduct its operations, take account of the necessary health, safety and welfare requirements for that new organization or location

(vi) provide all new employees, and those redeployed to different jobs and/or departments, with information on health and safety, welfare, fire precautions, first aid and medical matters, as appropriate to their occupations and locations

(vii) ensure that all the requirements of the parent Group's health and safety policy, as they affect the Company's operations, are complied with.

3. Arrangements for the operation of this health and safety policy

Management of health and safety

Responsibility The (Managing Director) may delegate authority for specific health and safety matters to (senior location/department managers). They will be personally responsible for health, safety, welfare, and fire precautions within their sphere of operation, as a part of their normal management duties, as follows:

- ensuring that this policy is complied with
- ensuring job safety; reviewing the systems of work in their (locations or departments)
- ensuring (on-site) safety in (installations); ensuring health and safety in new and changing situations
- ensuring the use and wearing of safety protective equipment, PPE and clothing by employees, contractors and visitors, as appropriate.

Health and safety committee A statement on Company policy concerning health and safety committees. (A health and safety working party is an alternative in very small businesses.)

Safety representatives A statement on Company policy concerning health and safety representatives (trade union or non-trade union members).

Health and safety monitoring (The following is an example of what you could put.) Standards of health, safety and welfare and the compliance with this policy statement will be monitored by the (Managing Director), assisted by any necessary specialist health and safety adviser.

Suggestions The Company welcomes suggestions.

Safety management structure Following is the management structure. The positions shown have accountability to the (Managing Director) for health, safety and welfare, through existing lines of authority as follows.

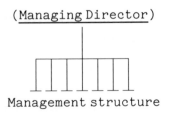

Management structure

Responsibilities and accountabilities

(Here, list the duties and responsibilities of each type of management and supervisory and other positions in the Company, for example the following.)

Executive responsibilities The (Managing Director) is responsible for . . .

Senior managers Senior managers have responsibility for . . .

Personnel manager/safety officer The Personnel Manager is responsible for . . .

Line managers and supervisors Line managers and supervisors are responsible for . . . (for example: induction training, including health and safety law, job safety, fire precautions, emergency procedures, location of fire exits, correct use of firefighting equipment, first aid and accident reporting

- ensuring that subordinates and contractors are aware of health and safety policy and that they obey the rules
- keeping up to date with health and safety matters
- ensuring good housekeeping standards
- ensuring that all access and egress routes are clearly marked and kept clear and that access to all fire doors and firefighting equipment is clear at all times
- reviewing all existing plant and equipment periodically and all new plant and equipment as it is ordered and installed
- carrying out regular health and safety checks
- ensuring accident reporting is carried out according to RIDDOR
- ensuring that appropriate disciplinary action is taken in cases of clear breaches of health and safety rules

- monitoring welfare arrangements under the guidance of . . . (for example, the Personnel Manager).)

Employees (Enter here what it is that you expect of your employees. They are to, for example:

- obey health and safety legislation and company rules
- cooperate with managers and supervisors
- receive and act on health and safety training, instruction and information
- report faults, hazards, non-injurious incidents and injuries to management
- raise with their immediate manager/supervisor any situation of conflict between health and safety requirements and the demands of the job
- wear and/or use safety protective equipment, PPE and clothing
- not interfere with, abuse or remove anything provided in the interests of health and safety
- keep all access and egress routes and access to all fire doors and firefighting equipment clear at all times.)

Fork-lift/power truck drivers (List here the duties of drivers, including, for example:

- the safe operation, transportation, depositing and storage of loads
- keeping access and egress routes clear and access to fire doors and firefighting equipment
- speed limits
- maintenance and records.)

Health and safety representatives (Enter here a statement of their duties and privileges.)

Health and safety committee/working party (Enter here a statement of their functions.)

Health and safety training

(Enter here your policy on health and safety training.)

Accident prevention

(Enter here your policy on accident prevention methods and involvement.)

The Control of Substances Hazardous to Health (COSHH) Regulations

(Enter here a statement of the Company's commitment to the COSHH Regulations, including, for example:

- initial and periodic assessments
- exposure, prevention and control
- recording
- monitoring
- control
- health surveillance.)

Duties to non-employees

(Outline the Company's duties towards visitors, contractors, the public and so on under section 3 of the HASWA.)

Duties as a (manufacturer/supplier/installer/seller)

(Enter here a statement of these duties to customers and so on under sections 3 and 6 of the HASWA.)

Personal protective clothing and equipment

(Enter here the Company's policy on what is issued to whom (including contractors and visitors) under what conditions. For example, helmets or hard hats, face masks/visors, goggles/glasses, ear defenders, overalls, gloves, boots/shoes, ventilators, harnesses and so on.)

Machine guarding and fencing

(Enter here the Company's policy on guards and fences, including warnings about interference and unauthorized removal.)

Accident/incident reporting

(Here, enter details of the Company's accident, incident and injury reporting and recording procedures.)

First aid

(Here, write down the Company's policy on first aid, for example regarding:

- first aid boxes
- first aid attendants
- obtaining first aid
- first aid medical room
- company doctor and so on.)

Housekeeping

(A statement of how important good housekeeping standards are to health, safety and welfare should be entered here.)

Hygiene

(Say here that hygiene in the workplace and personal standards of hygiene in relation to food, working with lead, wood and metal dust, oils and chemicals and so on is of great importance.)

Canteens and restaurants (State the importance of hygiene and of adherence to standards required by the Food Safety Act 1990 and associated Regulations.)

Health and safety signs

(State the importance of obeying these and note the types displayed on the premises, that is:

- red = prohibition
- yellow and black = warning
- green = safe condition
- blue = mandatory, that is, *must* do.)

Storage and handling

(Enter a statement of the Company's policy on the safe storage and handling of articles and substances, including temporary storage.)

Petrol

(Here you should write down your policy if petrol is used and/or stored on the premises.)

Lead

(Here, enter the Company's policy regarding lead if any is used in the manufacture of products, stating the methods and frequency of assessments, maximum exposure limits (MELs) (0.10 mg or 0.15 mg pm-^{3} in 8-hour TWA), protection, medical surveillance, and rules in areas where lead is worked. The following is an example of the points that could be made.)

- Food and drink are not to be consumed at workbenches.
- No one is to smoke in the workplace.
- Protective gloves, impervious aprons, masks/visors (if appropriate) are to be worn.
- Employees are to wash hands before eating.
- Employees are to avoid contact of gloved hands or ungloved lead-contaminated hands with their mouth and eyes.

Nickel

(Enter a statement here on the Company's policy regarding nickel if any is used in the manufacture of products, stating frequency of assessments, maximum exposure limits (MELs) (0.10 mg or 1.00 mg pm-^{3} in 8-hour TWA), that face masks are to be worn and ventilation/extraction to be provided.)

Asbestos

(State what procedures are to be followed if types of asbestos are discovered in the process of installations, demolitions and so on in compliance with the Asbestos at Work Regulations.)

Other hazardous substances

(State the Company's policy in similar manner to those on lead, nickel, asbestos.)

Fire equipment

(Enter the Company's policy on the types and use of fire-fighting equipment, including who is authorized to take what action.)

Fire and emergency drills

(Outline here the fire drill to be followed, from raising/ hearing the alarm and evacuation of the premises through to calling the fire brigade, first aid firefighting, handing over to the fire brigade.)

Smoking

(State here the Company's policy on smoking, if one exists.)

Office safety

(This entry is a reminder that offices as well as factories can be dangerous places and here policies should be stated on handling, storage, paper, smoking, fire-prevention measures and so on.)

Abrasive wheels

(State here the Company's policy, which must comply with the requirements of the Abrasive Wheels Regulations.)

General safety rules

(State here those health and safety rules that apply to every employee.)

Health and safety audits and inspections

(Enter here what audits and inspections will be carried out, by whom, with what frequency and who will act on the findings of audit reports.)

Welfare

(Here, details should be given about what welfare facilities are provided, such as wash basins, sanitary conveniences, wash rooms, rest rooms and so on, plus a statement exhorting the necessity for cleanliness and hygiene of the facilities provided to protect the interests of employees.)

Checking-in and out procedures

(Include here a statement about the importance of checking in and out for reasons of fire safety.)

Electrical safety

(Here, state what rules the Company works by, including 'no unauthorized person is to carry out electrical work', to ensure safety regarding electrical equipment.)

Isolation and locking-out procedures

(State here the Company's rules on isolating and locking-out plant and equipment when under maintenance, especially electrical and large mechanical plant.)

Communication and cooperation

A statement on the importance of good communication and cooperation to effective implementation of health and safety policy should go here.)

Appendices

(Enter here a statement to the effect that any appendices are integral parts of the main policy document.)

Reviews and updates

(Here, write down a statement that says how frequently this policy will be reviewed and updated and how any amendments will be made known.)

Date of this policy:

Revisions   Serial number   Date

Appendices

There are the following appendices to this policy:

Description   Date

For example:
1: Policy for on-site health and safety
2: Policy for dealing with . . .
3: Policy for installations.

Appendix 2: Examples of COSHH assessment forms

The following are examples of forms used when carrying out assessments as required by the COSHH Regulations 1988. There are other COSHH assessment forms that should be maintained, but the concern here is *only* with the protection of your employees, for which this and the example of a health surveillance record form in Appendix 3 will suffice. You should also undertake assessments and record-keeping in other matters relating to substances, products, processes and customer information as required by the COSHH Regulations.

These forms are suggestions only. There is no set formula. You should adapt them to meet your requirements.

Under certain Regulations (say, those for lead, asbestos), such medical surveillance (Appendix 3) *must* be carried out by an appointed employment medical adviser approved by the Employment Medical Advisory Service (EMAS) of the HSE.

Control of substances hazardous to health (COSHH) assessment

1. COSHH assessment of job/process

Location or department: _____		Assessment number
Title of job: _____		
Description of work undertaken:		
Substances in use: *Common/brand names:*	*Chemical name/formula:*	*Product data sheet suppliers:* *Numbers:*
Assessments: *Frequency:*	*Method/equipment:*	*Dates of assessments:*
Next assessment: *Date:*	*Responsibility:*	*Signature:* (done)
Usage and exposure: *Frequency of use:*	*Amount used:* (Per day/week/month)	*Exposure duration:* (Minutes/hours)
Control measures employed: *Minimize exposure:* *Enclosure:* *Protection:* *Extraction:* *Neutralize:*		
Required action: *Action to be taken:*	*Responsibility*	*Date action taken:*
Signature of assessor: (Safety Officer or Department Manager)		*Date:*

Control of substances hazardous to health (COSHH) assessment of substances under the COSHH Regulations 1988

2. COSHH assessment of substances

Details of substance: *Common or brand names:*	*Chemical name:*	**Assessment number:**

Chemical ingredients:
Chemical names:
1.
2.
3.
4.

Chemical formulae:
(of each ingredient):
1.
2.
3.
4.

Physical properties (description):

Product data sheet: Held? Yes/No (if No, obtain)
Name of supplier:

Date requested:

Number:

Date received:

Associated hazards/ill-health effects of exposure:

Tested/measured emission or vaporization:

_____ ppm; or

_____ mg pm^{-3} per TWA of _____ hours

Method of testing/measurement:

Type of test/measurement equipment used: *Tube No:*

Occupational exposure limits: (e.g., ppm, X mg pm^{-3} TWA X hours)

Appendix 3: Example of a health surveillance record form

COSHH personnel health surveillance record

Surname: **Forename(s):** **M/F** **Date of birth:**	
Date of this surveillance: **Date of last surveillance:**	

Location or department: **Surveillance record No:**

Job title:

Description of work undertaken:

Substances to which exposed:
Common name: *Chemical name/formulae:*   *COSHH assessment No:*

Date of assessment:

Occupational exposure limits:
(For example, ppm, X mg pm^{-3} TWA X hours.)

Details of medical surveillance:
(Such as urine analysis, blood tests/pressure, skin tests,
X-rays, peak-flow meter.)

Results of medical surveillance:

Recommendation of medical practitioner: **Treatment:** (If any.)

Signature: (Dr) Appointed Employment Medical Adviser or:
              (Dr) (SRN) Occupational Health Service

Date of next medical surveillance:

Appendix 4: Example of a substance and medical treatment data sheet

For the guidance of medical officer

Attention Casualty Department

Re: Mr/Mrs/Miss .... Age ....

Home Address ....

Employed by   The   Co. Ltd.

This patient was exposed to: (✓ appropriate line)

Carbon Tetrachloride   _____

Chloroform   _____

Tetrachloroethane   _____

1,1,2-Trichloroethane (Vinyl Trichloride)   _____

at   ....am/pm   On   ....19............

Degree of exposure: (✓ in appropriate square)

☐ moderate   ☐ severe

This substance is a narcotic and systemic poison and may cause:

a) Anaesthesia, all stages (giddiness, weakness, numbness of the legs, staggering gait, stupor, coma) which may lead to paralysis of the respiratory centre
b) Nausea, vomiting
c) Cardiac failure
d) Kidney and liver damage
e) Irritation of skin and eyes

It should be realized that vapour can be inhaled from contaminated clothing or liquid spillages. The liquid is absorbed through the skin.

A   FIRST AID

It is important for the safety of rescuers that they wear appropriate respirators during rescue. See introduction.

(✓ indicates action already taken)

1. Remove from exposure.   _____

2. Apply artificial respiration immediately if breathing has stopped
   or shows signs of failing.   _____

3. Apply external cardiac massage in the event of cardiac arrest.   _____

4. Remove contaminated clothing, loosen remaining clothing, place
   in most comfortable position and protect from cold.   _____

5. If breathing is laboured or patient is cyanotic, give oxygen
   through a face mask.   _____

6. For eye or skin contamination:

   Eyes — irrigate with water for at least 10 minutes   _____

   Skin — Wash copiously with water and, if necessary,
            cover with a dry dressing.   _____

7. Copious drinks.   _____

8. Keep at rest and arrange for patient to be transported to
   hospital as quickly as possible.   _____

B   MEDICAL TREATMENT

1. Continue oxygen if necessary.
2. Do not give vasopressor drugs (e.g. adrenaline, ephedrine,
   epinephrine, etc.) as there may be danger of producing cardiac
   arrhythmia.
3. Keep under observation for at least 48 hours for the possible development
   of liver and kidney damage.
4. Otherwise treatment symptomatic.

NOTES

Signature .... First Aider

Date and Time .... am/pm

Note to First Aider: Patient should always be accompanied to a doctor

This information is sent as a matter of routine and is based on
information compiled by a medical panel of the Chemical Industries
Association.

Appendix 5: Example of a fire precautions manual

Introduction

Companies have a duty of care to both employed and non-employed, including visitors to their operations. Premises must be free from fire risks and hazards, and management must be seen to have a responsible attitude by taking every available measure to ensure the safety of employees, visitors and the public.

To assist you, this fire precautions manual has been included, which can be adapted to suit the requirements of your company and its situation, to comply with all legal requirements of the Fire Precautions Act 1971 and the fire authorities.

Where examples of recording methods are given, they contain only a few lines and you will need to extend each page as necessary for your operation.

Fire precautions manual

All necessary tests, drills, inspections, servicing and training, whether on a daily, weekly, monthly, six-monthly or yearly basis, must be recorded in this manual along with any occurrences that take place. The responsibility for ensuring that these tasks are undertaken and recorded (in offices, factories or training centres to which this fire precautions manual is adapted) rests with the Chief Executive or other senior manager appointed with accountability for health and safety of those premises. Individual tasks within this manual may be delegated to a subordinate member of management or staff, but such delegation does not diminish the overall responsibility of that executive or senior manager.

This fire precautions manual must be kept up to date and be readily available for inspection by an appointed manager or health and safety auditor of the Company, by a licensing authority or an appointed fire officer of a local fire authority. Whenever an auditor, environmental health officer or fire officer visits the premises, they are to be given the opportunity to inspect this manual, signing and recording any comments in its sections.

It is stressed that simply to carry out audits, checks and tests is (in law) not enough. Full *records* of all audits, checks and tests must be maintained — they may prove an important item in the defence of the Company's position in any possible future occurrence.

Details of the premises to which this record applies

Name of location: _____

Address of location: _____

_____

_____

Fire certificate No.
(if applicable): _____

Date of issue: _____

Details of person with overall responsibility for fire precautions for these premises:

Name: _____ **Position:** _____

Names and positions of other persons at this location with delegated authority for fire precautions, tests and inspections of these premises:

1. **Name:** _____ **Position:** _____

   Responsible for: _____

2. **Name:** _____ **Position:** _____

   Responsible for: _____

3. **Name:** _____ **Position:** _____

   Responsible for: _____

What is an occurrence or a fault?

An occurrence or a fault, in fire safety, is any of the following events.

Fire alarm

- False or actual activation of the fire alarm.
- Damage to or failure of break-glass call-points.
- Failure of any audible or visual alarm indicator (siren/bell/light).
- Any defect or fault in the system as indicated by tests.

Automatic detection

- False or actual fire alarm.
- Damage to or failure of any fire or smoke detector.
- Disconnected alarm or outstanding service/maintenance work.
- Any defect or fault in the system as indicated by tests.

Fire doors

- Fire doors or lintels damaged or interfered with; unauthorized alterations.
- Faulty, damaged or disconnected electronic/magnetic self-closing devices.
- Failure of fire door(s) to close properly (or difficulty in closing).
- Missing or damaged fire exit and direction signs.
- Any defect or fault in fire doors as indicated by inspections/tests.

Emergency lighting

- Damaged or inoperable luminaires/lamps.
- Damaged or faulty fittings or wiring.
- Faults with battery or battery not recharging.
- Failure to meet duration test specifications.
- Automatic or manual switch-over failure (from mains to emergency lighting).
- Any defect or fault in the system as indicated by tests.

Firefighting equipment

- Damaged or vandalized extinguishers and other equipment.

- Fire extinguishers discharged (accidentally, mischievously or to fight a fire).
- Missing or stolen equipment.
- Fire extinguishers not in correct locations.
- Any defects or faults in equipment as indicated by checks/tests.

Fixed sprinkler systems

- Damaged or faulty sprinkler system, including water supply failure.
- Accidental or deliberate activation of the system.
- Failure in central control panel monitoring (incorrect or absent indicator).
- Fault discovered during servicing and maintenance.
- Any defects or faults in the systems indicated by inspections/tests.

Building structures

- Any building faults that would affect the safety of any means of escape (MOE).
- Any breaches in a fire-resisting construction.
- Any vertical fire-resisting construction that does not reach to the roof.
- Any MOE that is breached by holes/cracks in ceilings and walls.
- Any sections/compartments that have holes/cracks in ceilings and/or walls.
- Any defective fire doors and fire exits in MOE and fire-resisting walls.

Check-list of weekly, monthly, biannual, annual checks of fire-safety and fire-prevention systems

The following check-list will help you to remember when specific checks, tests and other fire-safety and fire-precautions actions outlined in this manual are to be taken.

Daily

- Fire doors clear and free of obstacles.

Weekly

- Means of escape.
- Fire alarm systems.
- Fire doors.
- Hand lamps.
- Emergency back-up batteries checked.
- Emergency generating plant — start up and run.

Monthly

- Self-contained emergency lighting systems checked.
- Emergency generating plant tests (with and without standby battery).
- Physical check of firefighting equipment.

Biannually

- Fire drills.
- Emergency lighting systems.
- Emergency lighting luminaires/lamps.
- Emergency back-up batteries, full test.
- Self-contained emergency lighting systems, full test.

Annually

- Full service and maintenance of firefighting equipment.

Regularly/periodically

- Fire-safety and fire-precautions training.
- Automatic detection systems.

Fire authority or environmental health authority visits

Whenever a fire officer or environmental health officer visits the premises for fire precautions inspections, this manual is to be shown to them and they are to be provided with the opportunity to sign below and make a note of any comments or remarks on the manual's upkeep, as they feel relevant.

Date	Name	Comments/remarks	Signature

Senior management inspections

This section is to be completed by the Operations Manager/a senior manager on site, to confirm that they have inspected this record book and undertaken the physical fire inspections as laid down in the health and safety management instructions.

Date	Inspected by	Comments/remarks	Signature

Means of escape inspections

Every means of escape — including fire doors, fire escape stairs, egress routes, main stairway, entrance and external egress routes — *must* be checked by the Operations Manager (or a senior manager on site) *weekly*. (This duty may be delegated to the Unit Health and Safety Coordinator.)

If any means of escape is found to be even partially blocked, say, by boxes, ladders, light tubes or rubbish, or if the egress route is very dirty and dust-covered, *immediate* action must be taken to clear any obstruction or hazard to personal safety. Any parked vehicles or obstructions in front of external fire doors must be moved immediately and action taken to prevent any recurrence.

During the inspection, all lighting (including emergency lighting) and signs applicable to fire safety must be checked to ensure that they are in place or operating; any faults or missing signs *must* be rectified immediately.

The named persons below are accountable for carrying out the means of escape inspections.

Regular inspections to be carried out by:

Name: _____ Position: (Senior manager)

First deputy:
Name: _____ Position: (Health and Safety coordinator)

Second deputy:
Name: _____ Position: _____

Regular means of escape inspections

Inspections should include checking that all doors forming part of the means of escape are easily and immediately available, including access and ease of opening, that all internal and external escape routes are free from obstruction and that all signs are clearly visible and lighting is operating.

Date	Inspected by	Where inspected	Faults found	Action taken

Fire alarm system

Fire alarm systems *must* be tested *weekly*. All fire alarm tests must be conducted at exactly the same time and on the same day of each week, with prior notice given to all employees, including trainees, that these tests occur. No action under the fire drill procedure is required on these tests.

In some multiple-occupancy locations, fire alarm tests may be the responsibility of the owners/landlords (or their representatives), in which case, the completion of this section is optional and at the discretion of the Operations Manager.

Everyone must be instructed that any sounding of the alarm outside of the strict test time each week is to be treated as a real alarm situation. Any activation of the alarm system outside the specified test times *must* be treated seriously and the fire and evacuation procedures acted on.

If the fire alarm system is connected to a central control or the local fire authority, they *must* be informed of these tests and a check made with them at the conclusion of each test to ensure that they received the alarm signal and are aware that the test has been completed.

The British Standard requires that each circuit or zone should be tested on a 13-week cycle and that the fire alarm system as a whole should be tested weekly. This implies that if the system is wired in series with loops connecting, say, call-point numbers 4, 5 and 6 together before returning to the control unit, then the loop requires testing every 13 weeks.

A different break-glass point should be operated each week (by use of an alarm key). A record of each different break-glass point test and each circuit or zone test must be recorded with each test record.

During the system test, all audible and/or visible alarms (for example, where deaf people work), must be checked to ensure that they are working correctly. Any faults or failures *must* be recorded in the 'Faults and action taken' column of the weekly test record (page 325) and action taken to remedy those faults or failures *immediately*.

Contractors When contractors check and service the fire alarm systems, they must be requested to record their check and details of service given in the test record of this manual.

Spare replacement pieces of alarm glass must be retained in each location and any accidental activation, fault or problem with the system recorded in the 'Faults and action taken' column as above and the appropriate remedial action taken *immediately*.

(Note that the type of alarm system and the manner in which it is wired up will need to be known when formulating a testing policy to ensure that the method of testing is appropriate to the system.)

Installation details of fire alarm system

This information is to be completed by the Operations Manager (assisted by the installation or service contractor where necessary).

1. Location of control panel: _____

2. State whether open- or closed-circuit, mains only, etc.: _____

3. Number of zones: _____

4. Number of call-points in each zone: _____

5. Number of alarm indicators: _____

6. Types of indicators (bell, siren, visual, etc.): _____

7. Location of indicators: _____

8. Is the system interlinked with other premises/ buildings? If so, state what they are: _____

9. Is the system linked to a central control or the local fire brigade? State which: _____

10. Type of cable used in this installation: _____

11. This system conforms to British Standards number: BS ___

Weekly tests of fire alarm system by responsible person

The persons named below are responsible for carrying out the weekly fire alarm tests and ensuring that the correct test procedures are followed. They are also responsible for ensuring that any faults, failures or difficulties are recorded in the 'Faults and action taken' column of the weekly test record and that any remedial action necessary is taken immediately.

Fire is a serious matter when it occurs. Prevention of it can only be achieved by taking swift action *before* the event.

Weekly tests to be carried out by:

Name: _____ Position: _____

First deputy:
Name: _____ Position: _____

Second deputy:
Name: _____ Position: _____

Weekly tests of fire alarm system

Record below when tests are carried out and any occurrences of damaged or faulty call-points, failures of the sounders (bells, sirens and so on), false alarms or actual alarms and fire drills.

Date	Call point No.(s)	Zone No.(s)	Tested by	Audio/visual indicators	Faults and action taken

Fire doors

All fire doors are to be tested and inspected *weekly*, including:

- hinges
- panelling
- door frames
- glazing
- smoke seals
- push-bar mechanisms
- the closing of the door for distortion and gaps
- self-closing devices (electronic/magnetic) (if fitted)
- fire door 'Keep shut' signs or 'Push bar to open' signs.

Any faults or problems are to be recorded in the 'Faults and action taken' column of the weekly test record and remedial action taken.

Fire doors *must not* be wedged or otherwise held open with fire extinguishers, chairs or any other item (this is a criminal offence).

Under *no* circumstances are fire doors to be kept locked during hours when work is undertaken (unless fitted with glass-tube bolt release or a key is available in a glass-fronted box at the door, though this will be *outlawed* in 1996).

Also, under *no* circumstances must fire doors be obstructed by any object at any time.

All fire doors are to be numbered and their locations recorded in this manual.

The persons named below are responsible for inspecting and testing fire doors weekly.

Weekly tests and inspections to be carried out by:

Name: _____ *Position:* _____

First deputy:
Name: _____ *Position:* _____

Second deputy:
Name: _____ *Position:* _____

Locations of fire doors

Door No.	Location (exact*)

*Give *exact* locations with sufficient detail to enable a person unfamiliar with the premises (new responsible person, EHO, HSE inspector or health and safety auditor) to find them easily.

Weekly tests and checks of fire doors

All occurrences (including faulty mechanisms, stiff doors, failures to open or close properly, poor condition, blockages inside/outside, before/after, obstacles, illegal actions, missing signs and so on) are to be recorded below.

All faults and occurrences *must* be reported to management and remedial action taken *immediately*. Remember that fire can occur at any time.

Date	Tested by	Faults found (Yes/No)	Faults, occurrences and action taken

328 THE HEALTH AND SAFETY SURVIVAL GUIDE

Fire drills

A fire drill is required (by the Company's health and safety policy) to be held in every Unit *not less than* once every six months. Where large numbers of trainees are present, undergoing training, fire drills should be held on a more frequent basis and not less than once in their training period.

In multiple-occupancy premises where routine fire drills are the responsibility of the owners/landlords (or their representatives), the Operations Manager is to make independent arrangements for the monthly drills, with the necessary liaison with the owners/landlords (or their representatives).

Every fire drill incorporating the activation of the fire alarm bell must also be entered on the record of tests of the fire alarm system.

A fire drill is the physical practising of the procedures to be followed in the event of a real fire and/or emergency evacuation. Discussion of those procedures forms part of employee/trainee instruction and training.

All fire drills must be entered in the record of fire drills and the record maintained in this recording system.

Note that the *absence* of records of fire drills, even if they *have* taken place, will mitigate against the Company in the event of any injurious fire.

The people named below are responsible for carrying out the fire and emergency evacuation drills.

Fire drills to be carried out by:

Name: _____ Position: _____

First deputy:
Name: _____ Position: _____

Second deputy:
Name: _____ Position: _____

Record of fire drills

Date of drill	Nos in drill	Evacuation time: optimum	actual	Extent of drill (full, trainees)	Method of roll call	General assessment of fire drill	Remedial action necessary	Conducted by (name)	Manager's comments and signature

Record of staff/trainees participating in fire drills

Record below the names of each member of staff/trainee participating in the drill and obtain their signatures (as proof).

Date	Name (printed)	Signature	Comments of person conducting drill

Emergency lighting system

The emergency lighting system (or secondary escape lighting) must be tested every six months, or more frequently as laid down in the relevant British Standard (a fire certificate, if issued, will refer back to the British Standard). The mains power (and generator, if applicable) must be switched off and the emergency lighting operated for *not less than* one hour to ensure that the batteries hold their charge and that they recharge when mains lighting is restored. Checks by auditors will be *additional* to these six-monthly tests, but then there will be only a brief period of operation of luminaires/battery testing.

Maintenance must also be carried out in line with the British Standard as good practice and to comply with section 2(2(a) of the HASWA.

All emergency lighting luminaires/lamps are to be numbered and a record maintained. Tests of the system are to be recorded, together with details of any faults, repairs, servicing and occurrences, including fires and false alarms.

Emergency lighting should illuminate the following areas in the event of the failure of normal lighting in a fire:

- all emergency egress routes
- all exit and emergency exit doors, including fire doors
- all fire alarm call-points and firefighting equipment
- all exit and emergency exit signs and instructions (if fitted with lighting).

Responsibility

The persons named below are responsible for carrying out the six-monthly tests of the emergency lighting system.

Normally responsible:

Name: _____   Position: _____

First deputy:
Name: _____   Position: _____

Second deputy:
Name: _____   Position: _____

Installation details of emergency lighting system

To be completed by installing or servicing contractor.

1. Location of batteries and/or generator: _____

2. Details of whether maintained, non-maintained, sustained and duration of lighting, for example, 1 hour, 2
   hours, etc.: _____

3. Total number of luminaires/lamps: _____

4. Type of cable used in installation: _____

5. The system conforms to British Standard Specification
   BS _____

6. Additional relevant information:

Locations of emergency lighting system's luminaires/lamps

Luminaire/lamp No.	Location

Emergency lighting tests

Emergency lighting systems should be tested in accordance with the relevant British Standard and manufacturer's/ installer's instructions. Following is a summary of the tests and maintenance set out in BS.5266:Part 1:1988 for emergency lighting.

Test type	System	Summary of test
1	Hand lamps	*Weekly check:* to ensure correct functioning, charge batteries as required, replace when defective.
2	Battery systems	*Weekly check:* battery tops, terminals and cases; top-up electrolyte levels as necessary.
3	Battery systems	*Six-monthly check:* simulate an electrical sub-circuit failure for a continuous period of one hour; *during* this period, check all luminaires and signs for correct functioning; *after* one hour, restore mains supply and ensure battery system is recharging correctly.
4	Self-contained systems	*Monthly check:* energize each luminaire and sign from its battery by simulating an electrical sub-circuit failure, check each for correct functioning and maintenance.
5	Self-contained systems	*Six-monthly check:* energize as in test 4 for a continuous period of one hour, then check each luminaire and exit or directional signs for correct functioning and maintenance and recharge batteries.
6	Generating plant	*Weekly check:* start up plant and run for 5 minutes, checking that generating plant supplies power within 5 seconds (minimum) to 15 seconds (maximum).
7	Without standby battery	*Monthly check:* simulate electrical subcircuit failure to energize system and run *continuously* for a period of one hour, checking that all luminaires and exit directional signs function correctly; after one hour, restore to normal operation; check starting battery, where fitted, and recharge.
7A	With standby battery	*Monthly check:* if the system is started from a separate mains supply but *also* has a standby starting battery, re-energize by use of the standby facility after switching off the mains supply.

Six-monthly emergency lighting system tests

Every test of the luminaires/lamps and every occurrence in which there is less than 100 per cent operational availability of luminaires/lamps (except during routine service) *must* be recorded below.

Date	No. of luminaires/ lamps checked	Checked by	Fault/occurrence and action taken

Firefighting equipment

Maintenance of the correct type of firefighting equipment in the correct locations is essential to control and extinguish any outbreak of fire. Locations of equipment as recommended by the fire authority will normally be accepted. However, in the absence of a fire certificate, firefighting equipment should be sited in accordance with BS. 5306:1985, Part 3 and the advice of a health and safety adviser should be sought.

All extinguishers must be numbered, with the number recorded on the Inventory of firefighting equipment (page 336). They must be correctly located, either on wall brackets or in a designated fire point, identified by markings painted in red and 'Fire extinguisher' or 'Fire point' signs. Fire blankets must be affixed to the wall not more than 1.5 metres above floor level.

All fire points *must* be kept clear of any obstruction at all times.

A physical check of all firefighting equipment must be carried out at least once per month. Any damaged and/or discharged extinguishers must be noted in the Record of monthly inspections of firefighting equipment and action taken *immediately* to service and restore them to operational use. Any extinguisher that has been discharged must be recorded with the reason or cause of this stated in the above Record, including if it was accidental.

Annual checks must be made by a competent person in accordance with BS.5306:1985, Part 3 and the requirements of fire certificates.

Monthly firefighting equipment checks

The persons named below are responsible for the monthly checks of firefighting equipment:

Normally responsible

Name: _____   Position: _____

First deputy:
Name: _____   Position: _____

Second deputy:
Name: _____   Position: _____

Annual firefighting equipment checks

The following Company is responsible, per contract, for carrying out annual servicing and maintenance of firefighting equipment and should be contacted in the event of any major problem, including discharged extinguishers.

Company name: _____

Address: _____

Contact name: _____ Telephone number: _____

Inventory of firefighting equipment

Type	Quantity	Size	Location
Water extinguisher			
CO^2 gas			
Dry powder			
Halon (BCF)*			
Foam			
AFFF			
Hose reels			
Fire blanket			
Sprinklers (if fitted)			
Other equipment			

*Replace as soon as possible as halon 1211 is a banned substance from 1 January 1996.

Record of monthly inspections of firefighting equipment

Every inspection and occurrence *must* be recorded in this section. Any equipment that is damaged or discharged *must* be serviced *immediately* and details of the occurrence/damage/discharge/service recorded below.

Date	Number	Type	Location	Fault/occurrence and action taken

Fire-safety and fire-precautions training

Training in fire-safety and fire-precautions procedures is a requirement of both the Fire Precautions Act 1971 and section 2(2)(c) of the Health and Safety at Work, etc., Act 1974, for *all* employees, including trainees. Training in instructional techniques should also be given to fire-safety trainers.

Every new manager and employee, including trainees, *must* be trained as part of their induction training on all the basic aspects of fire safety and fire precautions to be taken and observed in the workplace and the emergency evacuation procedures (fire drill). Continuation, updating and refresher training must be given to all managers and employees including trainees, as frequently as necessary, but not less than once every year or more frequently if required by a fire certificate.

Details of all fire-safety and fire-precautions training must be entered in the Fire-safety and fire-precautions training record and will include the following:

- the date on which training and instruction was given
- the type of training (lecture on . . ., demonstration of firefighting techniques, etc.)
- the names and signatures of those trained (to protect against lapses of memory — evidence of training is important in real occurrences)
- the name and position of the person conducting the training
- any comments the tutor/lecturer/instructor may wish to make.

The trainers named below are accountable for carrying out fire-safety and fire-precautions training of employees, including trainees.

Regular/principal tutor

Name: _____ *Position:* _____

First deputy:
Name: _____ *Position:* _____

Second deputy:
Name: _____ *Position:* _____

The content of fire-safety and fire-precautions training

Fire-safety training is designed to prevent fires occurring in the first place, while *fire-precautions* training is designed to ensure prompt and correct action by all personnel should a fire occur — how to control a fire, prevent it from spreading, prevent injury and protect life.

Fire-safety and/or fire-precautions training and/or instruction sessions must include at least one of the following subjects on each occasion. It is unlikely that one long, continuous session covering *all* subjects in one go will be productive.

Content of training for emergency plan manager/ supervisor

Under the Fire Precautions (Places of Work) Regulations 1995 (FPR 95) every senior person detailed in the emergency plan as responsible for supervising and controlling the plan (or specific parts of the plan) must receive training and instruction in the following:

- the method of supervision and control of the emergency plan
- the arrangements for ensuring that the MOE are maintained clear of all hindrance and immediately available at all times
- the action to be taken in the event of fire to prevent (unauthorized) persons entering the building, that is, those not directly involved in firefighting or marshalling
- the arrangements for calling the fire brigade in the event of a fire, informing them of the nature and source of the fire and of flammable or explosive substances used and/or made in the workplace.

Any construction safety supervisor must receive adequate training and instruction to fulfil their role of ensuring that the elements of fire safety and fire precautions on any construction site are strictly observed.

Content of training for trainers They must learn:

- instructional techniques for *fire-safety and fire-precautions trainers*
- training in the technical and management aspects of fire safety/precautions.

(including the following:)

Content of general training for the Fire Precautions (Places of Work) Regulations 1995 Under

FPR 95, all employees, including managers, supervisors and trainees, must be given general training so that they are familiar with fire safety and the fire precautions to be taken and observed in the workplace. This must include, as a minimum, the following:

- the MOE from the workplace in the event of fire or other emergency
- the action to be taken by them in the event of fire
- the types and safe uses of firefighting equipment
- the locations of, and methods of operating, firefighting equipment
- the locations and use of the means of warning of fire, for example, where the fire alarm system is and how to activate it
- the names and locations of people detailed in the emergency plan as responsible for supervising and controlling the plan and fire drills.

In addition, the following should be included in the general fire-safety and fire-precautions training programme:

- what is necessary for a fire to occur and what the causes of fire are
- the Company/unit/location fire and emergency drill procedures
- the names/locations of fire marshals or manager(s) responsible for overseeing fire drills (practice or real)
- fire prevention checks: electrical equipment, paper, deep-fat fryers switched off/not overheating, no temporary repairs, any combustibles left in dangerous places, oils/petrol/solvents in hazardous condition, and so on
- the location and types of all fire alarm points

- the types, identification and safe use of all extinguishers, including demonstrations of this, and what types of fire *not* to use them on
- the locations and types of all fire extinguishers
- the care of flammable materials
- good housekeeping and storage
- correct and safe waste disposal
- action if all lighting fails or is obscured by smoke
- safety of valuables versus the safety of people
- prevention of the spread of smoke and flames (construction, maintenance, alteration, and action in event of fire)
- safety precautions to take when searching premises
- safety precautions to take when fighting a fire
- what to do once full evacuation has been accomplished
- keeping calm in the event of fire and the avoidance of panic.

Contractors and others not normally employed, but who are allowed access to the premises for the purposes of carrying out their activities, must also receive at least the minimum training and instruction in fire precautions as for managers and employees, above.

Fire-safety and fire-precautions training record

1. Details of fire-safety training given

To be completed by the person presenting the training/instruction.

Date	Subject(s) covered	Duration	Comments	Signature

2. Register of training sessions

The names of every trainee must be recorded and a signature acknowledging that the fire-safety training has been given obtained from each trainee.

Date	Name	Signature

Automatic detection systems

Many establishments have automatic fire-detection systems that are a part of the overall fire alarm system. Automatic detection systems *must* be serviced and tested regularly as directed by the installer, fire certificate (if issued) or British Standard (BS), which is the minimum standard.

A record of the details of the system and its detector heads is to be made, all automatic detector heads must be numbered and their location recorded in this section and details of faults and occurrences given in the form of a Test/servicing/maintenance contractor's report.

Any activation of the automatic detection system by a detector head (where installed) must be treated seriously, as a real fire, and the fire and emergency evacuation drill put into action *immediately*.

Details of automatic detection systems

To be completed by the installation or service engineer.

1. Location of control panel: _____

2. State whether open- or closed-circuit: _____

3. Total number of automatic detector heads: _____

4. Type and numbers of detector heads: heat: _____
    smoke: _____

    ionization/optical: _____ other: _____

5. Type of cable used in installation of automatic detection system: _____

6. This system conforms to British Standards number:
    BS _____

Locations of detector heads

Detector No.	Type	Location

Servicing and maintenance

All firefighting equipment and fire-detection installations require regular servicing and maintenance if they
are to operate effectively and efficiently when the need
arises (which could be at any time).

Details of the servicing and maintenance contractors for
each type of system need to be entered in the Record of
servicing and maintenance contractors, so that the Unit
Manager can contact the appropriate agent in time of
need.

Whenever annual, biannual or 'call-out' emergency servicing and maintenance is undertaken by any contractor, a
record of it must be completed by that contractor in the
Test/servicing/maintenance contractor's report.

Record of servicing and maintenance contractors

1. Firefighting equipment

Name of contractor: _____

Address: _____

Routine telephone No.: _____ *Emergency telephone No.:* _____

Contract period from: _____ *To:* _____ *Annually/biannually*

2. Fire alarm system

Name of contractor: _____

Address: _____

Routine telephone No.: _____ *Emergency telephone No.:* _____

Contract period from: _____ *To:* _____ *Annually/biannually*

3. Emergency lighting system

Name of contractor: _____

Address: _____

Routine telephone No.: _____ *Emergency telephone No.:* _____

Contract period from: _____ *To:* _____ *Annually/biannually*

4. Fire doors and (if installed) automatic electronic/magnetic closing mechanisms

Name of contractor: _____

Address: _____

Routine telephone No.: _____ *Emergency telephone No.:* _____

Contract period from: _____ *To:* _____ *Annually/biannually*

5. Automatic detection system (where installed)

Name of contractor: _____

Address: _____

Routine telephone No.: _____ *Emergency telephone No.:* _____

Contract period from: _____ *To:* _____ *Annually/biannually*

Test/servicing/maintenance contractor's report

To be completed by the contractor on the occasion of each test, servicing, and maintenance of fire-protection systems.

Date: _____ Time: _____

Installation/equipment tested/serviced/maintained:
_____

Work undertaken: _____
_____

Parts fitted/exchanged: _____

Outstanding or additional items: _____

Name of contractors: _____

Name of engineer (PRINT): _____

Next visit due: _____ Signature: _____

Date: _____ Time: _____

Installation/equipment tested/serviced/maintained:
_____

Work undertaken: _____

Parts fitted/exchanged: _____

Outstanding or additional items: _____

Name of contractors: _____

Name of engineer (PRINT): _____

Next visit due: _____ Signature: _____

(Managers should reproduce this page for regular repeated use)

Appendix 6: Example of a risk assessment form

RISK ASSESSMENTS

1. Competent person(s)

Is there a suitably qualified and experienced competent person appointed to advise management on health and safety and to exercise overall control of health and safety on behalf of management? (Required by Regulation 6 of the Management of Health and Safety at Work Regulations 1992.)

Details:
(Internal/external)

2. Manual handling

(a) Does the work involve manual
handling?   Yes/No
Which jobs?   How?
(b) Is there risk of injury?   Yes/No
Which jobs?   How?
(c) Is it reasonably practicable to
avoid moving loads?   Yes/No $\left\{\begin{array}{l}\text{Automate or}\\ \text{mechanize?}\end{array}\right\}$ Yes/No
Which jobs?   How?   How?
(d) Does some risk of manual hand-
ling injury remain after (c) above?   Yes/No
Which jobs?   How?
(e) What manual handling practices do you observe in the factory and ancillary departments?

Department: *Observation:*

(f) What measures are necessary to reduce the risk of injury to the lowest level practicable?
Which job?   What measures?

3. Mechanical handling

(a) What kinds of mechanical handling are in use?
Are drivers/operators properly trained?

Types: *Purpose:*   *Trained:* (Yes/No)

(b) What are the hazards associated with these methods of mechanical handling?

Types: *Hazards:*
To people:
To machinery:
To materials:
To the handling equipment itself:
To premises:

4. Working environment

(a) What are the conditions and risks in the environment in relation to:

Heating?
Lighting?
Ventilation?
Dust?
Humidity?
Ammonia?

5. Electrical safety

(a) What are the risks in the use of electricity at work in relation to:
electrical supply?
to the factory?
(include phasing, voltages, extensions, cables — overhead versus body level — etc.)
to office machinery?
(include cable loads, fuses, extension leads, etc.)
to other departments?

6. Hazardous substances (including those mentioned in the COSHH Regulations)

(a) Have COSHH assessments been carried out?   Yes/No
When?_____ (date)
(b) Have all product data sheets been obtained?   Yes/No

Comments:

(c) What substances are in use in the factory?

Substances: *Uses:*
Chemicals:
Oils:
Gases:
Powders:

(d) What are the hazards associated with those substances?
Substances:
Chemicals:
Oils:
Gases:
Powders:

(e) What are the risks to which employees may be exposed?
Substances: *Risks:*   *Groups/individual at risk:*
Chemicals:
Oils:
Gases:
Powders:
Steam:

(f) What are the storage arrangements and facilities for hazardous chemicals?
Chemicals compound:
(Including how designed.)
Are all flammables, corrosives, etc., stored separately?   Yes/No
What quantities of chemicals are kept in use in production areas?
(The maximum quantity permitted is 50 kg/110 lbs.)
Is there a person appointed who has responbsibility for controlling/coordinating the storage and use of hazardous substances?

7. Upper-limb disorders

(a) What are the risks of suffering upper limb disorders due to repetitive upper-limb actions in production?
Type of job: *Activity:*   *Parts of limbs used:*

8. Repetitive strain injury (RSI)

(a) What jobs are there where there is a risk of RSI, e.g., tenosynovitis, especially with continuous repetitive use of the hands/fingers?
Type of job: *Activity:*   *Parts of hands/arms used:*

9. Radiation

(a) What risks of exposure to radiation are there in the workplace? (Excluding VDUs — dealt with separately.)

10. Bacteriological/microbiological

(a) What risks of exposure to bacteriological or microbiological organisms are there (pathogenic)?

11. Visual display units (VDUs)

(a) What are the risks to which VDU users (excluding self-employed people) are exposed?

Department:	Equipment details:	Usage duration: (In an 8-hour day)	Condition of equipment: (In relation to DSE Regulations)
	Screen:		
	Workstation:		
	Chairs:		
	Lighting:		
	Decor:		
	Background noise:		
	Humidity:		

(b) What breaks are users (excluding self-employed persons) given away from workstations?

Department:	Breaks:	Usage duration (in 8 hours):

(c) What arrangements are made for eye and eyesight tests for VDU users?
(d) What is the policy on the issuing of spectacles to those whose eyes are affected by VDU operations (as confirmed by an ophthalmic optician's report)?

12. Machinery

(a) What types of machinery are in use and what guarding, fail-safe and other devices are employed?

Department:	Machinery:	Fitted with guards:	Fail-safe devices:

(b) What problems of reasonableness and practicableness are there with regard to the provision of guards or fail-safe devices to machinery?

Department:	Machinery:	Nature of problem:

(c) Are all dangerous machines securely fenced, where appropriate (especially where operator access is not regularly required)?

13. Lead

(a) Is there any lead present in the buildings or in use in any production area? Is there any risk of exposure to lead in any area?

14. Asbestos

(a) Is there any asbestos present in the building?
(b) Is there any risk of exposure of employees or non-employees to that asbestos?

15. Fire safety

(a) *Competent person:* Is a competent person appointed with overall responsibility for fire safety and for emergency evacuation of personnel (for all reasons) on site? (As required by Regulation 7(1)(b) of the Management of Health and Safety at Work Regulations 1992.)

Yes/No *Name:* *Appointment:* *Department:*

(b) *Fire certificate:* Does the establishment hold a fire certificate? Yes/No (One is required if more than 20 are employed on the ground floor, *or* if more than 10 are employed on *any* floor above or below ground level.)
(c) *Fire drills:* Are fire drills held regularly? Yes/No
(d) Are there safe assembly points? Yes/No Away from traffic routes? Yes/No
(e) Give details of fire drills held and recorded.

Date: *Time:* *Time to full evacuation:* *Number evacuated:*
Comments:

(f) What fire extinguishers are provided?

Department: *Types held:* *Number:* *Date last checked:* *Access free?*

(g) Give details of fire doors.

Department: *Numbers:* *Locations:* *Condition:* *Access free?*

(h) *Emergency lighting:* What emergency lighting is installed?

Locations: *Checked regularly (batteries)?*
Comments:

(i) *Fire manual:* Is there a fire manual in use? Yes/No
(j) Is the fire manual (if held) fully operated in all sections? Yes/No
Comments:

(k) What other items require comment?
(l) *Recommendations:* What are the recommendations for changes/improvements in fire safety?

16. Statutory documentation

Are all the following statutory documents required held, used and, where appropriate, displayed?

Employer's liability certificate:
Company:
Expiry date:
Displayed?   Yes/No

Poster:
'Health and safety law — What you should know'   Yes/No
Accident recording:
DSS Form BI510 (accident book)   Yes/No
HSE Form F2508 (for reportable accidents)   Yes/No
HSE Form F2508A (for notifiable diseases)   Yes/No

Company accident/incident investigation and report form: Yes/No
Comments:

First aid boxes:
Are first aid boxes held and in place?   Yes/No
Are they of the correct pattern/construction?   Yes/No
Comments:

Are the contents maintained up to standard?   Yes/No
Comments:

First aid/Medical room:
Is there a first aid/medical room?   Yes/No
If 'Yes', does it conform to the 1990 ACOP standards?   Yes/No
Comments:

Abrasive Wheels Regulations poster: Yes/No
Are personnel trained according to the Regulations?   Yes/No
Comments:

Are any *unnecessary* posters displayed?   Yes/No
Details:

17. Accident summary

(a) Give the following information from the accident book.

Dates: Types of injury: Numbers: Predominant department:

(b) Give the following information regarding reportable accident HSE Reports made.

Dates: Types of injury: No. of days off: Department:

18. Vehicle movements and marshalling

(a) What is the nature and extent of vehicle movement on the premises?
(b) Is there a set/recognized route for all traffic?   Yes/No
Comment:

(c) Is there a system of marshalling for lorry reversal in existence? Yes/No
Comment:

(d) Is marshalling of lorries in reverse actually carried out?   Yes/No
(e) Who is responsible for marshalling of lorries?

19. Physical health and safety audit

(a) Give details of observations, other than those specified in the risk assessment above.

Department: *Observation:*   *Remedy:*   *Legislation:*

Appendix 7: Check-list for health and safety audits

Location   *Date*

Employers' liability insurance certificate   Held?   Yes/No
                                                    Displayed? Yes/No
                                                    In date?   Yes/No

Public liability insurance certificate   Held?   Yes/No
                                                    In date?   Yes/No

Fire certificate   N/A/Held/Shared occupancy (Delete as appropriate)

Health and safety policy   Yes/No/Under 5 employees

Poster 'health and safety law — what you should know'
                                               Displayed?   Yes/No

Fire equipment checked   Yes/No/Date checked____ Certificate? Yes/No

Access to fire equipment

Smoke detectors

Fire drills   Procedure written? Yes/No   Drills held? Yes/No

Fire escape routes   Clear? Yes/No

Fire-safety and fire-precautions training   Yes/No?   Who is trained?

Rules for isolating plant and equipment

First aid boxes   Held? Yes/No   Correct design?   Fully stocked?

First aid attendants

First aid register (e.g., DSS Form BI510)

Reportable injuries/occurrences report form (HSE Form F2508/F2508A)
Held? Yes/No Used? Yes/No

Accident report forms

Accident reporting procedure

First aid register summary (BI510)

Risk assessments completed/started?	Yes/No	Reports available?
• overall health and safety	Yes/No	Yes/No
• display screen equipment	Yes/No	Yes/No
• manual handling	Yes/No	Yes/No
• workplace	Yes/No	Yes/No
• work equipment/machinery	Yes/No	Yes/No
• personal protective equipment (PPE)	Yes/No	Yes/No
• Legionellae	Yes/No	Yes/No

Details of health and safety training for:
• management   Yes/No
• clerical staff   Yes/No
• contractors   Yes/No
• operatives   Yes/No
• installers   Yes/No
• customers?   Yes/No

Fork-lift/power trucks operated?   Yes/No
• Drivers trained to JCITB/MOTEC standards?   Yes/No
• Drivers authorized/licensed?   Yes/No

Noise: problem?   Yes/No
                                   If Yes, assessments done?
                                   Yes/No

Health and safety committee?   Yes/No
                                   Constitution   Meetings

Health and safety representatives?   Yes/No
• Their views on health and safety?

PPE used:
• policy?
• issued?
• practice?
• worn/used?
• enforced?

Welfare and hygiene arrangements   Nos employed: M____ F____
• Toilets: M____ F____ Wash-basins: M____ F____ Urinals: ____
• Condition

- Drinks facilities
- Food consumption (workshops)

Working environment
- Heating
- Lighting (natural/artificial)
- Ventilation/extraction
- Atmosphere
- Noise

Plant and machinery and electrical equipment
- Types/makes
- Guards
- Fences
- Insulation
- Lock-out procedure

Pressure (oil/compressed air/pneumatics/hydraulics)

Power presses
- Types
- Numbers
- Certificates?
- Hand-over arrangements/certificates?

Pressure vessels — inspection/maintenance certificates/records held?

Housekeeping

COSHH Regulations
- Chemicals used
- Gases
- Petrol
    —more than 4.55 litres held in building?
    —more than 22.75 litres held outside building?
      (If Yes to either, this is illegal unless, in latter case, you are licensed.)
- Oils
- Resins
- COSHH assessments done?   Initial ......   Periodic ....
    —Substances covered
    —Arrangements
- Carcinogenic substances
- Training

Electricity at Work Regulations
- Arrangements
- Compliance

Materials used in production

Asbestos encountered?

Glass
- Assembly/cutting
- Regulations complied with?

Company vehicles
- Vans:___
- HGV:___
- Cars:___
- Numbers/condition:___
- First aid kits carried?

Safe vehicle movement system in operation?   Yes/No

Departmental audits
- Manufacturing areas
- Workshops
- Assembly
- Warehouse/stores (especially housekeeping and handling there)
- Training area
- Restaurant/canteen
- Kitchen(s)

Appendix 8: Report writing

The following is a guide to writing reports, a suggestion for the presentation of a report on a health and safety audit. The items in parentheses are those details that you will need to add.

Report
on the
HEALTH and SAFETY AUDIT
carried out at
(location)
(Your company's name)
by
(auditor's name)
on
(date)

Introduction
A health and safety audit was carried out in the (location) by (your name) in the company of (names of others present) on (date of audit).

Terms of reference
The terms of reference for this audit were to:

1. inspect physical health and safety standards
2. observe working practices
3. identify specific hazards in the workplace
4. assess action that may be required to achieve satisfactory standards of health and safety
5. compile a report of findings and recommendations from the audit.

Objectives
The objectives of the audit were to:

1. provide management with a report on current health and safety standards in the workplace with recommendations for action

2. confirm the understanding of health and safety law and the principles presented during the seminar.

Summary

(Write here a summary of your findings (not recommendations), in one or two paragraphs, so that senior management has a brief overview of the report without having to plough through all the detail. Managers can then pass the report (or sections of it) to those individual managers who should take action.

This will need to be compiled *after* your report is finished, so leave a suitable gap here for your summary to be filled in later.)

Findings and recommendations

(The main body of the report.

Either:

Findings

(Write summaries of your findings first:

1.
2.
3.
4., etc.)

and then

Recommendations

(then write a list of your recommendations relating to your findings:

1.
2.
3.
4., etc.)

or:

Findings and recommendations

(Write each of your findings, complete with your recommendations, one by one.)

Do not go into great detail in this section, but give brief general findings and recommendations, and give your detailed analysis in your appendices, referring your reader to those appendices when appropriate.

Conclusion

(This section is the punch-line of your report. Think what you can say that will motivate your reader to take the action you seek. Perhaps some benefit that may be obtained from putting into practice the recommendations contained in the report.)

Appendices

(List the appendices to the report.)

Appendix 9: Suggested health and safety check-list for work placements

This health and safety check-list should be completed on a regular basis by a field staff member for each work placement company, not less than twice a year. A copy must be retained in the company's file. Any item of concern must be brought to the attention of the training provider's manager and, if necessary, the Training and Enterprise Council (TEC) or Local Enterprise Company (LEC).

Operations unit details

Address: _____

Operations Manager: _____ Field staff member: _____

Placement company details

Address of registered office: _____

Postcode: _____ Telephone number: _____

Contact name: _____ Job title: _____

Senior executive: _____ Job title: _____

Product(s) and/or service: _____

Premises address (if not as above): _____

Total number   Number of
of employees: _____ trainees: _____ Are they: ET/YT/IT

Check-list details

Registration   *Yes/No*
Have the premises been registered with the relevant
authority:
- offices/shops to environmental health officer
  on Form OSR1?   ☐☐
- factories/workshops to Health and Safety
  Executive (HSE) on Form F9?   ☐☐
- building or engineering construction to HSE on
  Form F10?   ☐☐

Insurance
Is a certificate of employer's liability insurance
displayed in a place where *all* employees can read it
daily?   ☐☐
Is it in date?   ☐☐
Is a certificate of public liability insurance
held?   ☐☐
Is it in date?   ☐☐

NB: Field staff *must* ask to see documents and note their
    contents, not just accept a person's word that they
    exist and are currently valid.
NB: All trainees are, by law, employees for the purposes of
    health, safety and welfare.

Policy
If the company has five or more employees
(including trainees), does it have a *written* health
and safety policy?   ☐☐
Does the policy cover *all* the company's operations,
materials and substances?   ☐☐
Are all employees (including trainees) and
contractors informed of its contents?   ☐☐

How is this done? Describe:_____

Posters
Are the following health and safety posters prominently
displayed where all those concerned, including trainees
and contractors, can read them (as appropriate)?
- 'Health and safety law — what you should know'
  (HSE)   ☐☐

Yes/No

- Woodworking Machines Regulations 1974 □□
- Abrasive Wheels Regulations 1970 □□
- Horizontal Milling Machines Regulations 1928 □□
- Power Presses Regulations 1965 □□

NB: There is no requirement to display the Factories Act 1961 or the Offices, Shops and Railway Premises Act 1963.

Thermometer

Is there a thermometer in the workplace? □□
Is the temperature above 16°C (60.8°F) within one
hour of commencement of work? □□

Fire certificate

Does the company have:

- *more than 10* persons working in a basement or above ground level □□
- *more than 20* persons working on the ground floor □□
including employees, trainees, contractors and
others who *regularly* work there?

If the answer to either of the above is 'Yes', is a
current fire certificate held □□
or has a fire certificate been applied for? □□

NB: All employer's premises, including hotels, guest houses and care establishments, with more than 10 persons in total working on all floors above or below ground level, or more than 20 persons working on the ground floor *must* have a fire certificate. If no fire certificate is held or applied for, *do not place the trainee there.*

Fire alarms

Is there a fire alarm system installed? □□
If 'Yes', is the complete system tested at least
once a week? □□
If 'No', what is the system for raising the alarm in a fire/
emergency?_____
Is the trainee aware of the tone/sound of the alarm
when it sounds? □□

First aid

Is/are first aid box(es) held, stocked up to 1990
ACOP level? (Check with list) □□

Yes/No

Are first aid boxes provided in company vehicles (where
trainees are conveyed)? □□

Is it/are they of the correct pattern (sturdy,
white cross on green background)? □□

Are first aiders trained and appointed? □□

Are their names prominently displayed on notice-
boards? □□

NB: If any answer is 'No', advise and supply copies of first
aid list and guidance card.

Documents

Does the company hold and complete the following
statutory documentation?

- Accident book DSS Form BI510? □□
- Reportable injuries Report HSE Form F2508? □□
- Notifiable diseases Report HSE Form F2508A? □□
- Own company accident/injury investigation/
  report form? □□

Fire safety

Are there adequate means of escape (MOE) (enclosed
corridors/stairs/fire doors)? □□

Are there adequate fire exits:

- 1.05 m wide (less than 40 m distance or fewer than
  100 working)? □□
- 2.10 m wide (more than 40 m distance or more than
  100 working)? □□

Are all MOE, fire doors, stairs, fire exits kept
clear at all times? (Inspect) □□

NB: MOE are routes provided for the safe evacuation of
persons in event of fire, etc.

What provision is made for the safe evacuation and account-
ing of disabled persons?

_____

Are the fire exit doors separate from any revolving
doors (where fitted)? □□

What fire hazards are there in the work process?____

_____

Is there adequate protection for persons against
those hazards? □□

Yes/No

Are all gangways, walkways, stairways, working areas kept clear at all times? □□

Fire precautions

Is there adequate provision of fixed and portable firefighting equipment? □□

Give details:_____

Does this provision include halon 1211 (BCF) extinguishers (green containers)? □□

NB: The Home Office has banned all use of halon (except MOD) from 1996.

Is there a set fire/emergency evacuation procedure? □□
Is it designed specifically for these premises?* □□
Is the procedure prominently displayed for all persons working there to see? □□
Is the trainee fully trained in the drill, including practice drills? □□

Assessments*

Have assessments of fire-safety and fire-precautions conditions/requirements been conducted as required by the Fire Precautions (Places of Work) Regulations 1995? □□
What particular concerns affecting employees/trainees did the assessments reveal?
Describe:_____

Fire training

Is the trainee *trained** in:
- the types and identification of extinguishers? □□
- the hazards associated with certain extinguishers? □□
- the practical use of extinguishers to fight a fire? □□
- health and safety matters related to the job and workplace? □□
- the fire/emergency evacuation procedure? □□

Signing in/out   *Yes/No*

Is there a signing/clocking-in and out procedure
for the purposes of fire safety?   ☐☐

All are legal requirements of the Fire Precautions
(Places of Work) Regulations 1995, which also requires *all*
fire exit doors to be kept unlocked during all hours when
work is in progress (since April 1996 a key in a glass box at
the door has *not* been acceptable).

Health and safety training
Induction
Is there a company induction programme that includes health and safety training?   ☐☐

General health and safety training
Is health and safety information, training and
instruction given to:
- managers?   ☐☐
- supervisors?   ☐☐
- other staff?   ☐☐

Does the training include information, as
appropriate, on:
- Duties under the Health and Safety at Work, etc.,
  Act 1974?**   ☐☐
- Abrasive Wheels Regulations 1970?   ☐☐
- Woodworking Machines Regulations 1974?   ☐☐
- Control of Substances Hazardous to Health
  Regulations 1988?**   ☐☐
- Noise at Work Regulations 1989?   ☐☐
- Control of Asbestos at Work Regulations 1987?*   ☐☐
- Electricity at Work Regulations 1989?   ☐☐
- Fire Precautions (Places of Work) Regulations
  1995?*   ☐☐
- Display Screen Equipment Regulations 1992
  (VDUs)?   ☐☐
- Manual Handling Regulations 1992?*   ☐☐
- Food Safety Act 1990 and Food Hygiene
  Regulations 1970 (as amended)?   ☐☐

How is the above information, training and instruction
given? Describe:_____

_____

Obtain copies of training handouts, etc., for review by
health and safety adviser

**It is a legal requirement for *all* employees to be given training in these laws; others are legal requirements for those employees engaged in the activities they cover.

Protective wear

What personal protective equipment (PPE) are trainees required to wear and/or use during their work? Describe:

	Yes/No
Are items provided free of charge?	☐☐
Are trainees engaged in occupations with legal requirements for protective wear?	☐☐
If so, are they:	
• construction?	☐☐
• engineering?	☐☐
• chemicals?	☐☐
• woodworking?	☐☐
• painting and decorating?	☐☐
• horticulture/agriculture?	☐☐
• other? Specify:_____	☐☐

What PPE are trainees required to wear and/or use in their work:
- helmet/hard hat? ☐☐
- visor? ☐☐
- face mask? ☐☐
- goggles/safety glasses? ☐☐
- gloves/gauntlets? ☐☐
- ear defenders? ☐☐
- safety boots/shoes? ☐☐
- overalls? ☐☐
- soft hat (painting and decorating)? ☐☐
- rubber mat (electricity)? ☐☐
- whites? ☐☐
- uniform? ☐☐
- other? Specify:_____ ☐☐

NB: It is an *offence* under section 9 of the HASWA to charge any employee, including trainees, for any item of PPE required by statute or company policy.

Manual handling

Will the trainee be required to lift heavy or awkward objects? ☐☐

If so, what information, training and instruction will they be given? Describe:

Display screen equipment (VDUs)***
Yes/No

Is display screen equipment (computers, word processors, VDUs) in use? □□

If so, are all screens fitted with:
- filter screens? □□
- twist-and-tilt mechanisms? □□
- *separate*/adjustable keyboards? □□

Is the lighting:
- fluorescent? □□
- filament bulbs? □□
- floor-up/wall-up? □□

Does the workstation equipment have non-reflective surfaces for the:
- keyboard? □□
- table/desk? □□
- printer? □□

Is the trainee's chair fitted with:
- correct lumbar (not shoulder) support? □□
- footrest, for use if required? □□

Windows
Are the windows fitted with blinds/curtains or filter film? □□
Which? Describe:_____

Humidity
Is there adequate provision for humidity around workstations? □□

Breaks
What breaks will trainees have away from their work-stations during working hours (separate from lunch-breaks)? Specify: _____ minutes at interval of every _____ hours.

Training
Will training be given in:
- the correct and safe operation of VDUs? □□

Yes/No

• the hazards associated with VDUs? □□

Eyesight
Will the trainee have access to:
• free eye and eyesight tests? □□
• free corrective spectacles?† □□

***Statutory requirements of the Health and Safety
(Display Screen Equipment) Regulations 1992.
†Where ophthalmic optician's test report states problem is
due to working with VDUs.

Control of Substances Hazardous to Health (COSHH) Regulations
Have assessments of hazardous substances in the
workplace been completed? □□
Have product data sheets been obtained from the
suppliers of the substances? □□
Have copies of the assessments been made available
for inspection and follow-up? □□

What hazardous substances are present in the area(s) in
which the trainee will work?
Specify and state whether toxic, radioactive, irritant,
harmful, corrosive or inflammable as defined in the Regu-
lations:_____

_____

What precautions will the company take to avoid exposure of
the trainee to substances? Specify:_____
What PPE will the trainee be required to wear? Specify:

_____

NB: *Do not* place a trainee in a company department where
COSHH assessments have not been completed. Any exposure of the trainee to a substance that has not been
identified and assessed may lead to legal action
against (your company name) and the placement's
managers.

Working hours
Under the Young Persons (Employment) Acts of 1938 and 1964,
no person under the age of 18 years is permitted to work
between 10.00 pm and 06.00 am, in any circumstances.

Factories

There are no restrictions on the hours worked by young persons under 18 years of age except as above, but employers are reminded of the duty in section 2 of the HASWA not to endanger the health and safety of any person, say, through fatigue caused by overextended working hours or lifting heavy objects.

Shops

The restrictions on the hours worked by young persons under the age of 18 years in shops was repealed by the Employment Act 1989, but, under the Shops Act 1950, they must be given a break of a minimum of 20 minutes during the course of every 6-hour working spell. Where that 6-hour spell includes the period 11.30 am to 2.30 pm, the minimum break given must be 45 minutes.

Offices

There are no specific restrictions on the working hours of young persons under the age of 18 years between 06.00 am and 10.00 pm, except for the caution given under Factories and the requirements for Display screen equipment.

Yes/No

Does the placement manager understand and apply these rules, as appropriate?   ☐☐

What hours will the trainee be required to work? Specify: from ____ am to ____ pm, Monday to Friday *or* Monday/Tuesday/Wednesday/Thursday/Friday* with breaks of ____ minutes during the morning and ____ minutes in the afternoon. *Delete as appropriate.

Dangerous machinery

What types of dangerous machinery are there on the placement premises? Specify:
List those prohibited to any person under 18 years of age

_____

_____

List those which persons may operate *only* after training

_____

_____

NB: Section 21 of the Factories Act 1961 specifies that it is *prohibited* for young persons under the age of 18 years to operate certain machines under *any* circumstances. These prohibitions include agriculture, brick presses, carding machines, 'dangerous machines', dough mixers, dough brakes, guillotine machines, horizontal milling machines, hydroextractors, examination and lubrication of unfenced machines, platen printing machines, power presses, prime movers, tile presses, transmission machinery, warehouse machinery including fork-lift trucks, woodworking machinery (unless trained) and so on. There is also prohibition of the employment of young persons under the age of 18 years in: work involving lead (where the lead content is more than 10 per cent of the raw material/product), pottery processes.

Electrical safety   *Yes/No*

Has the company had an assessment of electrical installations carried out? ☐☐

Will the trainee be required to undertake any electrical training/work? ☐☐

If so, will they be properly trained *and* *supervised*? ☐☐

NB: No unqualified or unauthorized person is permitted to undertake *any* electrical work.

Working environment/conditions

Is there adequate provision in the workplace of:
* lighting? ☐☐
* heating? ☐☐
* ventilation? ☐☐
* noise control? ☐☐
* humidity? ☐☐
* working space (minimum of 5 m^2 in factory or office) *or* 2 m^2 in shops? ☐☐
* fresh air from external source or from air-conditioning system? ☐☐
* sanitary conveniences and wash basins? ☐☐
* supplies of fresh drinking water? ☐☐
* adequate numbers of male/female sanitary conveniences? ☐☐

Note any unsatisfactory situations and discuss with the placement's management.

If unable to resolve any problems, refer to the Operations Manager and/or TEC/LEC's health and safety adviser.

Committee/representatives   *Yes/No*

Is there a health and safety committee in operation
in the company?   ☐☐

If so, are trainees given representation on the
committee?   ☐☐

Have health and safety representatives been
elected by the workforce?   ☐☐

If so, do the trainees know who their
representative is?   ☐☐

NB: Health and safety committees are not legal requirements, *unless* requested by health and safety representatives.

This health and safety check-list must be read in conjunction with the (your company name)'s health and safety
policy and, particularly, Appendix (add number), Health
and safety in placements, colleges and training centres.

Any problems that cause the placing of any trainee in a
placement company to be difficult or untenable must be
brought to the attention of the Operations Manager and
action taken as directed in (your company name)'s health
and safety policy under Action that will be taken in cases
of non-compliance.

Appendix 10: Example of an accident investigation and report form

Complete and photocopy this form, sending a copy to head office, one to the safety adviser and keeping one for your personal file.

Axident-prone Company Limited

Hazard House, Risky Road, Dangerfield,
Painshire DA1 1PA

Accident investigation/report form

Report of accident/injury investigated by:-
_____ (Name)

1. Personal details
Surname: _____ *First names(s):* _____
Date of birth: _____ *Age:* _____ *Sex:* M/F *How paid:* Monthly/
                                                    hourly
Home address: _____ *Telephone No.:* _____
Job title: _____ *Department:* _____ *Exact location:* _____
Name of manager/supervisor: _____ *Job title:* _____

2. Details of the accident
About the accident itself
Date of accident: _____ *Time of accident:* _____ am/pm
Place of accident, i.e., department: _____
Exactly where? _____
or location (if outside company's premises): _____

Circumstances leading to the accident
Precisely how did the accident occur? _____
_____
_____

Example of accident investigation and report form continued

Personal protective provision

Was there personal protective wear/equipment prescribed for the job being done? Yes/No

Was the injured person wearing/using the protective equipment/wear? Yes/No If Yes, what, *or*, if No, why? _____

3. Details of injury

What type of injury was sustained? _____

To what part of the body?* _____

Were hazardous substances involved? Yes/No If Yes, give brand and chemical names: _____

Give classification (as on label): †harmful/toxic/radio-active/irritant/flammable/corrosive

*Give full details of injured part (for example, not just 'hand'). †delete as appropriate.

4. Details of witnesses

First/main witness's name: _____ *Job title/department:* _____

Second witness's name: _____ *Job title/department:* _____

Statements of witnesses attached? Yes/No/N/A

5. Accident recording

Was/will there be absence from work as a result? Yes/No For how long? _____

If absence of more than 4 days, has a HSE Report Form F2508 (injury) *or* F2508A been completed? Which? _____ Date sent to HSE/EHO: _____

Has the accident/injury and treatment been recorded in the accident book? Yes/No

Was the accident/injury reported to the victim's manager/supervisor within 24 hours? Yes/No

6. First aid/medical treatment

Was first aid treatment given? Yes/No By whom: _____

Details of first aid treatment: _____

Was the person taken to hospital? Yes/No Were they detained overnight? Yes/No

Diagnosis (if known): _____ Name of doctor: _____

Example of accident investigation and report form continued

---

7. Results of investigation

Outline the conclusions of the investigation, i.e., what was the unsafe condition that existed? _____

_____

What was the unsafe act or omission (including tools/ machines)? _____

_____

How, in your opinion, could the accident/injury have been avoided? _____

_____

How can such an occurrence be avoided in the future? _____

8. Recommendations

What recommendations are there arising out of the investigation? _____

Signature of person investigating: _____ *Name:* _____

Appointment: _____ *Location:* _____ *Date:* _____

Appendix 11: A suggested management statement for the implementation of the health and safety policy and accident prevention

As has already been said earlier, accidents do not happen, they are *caused*. Similarly, health and safety and accident prevention will not just happen, they have to be *managed*.

Management statement for health and safety policy implementation and accident prevention

In order to achieve the aims of the Company's health and safety policy and every unit's local health and safety policy, and in order to achieve acceptable levels of accident prevention, every manager must see health and safety as a daily part of their management duties. It is not something we do providing there is nothing else to do, it is a *priority*.

Sections 2(1) and 2(2), with all the subsections, of the Health and Safety at Work, etc., Act 1974 (the HASWA) state that it is the *duty* of the Company and every manager to safeguard the health and safety of their employees, themselves and others who may be affected by their unsafe acts or omissions. Sections 7 and 8 of the HASWA lay down similar duties for employees towards themselves and others who may be affected by their unsafe acts or omissions.

Other pieces of legislation that directly impose duties on the Company, every manager and employee are the Fire Precautions Act 1971 (FPA), as supported by the Fire Precautions Orders (FPOs) of 1972, 1976 and 1979, the Fire Precautions (Places of Work) Regulations 1995 (FPR 95), and the Control of Substances Hazardous to Health (COSHH) Regulations 1988, and the Reporting of Industrial Diseases and Dangerous Occurrences Regulations (RIDDOR) 1986, as amended by the 1989 Regulations.

Policy

The Company's health and safety policy must be implemented at all levels throughout the organization and unit health and safety policies must be adhered to within the units to which they relate. It is important that both policy documents are kept up to date and so regular reviews of policy must be undertaken. Unit policies must be amended as appropriate in the light of developments within the units, while the Company's health and safety coordinator must be informed of any problems encountered in implementing the Company's policy, so that any necessary assistance can be given or suitable amendments made.

Organization

Every member of management at every level must know their specific accountabilities for health and safety. The operations manager (or senior manager on site) is personally responsible for all health and safety matters, but should delegate duties to their subordinates by means of either written instructions or including them in job descriptions.

Health and safety coordinators Every general manager (or senior manager on site) must appoint a mature and responsible person (not a trainee) within their location as a unit health and safety coordinator. They need not be qualified safety officers, but should have enthusiasm for health and safety and display a degree of safety awareness and consciousness (see Training below).

The duty of the coordinators is to coordinate, i.e., to ensure that all necessary health and safety action is taken (not necessarily taking it themselves), ensuring the organization of all necessary health and safety resources in order to meet requirements for advice and guidance.

In addition to their direct accountability to operations managers, health and safety coordinators will have a functional relationship with the Company's Health and Safety Coordinator at Head Office.

Fire

Fire can strike at any time. It is a function of health and safety management to prevent fires from occurring and injury being caused to employees. Managers are responsible for ensuring that the requirements of the FPA and of the fire certificate (if in force) are complied with (see Audits, inspections and hazard checks, below). Visitors and contractors must also be informed of fire-drill procedures so they know what to do should a fire occur during their visit.

These requirements call for regular checks on all fire precautions and firefighting equipment, with remedial action taken where appropriate. In this respect, a fire precautions manual has been designed to assist managers in carrying out their legal duties, with self-explanatory sections. Managers *must* take all the daily, weekly, monthly, biannual and annual action as appropriate and record the action taken, supported by their signature. The duty of maintaining the fire precautions manual may be delegated to the unit health and safety coordinators, if desired.

Accident and injury reporting

The Company's accident reporting procedure must be followed in all situations where an accident occurs. Every injury, no matter how trivial, must be recorded in the unit's accident book (DSS Form B510).

Any dangerous occurrence that does not result in injury, but could have resulted in serious injury, and every injury more serious than a minor cut or scratch, *must* be investigated and a Company accident investigation and report form completed. This completed form must be forwarded to the Company's Health and Safety Coordinator at Head Office, with details of the action taken to prevent a recurrence, as quickly as possible.

In the case of serious injury that results (or may result) in absence of four days or more or in hospital treatment, this *must* be reported immediately to the Company's Health and Safety Coordinator at Head Office who may decide on initiating an investigation by a specialist appointed by Head Office.

Additionally, for every 'reportable' accident (that is, one resulting in absence of four days or more or which is a dangerous occurrence as given in RIDDOR) an HSE Report Form F2508 *must*, by law, be completed and forwarded to the local environmental health officer or HSE office, as appropriate, with a copy sent to Head Office. In the case of notifiable diseases, an HSE Report Form F2508A must be used.

Health and safety discussion

Larger units may, at the discretion of their operations manager, institute a health and safety committee. Where no committee exists, health and safety must be included on the agendas of management meetings. Discussions should be so ordered as to ensure that all matters pertaining to health, safety, welfare and hygiene can be aired, plans of action determined and problems resolved.

Audits, inspections and hazard checks

The Company will arrange comprehensive health and safety audits by specialist health and safety practitioners on a frequent but irregular basis. It is the responsibility of every operations manager to personally conduct inspections of all workplaces within their sphere of responsibility not less than once per month to ensure that *all* health and safety requirements are being met.

Monthly inspections These shall include the following.

- Are the legal requirements complied with and up to date? (For example, employer's liability insurance, correct signs and posters, accident books, checking-in/out registers, first aid box.)
- Are all fire doors freely accessible and maintained in an operable condition and free of obstruction at all times?

- Are all emergency egress routes clear and free from all hazardous obstacles? (For example, overgrowth, discarded materials, boxes. Ensure that nothing is placed in the way of fire escapes/exits, even temporarily.)
- Are the surfaces of all egress routes away from fire doors safe? (For example, free of ice, moss, dirt/dust, rubbish.)
- Check the accident book — are particular types of injury occurring regularly and indicating the need for further accident-prevention action?
- What is the level of knowledge of health and safety of employees, especially trainees?
  (Checks on log books and brief questions will indicate this quickly. Do not assume that because they have been taught, they know.)
- Is adequate and correct firefighting equipment in place?
- Are all fire extinguishers serviced and in date (that is, checked less than one year ago)?
  (If out of date, contact your service contractor.)
- Has a fire drill taken place in the last six months (or as frequently as required according to the units' activities and employee trainee turnover)?
- Does the fire alarm work? Can it be heard by *everyone*?
- Is the evacuation procedure clearly known and posters displayed?
- If you have tools, machinery, ladders, scaffolding, electrical equipment and apparatus, are they all in a safe condition and stored correctly?
- Are all lights working efficiently and diffusers fitted?
- Are all employees, including trainees, fully trained in fire precautions and fire drills and firefighting procedures?

This is not an exhaustive check-list but includes all those items required by law.

Weekly checks Hazard-spotting exercises should be conducted weekly by briefly walking through each area (including outside) with safety 'awareness' in mind (see Training below). Any hazards found must be remedied immediately to prevent them causing an accident. If immediate remedial action is not possible, the offending area/

item should be adequately guarded, warning notices placed and action taken as soon as practicable.

Training

Under section 2(2)(c) of the HASWA, the FPA and FPOs and the COSHH Regulations, all employees, including trainees, *must* be given information, training and instruction in every aspect of health, safety, welfare, hygiene, fire precautions and COSHH, as they affect them. All employees, including trainees, must be given written information supported by verbal training and instruction in:

- the Company's health and safety policy, what it says and how it affects their particular unit and their specific occupations and skills
- the duties of every manager and employee, including trainees, under the law and Company policy (see the Company's health and safety policy)
- the rights and privileges of employees under the law and health and safety policy
- the units' fire drill procedures
- fire precautions procedures for the units
- firefighting equipment in use within the units and how to identify the various items
- which types to use on which types of fire and which types *not* to use in particular situations (such as water on electrical fires, halon in confined and unventilated rooms, CO_2 gas in the open air, etc.)
- electrical safety, including cabling and abuse of extension leads
- who the first aider(s) is/are
- the accident reporting procedure (its importance to *them* and the Company)

The above items are not in order of importance; *all* are important.

Occupational safety Every employee, including trainees, must be given health and safety training in their particular occupations and skills, including laws, Regulations and EC Directives relating to them, for example:

- health and safety consciousness and awareness, that is:

—*consciousness* 'thinking safety' about what they are doing and the consequences of their own unsafe acts and omissions

—*awareness* watching for safety in the workplace, noticing and rectifying or reporting unsafe conditions that exist and present hazards to the health, safety and/or hygiene of themselves and others

- use of VDUs and VDTs (including EC Directive)
- Construction Regulations
- woodworking (carpentry and joinery) Regulations
- catering: food safety and hygiene (including the Food Safety Act and Food Hygiene Regulations)
- dangerous machinery and rules concerning prohibition or training, supervision and authorization
- engineering; rules for safety
- agriculture, horticulture and floristry; rules for safety
- personal protective wear (including EC Directive)
- correct manual (kinetic) lifting methods (including EC Directive)
- good housekeeping.

Appendix 12: Suggested proforma for the assessment of personal protective equipment (PPE) requirements

Parts of the body

Risks assessed

Various	Lower limbs			Upper limbs			Head						Risk	Category	
Whole body	Trunk/abdomen	Skin	Lower legs	Upper legs	Feet	Lower arms	Upper arms	Hands	Whole head	Face	Respiratory tract	Eyes	Ears	Cranium		
															Falls from heights	Mechanical	Risks to which all sections of the PPE at Work Regulations 1992 apply
															Blows, cuts, impact, crushing		
															Stabs, cuts, grazes		
															Vibration		
															Slipping, falling over		
															Scalds, heat, fire	Thermal	
															Cold		
															Immersion		
															Non-ionizing radiation	Other	
															Electrical		
															Noise		Risks to which Regulations 4, 6 to 12 of the Personal Protective Equipment (PPE) Regulations do not apply (being covered by existing specific Regulations):
															Ionizing radiation		
															Dust fibre		
															Fumes		
															Vapours		
															Splashes		
															Gases, vapours		
															Harmful bacteria		
															Harmful viruses		
															Fungi		
															Non-micro-biological antigens		

Appendix 13: Example of a check-list to use when assessing manual handling operations

Manual handling of loads

EXAMPLE OF AN ASSESSMENT CHECKLIST

You may find it helpful to use a checklist when making a manual handling assessment. If so, here's an example.
This checklist may be copied freely. It will remind you of the main points to think about while you:
— consider the risk of injury from manual handling operations
— identify steps that can remove or reduce the risk
— decide your priorities for action.

SUMMARY OF ASSESSMENT	Overall priority for remedial action: Nil/ Low/Med/High*
Operations covered by this assessment:	Remedial action to be taken:.............................
....	....
....	....
Locations:	Date by which action is to be taken: ....
Personnel involved:...................................	Date for reassessment:...............................
Date of assessment:	Assessor's name: .... Signature: ....

*circle as appropriate

Section A — Preliminary:

Q1   **Do the operations involve a significant risk of injury?**   Yes/No*
      If **'Yes'** go to Q2. If **'No'** the assessment need go no further.
      If in doubt answer **'Yes'**. You may find the guidelines in Appendix 1 helpful.

Q2   **Can the operations be avoided/mechanised/automated at reasonable cost?**   Yes/No*
      If **'No'** go to Q3. If **'Yes'** proceed and then check that the result is satisfactory.

Q3   **Are the operations clearly within the guidelines in Appendix 1?**   Yes/No*
      If **'No'** go to Section B. If **'Yes'** you may go straight to Section C if you wish.

Section C — Overall assessment of risk:

Q   **What is your overall assessment of the risk of injury?**   Insignificant/Low/Med/High*
      If not **'Insignificant'** go to Section D. If **'Insignificant'** the assessment need go
      no further.

Section B — More detailed assessment, where necessary:

Questions to consider: (If the answer to a question is 'Yes' place a tick against it and then consider the level of risk)	Level of risk: (Tick as appropriate)			Possible remedial action: (Make rough notes in this column in preparation for completing Section D)
Yes	**Low**	**Med**	**High**	
The tasks — do they involve:				
◆ holding loads away from trunk?				
◆ twisting?				
◆ stooping?				
◆ reaching upwards?				
◆ large vertical movement?				
◆ long carrying distances?				
◆ strenuous pushing or pulling?				
◆ unpredictable movement of loads?				
◆ repetitive handling?				
◆ insufficient rest or recovery?				
◆ a workrate imposed by a process?				
The loads — are they:				
◆ heavy?				
◆ bulky/unwieldy?				
◆ difficult to grasp?				
◆ unstable/unpredictable?				
◆ intrinsically harmful (eg sharp/hot?)				
The working environment — are there:				
◆ constraints on posture?				
◆ poor floors?				
◆ variations in levels?				
◆ hot/cold/humid conditions?				
◆ strong air movements?				
◆ poor lighting conditions?				
Individual capability — does the job:				
◆ require unusual capability?				
◆ hazard those with a health problem?				
◆ hazard those who are pregnant?				
◆ call for special information/training?				
Other factors — Is movement or posture hindered by clothing or personal protective equipment?				

Deciding the level of risk will inevitably call for judgement. The guidelines in Appendix 1 may provide a useful yardstick.

When you have completed Section B go to Section C.

Section D — Remedial action:

Q   **What remedial steps should be taken, in order of priority?**

i ....

ii ....

iii ....

iv ....

v ....

And finally:

    —complete the SUMMARY above

    —compare it with your other manual handling assessments

    —decide your priorities for action

    —**TAKE ACTION.........AND CHECK THAT IT HAS THE DESIRED EFFECT**

HSE

Appendix 14: Sample seminar on the essentials of health and safety management

All items in parentheses are to be completed by adding your own details.

Essentials of health and safety management:
A three-day seminar
for
senior and middle managers, supervisors and controllers

Seminar objectives
1. To achieve safety consciousness and safety awareness in delegates.
2. To promote accident prevention in all locations of (your company).
3. To stimulate personal interest in safe working practices and standards.
4. To enhance health and safety as a (your company) management function.

Seminar content
In-depth analysis of health, safety and welfare at all levels and in all situations with examination of the duties, responsibilities and roles of managers, supervisors and employees in health and safety.

Detailed examination of the Health and Safety at Work, etc., Act 1974 and recent European Community (EC) legislation affecting the duties and responsibilities of managers and supervisors, also the Factories Act, Offices, Shops and Railway Premises Act and the Fire Precautions Act, health and safety policy and management systems.

The *processes* of accident/incident cause and effect and the system of accident investigation.

Method

The seminar will be intensive and highly participative, with much discussion and some syndicate work. There will be handouts from the seminar to assist delegates in implementing seminar content in their own spheres of management responsibility.

Presenter

The seminar will be presented by (name of presenter). He/she has specialist knowledge and experience in health and safety (etc.).

Questions

There will be opportunities to raise queries and obtain practical advice on safety situations. Come prepared — someone else may benefit from your question.

However, because of the very intensive nature of the programme, particular complex problems will need to be adjourned to be discussed in separate meetings. A notetaker will be nominated for this purpose.

Certification project

The seminar carries a nationally recognized certificate. A condition of passing the course is that delegates *must* submit a report (following the health and safety audit carried out during the seminar) that demonstrates their understanding of the seminar content. Advice will be given on report writing (spelling, etc., will not be a concern).

Essentials of health and safety management: day one

Introductions
Introductions by the senior manager and the seminar's presenter.

Why safety?
Attitudes, accident rates, the size of the problem; costs of accidents; costs of fires.

Brief history of safety law: Acts, Regulations, Codes of Practice; conflicts, contempts and ineffectiveness. Brief review of the Robens Committee's 1970–72 report.

The Health and Safety at Work, etc., Act 1974
The Act examined; specific themes:

- 'It shall be the duty'
- 'At work'
- 'So far as is reasonably practicable'
- 'Innocent until proven guilty'
- Regulations and Codes of Practice (COPs) — their effect.

What the Act says
To companies (section 37)
To directors (section 37(a))
To managers and supervisors (section 37(b))
To employees.

Duties
Of managers (sections 2 to 6 and 9)
Of employees (sections 7 and 8)
To contractors (section 3(1))
To customers (section 3(1))
To non-employees (section 3(1))

The working environment: heating, lighting, ventilation, humidity, air quality, sick office/sick building syndrome.

Safety in systems of work, storage, handling, transportation, etc. Legal administrative health and safety requirements (insurance, fire, first aid, etc.).

Company health and safety policy.

Enforcement

Powers of enforcement officers (inspectors, environmental health officers and fire officers); improvement, prohibition, prosecutions; the Courts; some examples (sections 18–24, 33, 39, 40, 43).

Case study 1

A look at a real-life situation.

Delegates will examine an accident and determine the application of law and liability — who was responsible/liable, for what, under which section of the HASWA?

Essentials of health and safety management: day two

The terminology
Let's understand the terminology.

The accident process
The vicious circle.

Accident investigation. Accident reporting: the legal requirements. Group/Company policy and practice.

Case study 2
Another look at a real-life situation.

Delegates will investigate an accident as health and safety officers, they will ask the questions as in Case study 1, but also draw up an accident process (vicious circle), including cause and effect. How could the accident have been avoided, its recurrence be prevented?

EC Directives and 1992 UK Regulations implementing them
The concept of risk assessments.
The Framework Directive and the Management of Health and Safety at Work Regulations.
The Work Equipment Directive and the Provision and Use of Work Equipment Regulations.
The Workplace Directive and the Workplace (Health, Safety and Welfare) Regulations and ACOP.
The Personal Protective Equipment (PPE) and Labelling Directives and the Personal Protective Equipment at Work Regulations and ACOP.
The Display Screen Equipment Directive and the Health and Safety (Display Screen Equipment) Regulations.
The Manual Handling Operations Directive and Manual Handling Operations Regulations.

Case study 3
A further look at a real-life situation, in similar manner to Case study 2, but, this time, assessing how the EC Directives and the UK Regulations implementing them were applied. How would a detailed knowledge of the Directives and Regulations have prevented this accident?

Essentials of health and safety management: day three

Review of Day two

Further European Community Directives and 1995 UK Regulations implementing them

The Fire Precautions Act 1971.

The Fire Precautions (Places of Work) Regulations 1995.

Requirements of fire safety and fire precautions legislation.

Other specific safety matters affecting (company name) and its establishments.

The Control of Substances Hazardous to Health Regulations 1988 (COSHH).

Control of noise at work. Asbestos. Electrical safety.

Fork-lift and power trucks. Ladder safety (fixed and mobile).

Manual/kinetic handling (including handouts for managers to use in training).

Health and safety audit

In two syndicates in agreed areas of the factory/offices. Report writing.

Health and safety training

Delegates' questions

Queries and problems put to the presenter.

Advice will be given; some solutions sought. If the answers are not immediately available, they will be sought and follow-up consultations arranged with the delegates concerned.

Closing remarks

Evaluation of seminar.

Closing discussion with senior management.

About the seminar's presenter

A. N. Other, BSc, MIPD, MIMgt, MIOSH, MIRSM
(A biographical account of the seminar(s) presenter's background, qualifications and experience.)

Appendix 15: Sample seminar on health and safety matters concerning process, production, materials handling and other operatives and office workers

**Seminar on health and safety
for
process, production, materials handling and other
operatives and office workers**

Seminar objectives
1. To achieve safety consciousness and safety awareness in delegates.
2. To promote accident prevention.
3. To stimulate personal interest in safe working practices and standards.
4. To promote health, safety and welfare as a function of one's job.

Seminar content
An examination of health, safety and welfare at all levels and in all situations.

Examination of the roles and responsibilities of management, workers, safety representatives and committees.

The process of accident/incident causes and effects will be examined. Delegates discuss their own working situations and experiences and seek guidance and possible solutions to problems.

The Health and Safety at Work, etc., Act 1974, together with recent European Community (EC) Directives and UK Regulations, will be examined as they affect management and employees. Legislation covering various operations, occupations and functions will be discussed.

Method

The seminar will be participative, with discussions and lectures.

Certification

Delegates attending the seminar will receive a company certificate as recognition of having attended this training.

Delegates are encouraged to ask as many questions as they feel necessary, make full written notes of the seminar and full use of all handouts, as these will be invaluable for future reference.

Health and safety seminar programme

Introduction
Safety consciousness and safety awareness.
Responsibilities for health and safety.

Why health and safety?
Accident rates: the size of the problem; the human element.
Costs of accidents

The Health and Safety at Work, etc., Act 1974
What it says to employers and managers and to employees.

The Factories Act and the Offices, Shops and Railway Premises Act
Brief outline of its main sections.

Enforcement of the legislation
How and by whom.

Health and safety training
The law and company policy.

Health and safety policy
What it is.

The accident process
Accidents don't happen. The differences between accidents and incidents.
When does an 'accident' begin? The vicious circle.

Audits and investigations
When an accident occurs, how to prevent a recurrence and, when hazards and incidents arise, how to prevent them *becoming* accidents. Employees' roles in this.

Accident prevention
The process — breaking that vicious circle.

EC Directives and UK Regulations implementing them
In brief, the new duties of employers and employees. Particular parts of Directives/Regulations discussed according to relevance to delegates' jobs.

Other subjects, as appropriate to occupations represented
Fire. Office safety. VDU safety. Machine safety (guards, etc.).
Control of Substances Hazardous to Health (COSHH) Regulations.
Electrical safety — responsibilities and prohibitions.
Environmental protection. Control of noise.
Manual/kinetic handling. Safety in engineering.

Discussion with management: where do we go from here?

Seminar review
Discussion and completion of evaluation reports.

Appendix 16: Suggested safe reversing schedule/training document for lorries when on company premises

Items in parentheses are to be completed by filling in your own details.

(YOUR COMPANY NAME)

Reversing with safety

Operating schedule and training manual

Marshalling of lorries
while reversing

The following procedure is to be followed on *all* occasions when lorries (of any description) are being reversed on the Company's premises.

This procedure applies to *all* vehicles, including those operated by other vehicle owners and operators.

Timings of marshalling activities:

- am: delivery vehicles
- pm: other owners' vehicles and storage of trailers.

Introduction

Many accidents occur each year (nationally) when large vehicles are being reversed, people being knocked down or trapped by those vehicles. Reversing accidents usually occur at *low* speeds, with no other vehicle involved and often the result of carelessness, overconfidence on the part of drivers and/or failure to observe simple safety rules and take precautions.

The particular location may be unfamiliar to the driver and so there will be hazards of which they are unaware or, given familiarity with locations, the presence of unforeseen hazards may go unnoticed. At the end of long journeys, drivers may be tired, want to finish quickly or be otherwise preoccupied. Similarly, there may be people in the area who are unaware of the dangers of reversing lorries and possibly who have impaired sight or hearing.

This operating schedule for the reversing of lorries *must* be followed when any lorry (single chassis or articulated) is being reversed within the confines of the Company's premises:

Instructions to drivers

Marshalling

Drivers of *all* lorries must obtain the assistance of a (your company name) traffic marshaller whenever they intend to carry out a reversing manoeuvre. On no account is any lorry to be driven in reverse *except* under the guidance of a (company name) traffic marshaller.

Instruction slips All drivers are to stop at the security lodge at the main entrance gate and obtain an instruction slip from the security officer on duty.

Temporary parking The driver will then proceed to the marshalling area (area XXX), exercising caution where pedestrian zebra crossings are placed. They are then to park in the temporary parking area by reversing against the ( ) fence. This is an area that is completely free of pedestrians and private vehicles and a 'No pedestrians — authorized persons only' sign is displayed.

However, before reversing into the parking bay, drivers must satisfy themselves that no other lorry driver, unauthorized person, vehicle or other obstruction is in the road/pathway of the vehicle. For loading/unloading in the (another department), temporary parking is in ( ).

Company marshallers When satisfactorily parked, the lorry driver must then report to a (company name) traffic marshaller (in area XXX) and request to be assisted by marshalling into the required loading or unloading bay or position.

The lorry driver must then give the (company name) marshal full instructions as to where it is intended to reverse the vehicle. The driver will then drive forward to the position ready for reversing. From this point, the driver is under the control of the traffic marshaller, but retains responsibility for the vehicle. The driver must obey all the verbal directions and manual signals given by the (company name) traffic marshaller. However, if the driver is uncertain about signals given by that traffic marshaller, they must obtain clarification before reversing any further.

Do not commence *any* reversing movement unless and until signalled to do so by an authorized (company name) traffic marshaller.

Signals must be taken from *one* person only, except for *emergency* signals or verbal commands to stop, which must be accepted from anyone.

Speed The speed of your vehicle must be kept as low as possible, but, in any event, at a maximum of 5 miles per hour.

Warning devices The driver *must* ensure that the audible warning device on their vehicle is in working order and is *on*. Any defect must be drawn to the attention of the traffic marshaller and action taken to rectify any fault.

Main roads Lorries must *never* be reversed from a side road into a main road.

Instructions to traffic marshallers

Protective/identification gear
All (company name) lorry marshallers *must* wear luminous yellow *flak* jackets with the words 'traffic marshal' on the back. They must also either wear luminous red/orange gloves with a pointer/arrow on the palm or carry luminous red/orange bats, to ensure they give clear signals that are seen and understood by the driver, especially during hours of darkness. Marshallers must put this gear on *before* proceeding to the marshalling area.

The purpose of the luminous *flak* jacket is to ensure that marshallers are easily seen by drivers, especially during the hours of darkness.

Preparatory action
Before commencing marshalling operations, the marshaller is to:

1. receive instructions from the lorry driver as to which is their vehicle, where it is parked in the temporary parking area and into which position they intend to reverse the vehicle
2. assess the area in which the reversing manoeuvre is to be carried out and satisfy themselves that:
   - they fully understand the instructions given to them by the lorry driver, clarifying any points that may be necessary (*remember* the marshaller's personal

safety and the safety of others depends on clear mutual understanding between the driver and marshaller)

- there are no pedestrians in the area, instructing any pedestrians (other than authorized persons, such as lorry drivers attending their vehicles or transport supervisors) to leave the area
- there are no unauthorized vehicles moving or parked in the area and ensuring the removal of such vehicles
- other authorized vehicles parked or moving in the area will not constitute a hazard to the manoeuvre, requesting such movement of vehicles as may be appropriate and/or advising the lorry driver of their presence
- the area behind the vehicle and into which the vehicle is to be reversed is completely clear of all other possible obstructions
- the lorry driver understands the reversing signals to be used by the marshaller

3. inform the lorry driver of the signals to be used by the lorry marshaller and, if they indicate that they are unsure of them, showing them illustrations of the signals and explaining their meanings (as outlined under Hand signals, later in this schedule)

4. warn any authorized persons present that a reversing manoeuvre is about to commence.

Positioning of lorry marshaller

The position taken up by the marshaller will depend on the circumstances in which reversing manoeuvres are being carried out.

To ensure personal safety, the marshaller must *always* be in a position where they can be clearly seen by the lorry driver with the use of rear-view mirrors, if directing from behind, or, if directing from the front, clearly seen from the driver's side of the tractor. This will normally be on the offside (right-hand side) of the vehicle. If out of the driver's sight lines, the marshaller must shout 'Stop' and adjust their position.

However, if the tractor (towing unit) is turned sharply to the *left* (near side) at an angle of more than 25° to the trailer, then the marshaller must be positioned at the left (near side) rear of the vehicle if directing from the rear, as it is unlikely that the driver will then be able to see the marshaller in their off-side rear-view mirror.

If not in the driver's view, shout 'Stop' and adjust position so that the marshaller can be seen by the driver.

Beware The lorry marshaller must *never* position themselves immediately behind the trailer.

The lorry marshaller must *never* position themselves to the rear of the trailer and between any dead-end obstruction, such as a wall or loading bay platform.

Lorry marshallers must:

- always position themselves out of danger from the reversing vehicle and other vehicles in the vicinity
- position themselves to the side, at least 1 metre away from the vehicle *and* its intended route — remembering that the rear of a trailer will turn very sharply in a small turning circle, compared with the wide turning circle of the tractor and front end of the trailer
- *never* move around the *rear* of the lorry (unless sure that it has fully stopped and the handbrake is on). To move from one rearward side to the opposite rearward side, *always* move around the *front* of the vehicle, remaining in full view of the driver.

Hand signals
Hand signals must be:

1. clear
2. seen clearly by the driver (the marshaller must reposition themselves as necessary throughout the manoeuvre to ensure that there is clear visual contact between driver and marshaller at all times (whether via their rear-view mirrors or direct visual contact)
3. given in sufficient time to allow the driver to react and apply the necessary controls — *remember*, even at very slow speeds, a very large/heavy vehicle needs time to come completely to a halt.

Emergency It should be noted that, in the event of an emergency, a bang with the hands on the side or rear of an articulated trailer *cannot* be heard by the driver. Clear hand signals and a verbal command in a very loud voice are therefore *essential*.

Direction It must be remembered that, whatever type of vehicle is being reversed, the 'direction' or 'change direction' signal indicates to the driver the direction in which the *rear* of the vehicle is to be steered.

Types of hand signals Following are the recognized hand signals that are to be given by marshals.

- **Advance** Use the right hand and forearm vertically, palm away from the driver (towards the marshaller), drawing the driver onwards and calling out 'Come on', if necessary, in a loud, clear voice.
- **Reverse** The marshaller should be positioned to the *front* of the vehicle for this signal to be given. (This is particularly important when marshalling a lorry in reverse into a confined space or into a dead-end obstruction, such as a wall or loading bay.)
  Use both hands and forearms with palms facing the driver (away from the marshaller), pushing them back and calling out 'Go on', if necessary, in a loud, clear voice.
- **Change direction** The marshaller must be positioned well to the side of the vehicle, on the side towards which the trailer is to proceed, clearly visible in the rear-view mirror.

Face forwards towards the driver, maintaining in full view the whole length of the vehicle.

Extend one arm (the right arm to turn the vehicle to the off side/right; left arm to turn to the near side/left), hold the palm of the hand out flat pointing to the direction in which the *rear* of the trailer is to be steered.

- **Stop** Raise the right arm vertically, palm facing the driver (away from the marshaller), fingers extended and together. Shout 'Stop' loudly and clearly.
- **Clearance** To indicate the amount of clearance there is between the side of the trailer and a wall, side of a loading bay or other obstruction (such as another HGV). Raise the arms above the head, arms straight, palms facing inwards, towards the head.

Indicate the amount of clearance between the side of the trailer and the obstacle by raising or lowering the arms; the distance between the hands should approximate the amount of clearance available for the vehicle. Thus, if the arms are raised so that they are nearly vertical, there is a narrow clearance, but if the arms are lowered towards the horizontal, there is a wider clearance.

Bibliography and recommended reading

Appleby, Paul, and Rickman, Alistair, 'Sick Buildings: The facts and fallacies', *Safety and Health Practitioner*, November 1993.

Asbestos (Prohibitions) Regulations, The, 1992 (HMSO).

Brimson, Terence J., *The Employer's Survival Guide* (McGraw-Hill, 1992).

Buck, P. C., and Hooper, E., *Electrical Safety at Work: A guide to regulations and safe practice* (Paramount Publishing, undated).

Chemicals (Hazard Information and Packaging) (CHIP) Regulations 1993 (HMSO).

Control of Asbestos at Work Regulations 1987 and ACOP (HMSO).

Control of Asbestos at Work (Amendment) Regulations 1992 (HMSO).

Control of Carcinogenic Substances (Carcinogens ACOP, third edition), as amended 1992 (HMSO).

Control of Lead at Work Regulations 1980 (HMSO).

Control of Substances Hazardous to Health (COSHH) Regulations 1988 (HMSO).

Control of Substances Hazardous to Health (Amendment) Regulations 1991 and 1992 (HMSO).

Control of Substances Hazardous to Health (General ACOP, third edition), as amended 1992 (HMSO).

Dewis, M., and Stranks, J., *Health and Safety at Work Handbook* (Tolley and RoSPA).

Display Screen Equipment Work/Guidance on Health and Safety (Display Screen Equipment) Regulations 1992 and ACOP (HMSO).

Donaldson, Dr R. J., OBE, *Essential Food Hygiene* (Royal Society of Health, 1991).

Electricity in the Workplace: A guide to current legislation (Electrol, 1991).

Environmental Protection Act 1990 (HMSO).

Environmental Management (Croner Publications Limited, subscription-only publication).

Essentials of Health and Safety (HSE, 1986).

Everton, Ann, Holyoak, Jon, and Allen, David, *Fire Safety and the Law* (Paramount Publishing, 1990).

Factories Act 1961 (HMSO).

Farmer, D., *So Far as is Reasonably Practicable* (Croner Publications Limited, 1989).

Fire Precautions Act 1971 (HMSO).

Fire Precautions (Places of Work) Regulations 1995 (HMSO).

Fire Safety Management in Hotels and Boarding Houses — Fire Protection Association (HMSO, 1991).

First Aid at Work/Health and Safety (First Aid) Regulations 1981 and Approved Code of Practice 1990 (HMSO).

Five Steps to Risk Assessment (Guide IND(G)163L, HSE, 1994).

Food Hygiene (General) Regulations 1970 (HMSO).

Food Hygiene (Amendment) Regulations 1990 and 1991 (HMSO).

Food Hygiene Handbook, The (Institution of Environmental Health, 1991).

Food Safety Act 1990 (HMSO).

Food Safety: Your questions answered (Food Safety Advisory Centre, 1991).

Graves, Rod J., 'Grasping the Manual Handling Regulations', *Safety and Health Practitioner*, April and June 1993.

Guide to the Factories Act 1961 (HSE, 1991).

Health and Safety Commission Annual Reports 1987/88 to 1992/93 (HMSO).

Health and Safety at Work (Croner Publications Limited, subscription-only publication).

Health and Safety at Work, etc., Act 1974 (HMSO).

Health and Safety Monitor (Monitor Press, subscription-only publication).

Home Digest: Your useful food and household year book (Safeway, 1992).

Introducing the Noise at Work Regulations (Guide IND(G)75(L), HSE).

Legionellosis, The prevention or control of, ACOP (HMSO).

Lifting and Handling: An ergonomic approach (National Back Pain Association and Thorn–EMI, 1991).

Lighten the Load (Guide C.500, incorporating Guides IND(G)109/110(rev), HSE, 1993).

Management of health and safety at work: Guidance on Management of Health and Safety at Work Regulations 1992 and ACOP (HMSO).

Manual handling: Guidance on Manual Handling Operations Regulations 1992 and ACOP (HMSO).

Noise at Work Regulations 1989 (HMSO).

Offices, Shops and Railway Premises Act 1963 (HMSO).

Our Health and Safety Policy: Guide for small businesses (HSE, 1989).

Personal protective equipment at work: Guidance Notes on Personal Protective Equipment at Work Regulations 1992 and ACOP (HMSO).

Portable Appliance Testing (Electrol, 1991).

Practical Food Hygiene (Croner Publications Limited, subscription-only publication).

Record Keeping Book for COSHH (Croner Publications Limited, subscription-only publication).

Reference Book for Employers (Croner Publications Limited, subscription-only publication).

Reporting of Injuries, Diseases and Dangerous Occurrences Regulations 1985 (Guide) (HMSO).

Safety Reps/RoSPA Guide to the Safety Representatives and Safety Committee Regulations 1977 (RoSPA).

Storage of flamable liquids in containers, The (Guide HS(G)51, HSE).

Substances Hazardous to Health (Croner Publications Limited, subscription-only publication).

Substances Hazardous to Health: Emergency spillage guide (Croner Publications Limited, 1993).

Work Equipment/Guidance on Provision and Use of Work Equipment Regulations 1992 and ACOP (HMSO).

Workplace health, safety and welfare: Guidance on Workplace (Health, Safety and Welfare) Regulations 1992 and ACOP (HMSO).

You Can Do It: A learning package and self-help guide (HSE, 1994).

Index